S0-AAH-420

Agrarian Revolution and Economic Progress

HD
1415
S3.2   1115 15

⊕ PRAEGER SPECIAL STUDIES IN
INTERNATIONAL ECONOMICS AND DEVELOPMENT

Agrarian Revolution and Economic Progress

A PRIMER FOR DEVELOPMENT

Rainer Schickele

Published in cooperation with
the Agricultural Development Council, Inc.

PRAEGER PUBLISHERS
New York • Washington • London

GOSHEN COLLEGE LIBRARY
GOSHEN, INDIANA 46526

The purpose of the Praeger Special Studies is to make specialized research monographs in U.S. and international economics and politics available to the academic, business, and government communities. For further information, write to the Special Projects Division, Praeger Publishers, Inc., 111 Fourth Avenue, New York, N.Y. 10003.

PRAEGER PUBLISHERS, INC.
111 Fourth Avenue, New York, N.Y. 10003, U.S.A.
5, Cromwell Place, London S.W.7, England

Published in the United States of America in 1968
by Praeger Publishers, Inc.

Second printing, 1969

© 1968 by Frederick A. Praeger, Inc.

All rights reserved

Library of Congress Catalog Card Number: 68-18928

Printed in the United States of America

15.15

5-21-71

Craeger

FOREWORD

For the last twelve years, I looked, listened, and talked in all corners of the world. I looked at farmers working in their fields in Nepal and Bolivia, in Indonesia and Tanzania. I listened to them, I asked them questions, I talked with them. I talked with businessmen, houseboys, clerks, political leaders, and government officers from presidents, ministers, and directors to district officers and village-level workers.

My concern as an economist with the Food and Agriculture Organization of the United Nations was the acceleration of economic development and the special role that agriculture must play, as it comprises the largest sector of the economy in most developing countries. That was their concern, too.

I put myself in the place of a Minister of Agriculture, a Director of the Economic Planning Board, a Chief Engineer in the Irrigation Department, a District Agricultural Officer, a peasant, tenant, landlord, village trader and moneylender, a tribal chief, village elder, political leader and Member of Parliament. As I wrote this book, I had imaginary discussions with specific persons in these various positions whom I had come to know and in whose judgement I have confidence. These persons looked over my shoulder, figuratively speaking, while I wrote these pages.

I put much effort and self-discipline into imagining how each of these persons sizes up the nature of the development problem; what his specific motivations, hopes, and fears are concerning social and economic change; and what he might consider desirable and feasible.

This method of empathy, of experiencing and gaining insight, is not taught in school. But it is an indispensable method for learning to understand people of other nations and cultures. And economic development depends increasingly upon people in different countries, in different walks of life, understanding each other.

Perhaps this empathic method cannot be taught directly, as mathematics and languages can. But it can be described; its constructive functions can be demonstrated; its development and use can be encouraged. It is of strategic importance for leaders in politics and administration, and for teachers and researchers in the social sciences.

One needs to cultivate in oneself two qualities, possessed by any normal person but not commonly recognized as useful, for sizing up economic development problems and finding practical solutions: a warm heart, and the ability to detach oneself from one's own private and cultural environment. The first is an emotional quality of feeling about others; the second is an intellectual capacity to abstract from one's own immediate involvement and prejudices. These qualities support each other in the quest for deeper insights into economic affairs. They can be nurtured and guided to serve the cognitive and operational needs of accelerating economic progress. This method of empathy is indispensable for formulating promising hypotheses and for guiding development policies; hypotheses that can be tested, and policies that can be improved by trial and error.

Auguste Comte, a great Frenchman of the early nineteenth century and a founder of the social sciences, expressed the role of empathy in socio-economic studies and the formulation of policies for human progress most succinctly: "It is for the heart to suggest our problems; it is for the intellect to solve them. The only position for which the intellect is primarily adapted is to be the servant of the social sympathies." Let us remind ourselves that economics is a social, not a physical or math-

vi

ematical, science and that it is people who develop their economy and the institutions serving it, and not the laws of physics and mathematics.

This book is addressed primarily to civic leaders at all levels, to planners and government officials, to teachers and experts in public agencies and educational institutions in the developing countries throughout the world.

I have attempted to reflect _their_ points of view, to assess the nature of _their_ development problems, and to explore solutions in the interest of _their_ countries. The insights I gained from my contacts with them have shaped the approach I have taken in this book. It is to them that I owe deep gratitude for the time and effort, the courtesy and confidence, and the wisdom I have received from them.

My approach has been thematic rather than schematic. There are many aspects that are not discussed in detail. For instance, problems of price policy are mentioned only with respect to its task in accelerating adoption of modern techniques but are not elaborated in terms of price-support programs for specific products. Questions on basic agricultural research are not examined, but applied research on testing the adaptability of modern techniques to local farming conditions is discussed. I do not describe various methods used in comprehensive national planning, but stress the need for planning "from the bottom up" as well as "from the top down." I have sacrificed systematic coverage to a selective treatment in depth of a few crucial issues, which I feel are much neglected in the literature, whose importance is widely underrated, and whose nature is often poorly understood. This, I hope, will make the book more thought-provoking for a wider audience than a schematic treatment would do.

There is another reason for this selective approach: I am painfully aware of how little we know about the development processes now gaining momentum in the newly developing countries. With such a wide array of different nations, with such a variety of cultural traits, social structures, and economic conditions, we are bound to gain more insight and find practical solutions more readily by a rigorous examination of a few key issues than by attempting to build a general comprehensive scheme of development plans and policies.

There are six key issues or themes upon which the discussion is focused, and around which many other aspects are examined in their relationships to these key issues:

(1) Development planning must have two concurrent goals: to increase production and to reduce poverty; far from being antagonistic, these goals are inherently complementary;

(2) Industrial and agricultural development must go together; sacrificing progress in agriculture for building up industry by extracting excessive amounts of capital from agriculture retards self-sustaining development;

(3) Production processes and their human aspects are by nature so different in agriculture and in industry that different types of development policies and implementation measures are required; what works in industry often does not work in agriculture;

(4) Modernizing agriculture requires an agrarian revolution; in some cases it may be peaceful, in others violent, but a revolution in education, land tenure, and economic opportunities of the masses of small farmers there must be;

(5) Participation of rural people in planning and implementing development projects, and in group organizations such as cooperatives, farmers' associations, and political parties, is as important for raising production as it is for making them full-fledged responsible citizens;

(6) National development plans to succeed in agriculture must be translated into effective local

projects, each narrow enough in scope to focus energy, but broad enough to encompass complementary
activities without which success would be thwarted.
This involves local participation of farmers in
adapting modern production techniques and administrative measures to local conditions, and provides
"planning from below" as an integral part of the national planning process.

PLAN OF THE STUDY

First, let us take an over-all view of the most
critical issues people are facing in transforming
their economies from a traditional system oriented
toward maintaining the status quo to a dynamic system oriented toward social and economic progress.
Part I deals with the pervasive issues of linking
the world-wide sweep of a humanist-democratic ideology with the instruments of modern technology and
socio-economic organization, which must be harnessed
to serve human needs and aspirations for a better
life, for freedom from hunger, poverty, and oppression.

Second, we shall examine the problems of mobilizing agriculture for economic development. Part
II deals with the peculiar characteristics of agricultural production processes and their inherent differences from those in industry and trade, and with
the role agriculture must play in national development.

Third, we shall turn to the problems of implementing agricultural plans and policies in the field,
on farms and in villages. Part III deals with the
difficult task of making the masses of small farmers
who produce the bulk of the world's food and fiber
able and willing to adopt modern production techniques. The ominous slowness of the rate of growth
in agricultural output shows that this is not an
easy task. Farmers must become capable and willing
to produce much more to meet the needs of a rapidly
growing population and to support a rising living
level for all people, especially for those who now

live in hunger and humiliating poverty.

Last, we shall explore issues arising out of the growing interdependence of nations. Part IV leads us from the rural village back again to the world scene where national policies must be harmonized with the pressing necessity of international cooperation. Countries are becoming more dependent on each other. Multilateral arrangements are needed for organizing international capital markets and expanding convertibility of currencies. Technical assistance must become more effective; for this, the Food and Agriculture Organization and other United Nations agencies require strong support and delegation of authority from the member nations in the service of progress toward a peaceful world.

CONTENTS

PART IV

INTERDEPENDENCE OF NATIONS
IN ECONOMIC PROGRESS

LIST OF TABLES AND CHARTS

xix

PART I

CRITICAL ISSUES

IN DEVELOPMENT PLANNING

CHAPTER 1 A PROLOGUE

We are witnessing a drama of breath-taking sweep throughout the newly developing world.

We are in the second act on which the curtain rose after World War II. The first act started in the wake of the French and American revolutions, around the year 1800. The center of the stage in the first act was Europe and North America. In the second act, it has shifted from the West to the East and South, to Asia, Africa and Latin America.

The central protagonist is the worker, the peasant, the small craftsman, the clerk, the poor man working in the factory, field, workshop, and office. The plot of the drama deals with his frustrations and triumphs as he struggles along his way from subservience to human dignity and citizenship, from poverty to wealth, under the guiding spirit of humanist ideology, of democracy and the equality of man.

THE INDUSTRIAL REVOLUTION OF THE WEST

In the first act, during the Industrial Revolution up to World War II, technology brought about a tremendous increase in productivity. Application of science to the production processes increased the capacity of people to produce so much that, for the first time in the history of mankind, it became possible to wipe out hunger and poverty. The humanist ideology taught people that the purpose of an economic system is the creation of wealth for the satisfaction of human wants, and that men are created equal. This means that men of all races and creeds have a basic human right to equality of opportunity and

1

civic dignity, that the satisfaction of the human
wants of the poor is as important as that of the rich,
and that degrading poverty is incompatible with the
principle of human rights in a modern democracy.

The economic system during the Industrial Revolution was based mainly upon private entrepreneurs.
Although producers were always subject to various
public policies and regulations, these were in the
beginning formulated in the interest of industrial
producers and of commerce with no regard for expanding also the opportunities for the millions of poor
workers employed at starvation wages and working under most horrible sweatshop conditions. During the
nineteenth century, many people became rich, but
many, many more people remained extremely poor. As
late as the middle of the twentieth century, the
richest of the Western industrial countries still had
far too many families living in poverty, in the midst
of plenty.

This weakness of the private enterprise system
in distributing its rising output to also meet the
needs of the poor became apparent as early as the
middle of the nineteenth century. Our drama's hero,
the worker, farmer and small craftsman, with the help
of philosophers and economists, came forth with the
proposal of an alternative economic system, that of
state enterprise, whose purpose was to create wealth
for the satisfaction of human wants according to
physical and social need rather than ability to pay.
It was, however, only as late as the 1920's, and only
in one country, Russia, that a centralized state enterprise system was actually put into practice during
the first act of our drama. It performed well in reducing abject poverty among the masses of the people,
but was much less successful in the task of increasing productivity, particularly in agriculture.

The hero, when he saw more than half a century
go by without any Western country adopting the state
enterprise system, began struggling for a fundamental
reform, for a reorientation of the private enterprise
system which would strengthen its performance in sat-
isfying the human wants of the poor, without weakening

its performance in producing wealth. In their political ascendancy, people assigned to the state the
responsibility for guiding the private enterprise
economy with social and economic welfare policies so
as to reduce poverty and give equal opportunities to
the poor for education, health and bargaining power
in the market. These policies compensated, at least
in part, for the lack of the market system's response
to the needs of the poor, and still preserved the incentives and initiatives of private enterprise in
production.

This "mixed economy" where private enterprise
produces and trades within a framework of public policies and controls designed to promote the economic
welfare of people as a whole, and particularly of the
poor and disadvantaged, achieved a dramatic breakthrough in most of the Western industrialized countries during the 1920's and 30's. In the Scandinavian countries, poverty has almost been wiped out,
private enterprise is producing efficiently and profitably, and living standards are among the highest in
Europe. Also, in many of the other Western industrialized countries, the extent of poverty has been reduced more or less depending on the scope and efficiency of the public policies for equalizing opportunities and reducing poverty. There remains no
economic or moral justification for poverty in an in-
dustrially developed affluent society where excess
production capacity and surplusses are more trouble-
some than shortages. So our drama's hero continues
his struggle in the West, but with a strong stance
which promises to bring him soon within reach of his
economic goal--the abolition of poverty.

This is the state of affairs, the scenery and
the stage of the plot at the end of the drama's Act
I, the Industrial Revolution of the West.

THE AGRARIAN REVOLUTION
OF THE NEWLY DEVELOPING WORLD

As the curtain rises on Act II around the year
1950, the Agrarian Revolution of the East and South
has started. The scene is the vast region of Asia,

Africa, and South America, a rural region where most people live on farms and in villages and derive their livelihood from agriculture. Here, 800 to 900 million people achieved political independence from colonial rule in recent years, and another 400 million people are bringing about fundamental changes in their old traditional governments. Of the 1.25 billion people in this newly developing part of the world, 90 per cent live in countries with an average per capita income of less than $200 per year.[1] This simply means that the vast majority of the people are very poor indeed.

The people want to consummate their newly won political independence and strive toward their new aspirations of human dignity, freedom as responsible citizens, and equality of opportunity. This means they must raise their production and do so for the main purpose of reducing poverty.

The hero finds himself in a state of deep and widespread poverty. His trials deal with finding ways of harnessing the wealth-creating drive of private enterprise within a framework of governmental policies that satisfy the human wants of the poor, in order to unleash the pent-up capacities and energies of the people which are now stunted, suppressed by lack of education, health, food, and other bare necessities of life.

The drama's hero is not a heroic character. He takes on the shape of many different persons in all walks of life. He appears as an Indian farmer, overlooking his fields parched by the drought of the failing monsoon, with his wife, children and grandparents. Where will the food come from to keep his family alive? He appears as an office clerk in Nigeria who was fired by the manager to make room for a cousin, and who cannot find another job because he comes from the wrong tribe. He appears as a woman in a textile factory in Malaysia, a fisherman in Haiti, a blacksmith in the Northeast of Brazil--and whenever some little thing goes wrong he is down and out. There are so many little things over which he has no control and which can go wrong for him, because he

has no influence over his environment, no influence
with his employer, landlord or creditor in the conduct of public and community affairs. But he knows
that if he is given a chance, if he can get education, food, and other prime necessities of life, he
can do well, and he has proven it again and again on
the rare occasions when he did get a chance. He is
determined to get this chance for the multitude of
poor people everywhere.

There are leaders emerging who articulate the
aspirations of the people, who educate them in political and economic matters, who organize them into cooperative groups and political parties, who are rapidly learning the art and science of modern politics
and government. Some of these leaders come from poor
families, from peasant farms and shantytowns; but
many come from well-to-do families, from educated
classes, from professional and civil service ranks
and landed aristocracies. Gandhi, whose father and
grandfather were chief ministers of several Indian
states,[2] shared the life of the poor voluntarily in
the service to their cause. Nyerere was a teacher,
Senghor a philosopher and poet, Cardenas a general,
before they became great leaders of their people.
They identified themselves with them, they came to
political power with their support and held their
confidence. This emergence of progressive leaders of
the common people is proceeding everywhere, slowly in
some places, faster in others. There is today no
government, no group of rulers and wealthy merchants
and landowners who do not sense the political ascendancy of the poor.

This pervasive spirit of the times is our drama's
hero. This spirit is energized by the vision of man
coming into his own, as an individual on equal terms
with his brethren of all races, creeds and nations,
with equal opportunities to develop his talents, to
apply his productive efforts, and to be treated with
respect by other persons and by his government. This
is the freedom aspect of this ideology; its counterpart, fully as indispensable, is the responsibility
aspect--the vision of man as a member of the community, who accepts the obligation to serve the needs of

society, who participates in public affairs as a responsible citizen with the community's interest at heart.

The practical meaning of this ideology, this spiritual credo of our time, is that the individual has the right to choose and act freely within the limits of compatibility with community welfare; and that the government, in its promotion and safeguarding of the community's welfare, exercises its power with the consent of the people at large, and within the limits of compatibility with individual freedom and dignity.

Who is the villain in our drama? The plantation owner with a whip? The feudal prince in his palace with wives in silk brocades and thousands of peasants in rags and abject servitude? The colonial administrator backed by mercenaries?

These characters are disappearing rapidly with the demise of colonial empires, the achievement of political independence and the creation of representative democratic governments, although there are still areas where they are fighting covertly, but ruthlessly, for their power and social status.

The real antagonist is the old traditional spirit of privilege and power of the few over the many, of the elite over the "innately inferior," of the born aristocrat over the plebs, of the wealthy over the poor. This antagonist still has great strength which is rooted in past traditions of thousands of years. He also takes on the shape of many different persons in all walks of life. He appears as a peasant who has no respect for the dignity of his wife and mistreats her as a slave. How can his children grasp the belief in human dignity when they see their own mother mistreated? He appears as a government official who abuses the power of his office, who intimidates people and demands bribes. He appears as a landowner who keeps his tenants and laborers ignorant and poor and in debt to him, or as a foreman in a factory who bars his workers from advancement and keeps them in constant fear of dismissal.

This metaphoric prologue symbolizes the essence
of the forces underlying modern economic development
problems. For the first time in mankind's history,
technology offers the possibility of producing enough
for every man, woman, and child to live in decency,
free from hunger and stultifying want. This constitutes the material base upon which a democratic society can be built embracing all the people rather than
only a small elite.

GENERATORS OF PROGRESS

These are two powerful generators of economic
development: the humanist ideology, and science and
technology.

The great moral force which ushered in the American and French revolutions of the late eighteenth
century and shaped the concept of a modern democratic
social system was rooted in the belief that men are
created equal before God, or in worldly terms, that
men are equal before the law and have equal rights
for opportunities to develop their capacities, to reap
the fruits of their productive efforts, and to participate in the shaping of their communities, in the
molding of their institutions and governments. This
idea is still an infant in world history's perspective, and is very new indeed to the traditional cultures of two thirds of the world population.[3] But
this humanist idea is on the march everywhere, is
stirring in the minds and hearts of people throughout
the world, and will continue to shape the history of
mankind throughout the current and the coming centuries.

In the West, this humanist ideology transformed
a feudal elite society into a democratic society of
citizens in which universal suffrage, one-man, one-
vote, became the revolutionary invention for making
government responsible to the people. It transformed
a highly restrictive and esoteric educational system
for the privileged few into a universal, largely free
educational system for everyone. It abolished slavery and established a code of law and a system of

courts before which every man was considered equal in
his rights and responsibilities. It created the goal
of people's economic welfare, of equitable sharing of
the nation's wealth and opportunities, of abolition
of hunger and poverty--a logical sequel to the abolition of slavery. These were tremendously powerful
innovations which triggered a revolution of rising
aspirations and unleashed pent-up energies of people
for building a new society, new institutions and
standards of behavior, new laws and forms of government. Even after 150 years of political potency in
the Western industrial world, no one claims that this
humanist ideology has found its full realization in
modern Western society; it is still far from it. But
since the middle of the current century it has become
the dominant world spirit and driving force. It is
giving the direction, the orientation for progress
throughout the world, in the industrial West and newly developing agrarian countries alike.[4]

Science and technology transformed the traditional production processes in industry, agriculture,
and trade into instruments of amazing power for making the natural resources of the earth the servants
of the material needs of man. In the industrial
West, during the last hundred years, output per worker increased manyfold in every line of production.
It created a large variety of new goods and services
which were not even conceivable a hundred years ago.
This application of a rapidly expanding science to
practical production processes is now beginning to
spread throughout the developing world, and is bringing about new attitudes of people toward their work,
new forms of organization and group activities in
production techniques, in market structures and government functions. Science and technology has given
man the power to abolish poverty, for the first time
in history--but also to destroy himself by instantan-
eous mass-murder. The greatest challenge to mankind
in the coming centuries is to uphold the mastership
of the humanist ideology, of the spiritual and moral
values of modern society, over the application of
technology, over the use of science in human affairs.
This applies to the use of atomic energy as well as
to the use of mechanization and automation.

These two great generators of progress, the humanist ideology and the scientific technology, are
the West's constructive legacy to the newly developing regions of the world; they have to adapt them to
their own peculiar conditions, but they need not in-
vent them anew. Herein lies the hope for a victori-
ous outcome of the race against time.

If progress lags too much, there is real danger
of mankind losing control over technology. A serious
disintegration of the spiritual power which the idea
of the equality and dignity of man holds over our
hearts and minds may readily lead to an atomic holo-
caust, or to a technocratic society of robots along
the alpha-beta-gamma lines of Huxley's Brave New
World or the nightmare of Orwell's 1984.

The material aspect of the race against time is
that between food and population, between production
and poverty. Will we succeed in abolishing hunger
and poverty fast enough to prevent a world-wide breakdown of interhuman and international relations, of
national and world peace?

The ideological aspect is the question: Will
people's faith in the humanist idea of the respect
for our fellowman's and neighbor-nation's dignity and
right of self-government withstand the frustrations
and trials on the road to progress, or will this
faith falter in us before a modicum of realization is
reached?

These are the two basic disturbing aspects of
the race against time which leaders must ponder hon-
estly, at all levels, in all walks of life, in all
countries throughout the world.

NOTES TO CHAPTER 1

1. See Paul G. Hoffman, <u>One Hundred Countries</u>
<u>and One and One-Quarter Billion People</u> (Washington,
D.C.: Lasker Foundation, 1960). Mainland China is
excluded for lack of comparable information.

2.   Mohandas Karamchand Gandhi, <u>All Men Are</u>
<u>Brothers; Life and Thoughts of Mahatma Gandhi as Told</u>
<u>in His Own Words</u> (Paris: UNESCO, 1958), p. 4.

3. For a spirited account of this aspect, see
Barbara Ward, <u>The Rich Nations and the Poor Nations</u>
(New York: W. W. Norton & Co., Inc., 1962).

4. For a provocative essay on Western ideology
in the Asian context, see Raul S. Manglapus, "Asian
Revolution and American Ideology," <u>Foreign Affairs</u>,
Vol. 45, No. 2 (January 1967), pp. 344-52; and
Barbara Ward, <u>Spaceship Earth</u> (New York: Columbia
University Press, 1966), pp. 107-48.

CHAPTER 2

RACE AGAINST TIME:

PRODUCE OR PERISH

The facts are fairly well known. Food production is barely keeping pace with population, and in some countries during the last decade less food was produced per person than before (see Table 1). The average person in 1965 had only 1 per cent more food than in 1955--an insignificant gain for a whole decade which can easily be wiped out and turned into a loss any year by unfavorable weather alone, as the failing monsoon did to India in 1965.

POPULATION GROWTH AND FOOD

Population will continue to increase in the developing regions at an annual rate of 2.5 to 3 per cent for some time to come, and unless food production is increased to a rate substantially higher than that of population, say at least 5 or 6 per cent per year, progress will be much too slow to overcome hunger and malnutrition--the first step to better health and greater productivity, alertness, energy, and will power.

The food goal for the year 2000 must be at least three times higher than present production to feed a population twice as large adequately.[1] Modern scientists agree that technically there is no doubt that this goal can be achieved. The doubt lies in the capacity of the traditional local leaders, in their willingness and ability to bring about the economic, social, and organizational changes necessary to put modern technology to work on the millions of farms. Inducements and access to capital and services must be offered to farmers, otherwise they cannot increase production sufficiently.

11

To accomplish this, an agrarian revolution must open new opportunities to farmers. It will take much courage and imagination on the part of leaders, and active participation and confidence on the part of the people, of farmers, tradesmen, educators, and civil servants.

Throughout the newly developing world, a farm family produces now the food for itself plus that for one half or one other family; this is the basic economic meaning of the fact that 50-70 per cent of the labor force are in agriculture. Economic development, a balanced growth of agriculture, industry, and professional, technical, and administrative services, must enable a typical farm family, by the year 2000, to produce food for three or four other families-- otherwise industry and trade and all the essential services cannot develop sufficiently to sustain economic progress.

Nor can agriculture develop without such an increase in industrial goods and professional services, since they are essential to the application of science and technology to agricultural production. It took Western Europe seventy years to increase the non-farm labor force from 40 to 75 per cent;[2] this means that farmers increased their productivity so that around 1950 one farm family produced enough for four families as against only for one and one half in 1880. The newly developing countries are pressed by a much higher population growth than prevailed in Europe around 1880. This means that they must apply modern technology to agricultural production much faster to telescope this change into about thirty-five years, half the time-span it took in Europe. Nothing less than an agrarian revolution can do it.

This will require great effort and energetic leadership dedicated to the welfare of people rather than to the welfare of a small elite. This leadership with such an orientation is emerging throughout the developing countries. But it is a race against time, whose outcome is far from certain.

GROWTH IN AGRICULTURAL PRODUCTION

What has been the record so far? Table 1 reveals wide variations between individual countries in
their production increases achieved during the recent
decade of 1955-65. The annual rate of growth over
this ten-year period for the world was nearly 3 per
cent, with many countries falling well below this average and only a few countries exceeding 5 per cent.

A 3 per cent annual increase in agricultural
production for the world as a whole looks at first
sight quite impressive. To show what it means to
people, Table 1 indicates also the change in agricultural production per head. From that viewpoint, the
increase shrinks to a disappointing rate of less than
1 per cent, because population increases almost as
fast as production. In some countries population
during that decade increased even faster than production, as in Indonesia, Iraq, Peru, Chile, Cuba, and
some northwest African countries, so that actually
less was produced per person than before.

Considering the low level of food consumption
for the great majority of people in the developing
countries, an annual rate of 2 to 2.5 per cent increase per capita in agricultural production appears
necessary to bring an improvement of the situation
which can be consciously felt by people over a ten-
year period. If we can trust the statistics, only
five of the thirty-five developing countries in the
table achieved an annual rate of per capita increase
of 2 per cent or more. In twenty-three developing
countries the annual per capita increase was less
than 1 per cent, including eleven countries showing a
decrease.

These rates of growth are much too low. Many of
the developing countries depend upon agricultural exports for a major source of foreign exchange. This
means that although a part of their foreign exchange
earned by these exports can and is being used to import food, a good part of it must be used for industrial capital and other non-food imports, hence does

TABLE 1

Agricultural Production Increases During Decade 1955-65[1]

Country	Annual Rate of Increase			Country	Annual Rate of Increase		
	Total Pro-duction	Total Popu-lation	Per Capita Produc-tion		Total Pro-duction	Total Popu-lation	Per Capita Produc-tion
4% or more	%	%	%	2.0-2.9%	%	%	%
Israel	9.9	3.9	6.0	India	2.7	2.2	0.5
Mexico	6.3	3.1	3.2	Burma	2.5	2.2	0.3
Guatemala	5.8	3.1	2.7	France	2.5	1.2	1.3
Thailand	5.2	3.0	2.2	Netherlands	2.5	1.3	1.2
Venezuela	5.1	3.5	1.6	Colombia	2.4	2.8	-0.4
Yugoslavia	5.1	1.1	4.0	Finland	2.4	0.9	1.5
Greece	4.7	0.8	3.9	Germany	2.4	1.2	1.2
Syria	4.7	3.1	1.6	Peru	2.4	2.6	-0.2
Taiwan	4.3	3.4	0.9	Belgium	2.3	0.6	1.7
Malaya	4.2	3.1	1.1	Chile	2.2	2.6	-0.4
Brazil	4.0	3.0	1.0	Pakistan	2.2	2.4	-0.2
				Canada	2.0	2.3	-0.3
3.0-3.9%				Ireland	2.0	-0.3	2.3
Australia	3.7	2.2	1.5				
Egypt	3.7	2.5	1.2	0.1-1.9%			
Turkey	3.5	2.9	0.6	Denmark	1.8	0.7	1.1
Japan	3.4	1.0	2.4	Argentina	1.7	1.7	0.0
Panama	3.4	2.8	0.6	Italy	1.7	0.6	1.1
Iran	3.3	2.5	0.8	Morocco	1.6	2.8	-1.2
Korea	3.3	2.6	0.7	United States	1.6	1.6	0.0
Austria	3.2	0.3	2.9	Portugal	1.4	0.6	0.8
Philippines	3.2	3.2	0.0	Tunesia	1.1	1.8	-0.7
South Africa	3.2	2.5	0.7	Indonesia	1.0	2.2	-1.2
Ceylon	3.1	2.6	0.5	Switzerland	0.8	1.8	-1.0
Ethiopia	3.1	1.7	1.4	Cuba	0.7	2.2	-1.5
Honduras	3.1	3.1	0.0	Iraq	0.6	2.8	-2.2
Spain	3.1	0.8	2.3	Norway	0.4	0.8	-0.4
United Kingdom	3.1	0.6	2.5	Production Decline			
New Zealand	3.0	2.2	0.8	Sweden	-0.2	0.6	-0.8
				Algeria	-0.4	1.8	-2.2
World Average[2]	2.7	2.0	0.7	Uruguay	-0.4	1.5	-1.9

1. The State of Food and Agriculture, 1966 (Rome: Food and Agriculture Organization of the United Nations, 1966), p. 19 (compound rates).
2. The State of Food and Agriculture, 1965 (Rome: Food and Agriculture Organization of the United Nations, 1965), p. 16.

14

not augment the food supply of the people. Moreover,
in some countries production increases have been
greater in export products such as rubber, cotton,
cocoa, etc., than in domestic food products.

All this shows clearly the urgency for a strong
acceleration in agricultural development, for reducing hunger as well as for promoting industrialization
and general economic progress.

It will be difficult to increase agricultural
production rapidly enough to avoid disaster of one
form or another within the next twenty years or so.
In following chapters, we shall deal with the most
critical issues facing us, and shall draw from the
recent experiences of many countries for clues of how
these difficulties might best be overcome. But first
let us explore the process of economic development as
a whole, since agricultural progress cannot be
achieved in isolation from the other sectors of the
economy. Modernization of farming requires the support of industries and trade and many educational,
technical, economic, and administrative services
which are integral parts of general development.

PAST RATES OF ECONOMIC GROWTH

During 1860-1960, European countries increased
their total production at widely varying rates, but
ended up with remarkably similar growth rates of income per head, as shown in Table 2. England and
France produced about seven times as much in 1960 as
in 1860; with a moderate population increase of about
1.5 times over the 1860 population, they wound up
with an increase in income per head of four to five
times in 1960.

In contrast, Germany and Denmark increased their
production 15-fold, that is twice as much as England
and France; their population also grew nearly twice
as fast by trebling during the century. They wound
up with an increase of income per head of five to six
times. Note that instead of the "population explo-
sion" in Germany and Denmark keeping the people

TABLE 2

Growth of National Product,
Population, and Per Capita Product,
During the Century of Around 1860-1960

	Coefficient of Multiplication in a Century 1860-1960			Total Product Compound annual growth rates corresponding to multiplication factors (approximate)
	Total Product	Population	Product Per Capita	%
France	6.6	1.3	5.2	2
United Kingdom	6.8	1.8	3.7	2
Italy	10.7	1.9	5.6	2 1/2
Germany	15.0	2.9	5.2	2 3/4
Denmark	15.8	2.7	5.9	2 3/4
Sweden	23.2	1.9	12.1	3
United States	34.5	7.1	4.9	3 1/2
Japan	33.4	3.2	10.4	3 1/2

Source: Simon Kuznets, Modern Economic Growth (New Haven, Conn.: Yale University Press, 1966), p. 64.

16

poorer, compared with England and France, it actually
was associated with a somewhat higher rate of growth
in income per head. Kuznets concludes: "No clear
association appears to exist...between rates of
growth of population and of product per capita." Our
neo-Malthusian friends might well ponder this historical fact in the light of modern conditions.

Sweden is in a class by itself among the European countries: It increased its production 23-fold,
barely doubled its population, and wound up with a
12-fold increase in income per head. Although some
of this impressive growth rate might be attributed to
the lower level at the start, it is likely that much
of it was due to the much less dominant position of a
feudal elite placing obstacles in the way of people's
aspirations and opportunities for economic progress.
Moreover, it kept out of wars and concentrated its
national energies upon development at home, and upon
international cooperation and peaceful co-existence
abroad.

The U.S.A. and Japan achieved by far the highest
rate of growth by increasing their output 34-fold.
What is particularly noteworthy is that Japan produced this feat by only trebling her population,
winding up with a 10-fold rise in income per head.
The U.S.A. achieved the same increase, but with a
population growth more than twice that of Japan,
winding up with a 5-fold rise in income per head--
about the same as Northwestern Europe.

A century growth rate of 7-fold increase corresponds to an annual compound rate of 2 per cent, that
of 30-fold to an annual rate of 3.5 per cent. This
helps to compare them with recent growth rates over a
decade which we are observing currently in newly developing countries.

The Western countries in the 1860's and subsequent decades had annual increases in their national
production of 2 to 3 per cent. During 1950-64 many
newly developing countries achieved substantially
higher growth rates, as shown in Table 3. Over this
15-year period, of the 61 developing countries shown

in the OECD publication, 41 had a growth rate of 4
per cent or more, 30 a rate of 5 per cent or more,
and only 6 a rate of less than 3 per cent. Sixteen
of the 61 developing countries had a steady or consistently increasing economic growth rate (within 0.5
percentage points), an additional 8 had a higher rate
in 1960-64 than in 1950-54, and 12 had a consistently
declining rate. Note that India and Pakistan had
consistently increasing growth rates.

   In launching the "Development Decade" of the
1960's, the United Nations urged countries to press
forward with effective policies to reach a minimum 5
per cent growth rate as fast as possible, so that by
the end of the decade, every country would achieve or
surpass this minimum level of economic growth. Over
half of the developing countries at mid-decade were
below that level, and some of the countries now at or
above that level may slip back below it again in coming years unless they bend all their efforts to prevent it. As the population growth in most of those
countries is between 2 and 3 per cent per year, a national product growth of 5 to 6 per cent would be
necessary to make the majority of people consciously
experience substantial benefits from economic development within a time span of a decade. An annual
rate of less than 3 per cent increase in national
production per head is not likely to make most people
feel that they really are getting rewarded for the
anxiety and risk and harder work involved in breaking
away from many traditions and adopting modern production techniques and forms of organization.

   Many of the newly developing countries did substantially better during the 1950's and early 1960's
than did the Western European countries during the
1870-1913 period, with a prevailing growth rate of
only 2 to 3.5 per cent.[3] However, their population
growth (around 2.5 per cent) is more than twice as
high as in Europe (around 1 per cent), so that the
per capita income increase is much lower. This,
again, shows why the developing countries now are under much greater pressure for increased production in
the race against time than the industrial West was
during the period of the Industrial Revolution. To

TABLE 3

Growth Rates of National Production
(Real Gross Domestic Product) in Developing Countries, 1950-64

	Annual Compound Growth Rates			
	1950-55	1955-60	1960-64	1950-64
Europe	7.0	5.3	7.9	6.1
Africa	4.3	4.7	4.0	4.4
Latin America	4.8	4.9	4.4	4.8
Asia	4.5	4.5	5.2	4.6
All Developing Countries	4.9	4.8	5.0	4.8
Steady or Rising Growth Rates				
Yugoslavia	5.3	8.6	8.5	7.7
Egypt	4.3	6.6	6.4	5.6
Ghana	4.0	3.7	3.7	4.0
Sudan	4.8	5.0	4.6	5.2
Guatemala	2.3	5.3	6.1	4.4
Mexico	6.1	6.2	6.2	5.9
Costa Rica	4.9	4.9	4.6	4.8
India	3.4	4.1	4.4	3.7
Pakistan	1.9	3.6	5.4	3.5
Malaya	3.0	4.1	6.2	4.2
Thailand	6.5	6.1	6.9	6.3
Taiwan	8.2	6.5	8.2	7.4
Declining Growth Rates				
Turkey	6.4	5.2	4.0	4.6
Ecuador	5.4	4.5	4.0	4.5
Venezuela	8.7	6.4	5.0	6.6
Burma	7.0	5.7	2.0	5.0
Ceylon	4.9	3.0	2.9	3.4
Iraq	14.0	6.8	6.2	9.4

Source: Organization for Economic Cooperation and Development, Development Assistance Efforts and Policies: 1966 Review (Paris: OECD, 1966), p. 20.

make a noticeable impact on the welfare of the people,
per capita income must increase at least 3 per cent
per year over several decades, unless the birth rate
should drop considerably in the near future. In
practical terms, this means that with a population
growth of 2 to 3 per cent, growth rates of total national production of less than 5 or 6 per cent per
year are seriously deficient and are bound to invite
trouble.

INCOME GAP BETWEEN RICH AND POOR NATIONS

It is disconcerting to see how the income gulf
between the poor and the rich countries has actually
widened, rather than narrowed, since World War II and
the independence of the former colonial territories.
With the tremendous cost of the war, with all the reconstruction of the devastations suffered during the
war, the Western countries have become richer, in absolute terms, faster than the newly developing countries. The per capita income gap between the poor
and the rich nations has widened and continues to
grow wider (see Table 4).

This, of course, is bad and is often noticed
with alarm and resentment by the developing countries,
with embarrassment by the industrial countries. All
the more it is important to understand why this is
so, and what can be done about it.

The widening of the income gap will continue in-
evitably for some time and for many of the developing
countries simply because they start from a very low
level. For instance, if Taiwan has only one-tenth
the income per head of the United Kingdom, Taiwan's
annual growth must be ten times higher than that of
the U.K. just to keep the same income gap. A 1 per
cent increase of an $800 income is $8, of an $80 income
only $0.8. To maintain the same income gap of $720
while the U.K. income per head grows only by the very
moderate rate of 2 per cent per year, or $16, Taiwan
would have to grow by a rate of 20 per cent per year
to add $16 to its per capita income just to keep the
$720 gap from widening--an annual growth rate so high

TABLE 4

Economic Growth and the Income Gap

	Real National Income Per Caput at 1953 Prices (in U.S.A. $ equivalents)[1]		Annual Growth Rate Per Caput		Income Gap With Respect to the U.S.A.		Direction of Change in the Gap
	1953 $	1962 $	Real Income[1] 1953-61 %	Population[2] 1958-63 %	1953 $	1962 $	
United Kingdom	801	1,000	2.2	0.7	-1,279	-1,298	widening
West Germany	619	1,020	5.7	1.3	-1,461	-1,278	narrowing
Italy	353	571	5.4	0.6	-1,727	-1,727	same
India	65	74	1.4	2.3	-2,015	-2,224	widening
Taiwan	78	107	3.4	3.5	-2,002	-2,191	widening
Japan	189	401	8.8	0.9	-1,891	-1,897	same
United States	2,080	2,298	1.1	1.6			

1. United Nations, Yearbook of National Accounts Statistics, 1963 (New York: U.N., 1963). Computed by applying Annual Growth Rate of Real Income to the 1953 Income and cumulatively to the successive years.
2. United Nations, Statistical Yearbook, 1964 (New York: U.N., 1964).

as is practically impossible of achievement.   Table 4
shows changes in the income gap of selected countries
with respect to the U.S.A. during 1953 to 1962.

What would reduce the income gap would be the
cessation of growth, or even contraction of the economy, in the rich countries and at the same time a
sustained high growth rate in the poor countries.
This, of course, is neither desirable nor practically
feasible because a depression in the industrial countries would greatly hamper the development in the
poor countries, as prices of the poor countries' export goods would fall severely and unemployment in
the rich countries would make less capital available
for development.

Around 1960, there were nearly seventy-five
countries with per capita incomes of less than $200.[4]
Since the European countries with over $600 incomes--
that is, at least three times higher--are likely to
grow at rates of 2 per cent or more, a further widening of the income gap between them and the seventy-
five lowest-income countries appears inevitable at
least for the next decade. A required per capita
growth rate of at least 6 per cent per year (i.e.,
three times the European rate) will not be attainable
by most of the poor countries.

The widening of the income gap between the rich
and the poor nations for some time to come need not
have disastrous consequences for the developing countries. What is of crucial importance is that poor
countries do achieve a vigorous growth rate of around
3 per cent or more in their income per head. There
are two constructive ways by which the unfavorable
psychological and world political impact of this widening gap can be counteracted.

The first consists of the developing countries
increasing their national income in such a way that
the masses of the people become aware that economic
development is primarily benefiting them, is reducing
their daily hunger and want, is expanding their opportunities for achieving a better living and a respected citizenship participation in public affairs.

Their own personal experience of the beneficial impact of development on their opportunities and their
income will greatly stimulate their initiative and
productive efforts, their confidence and participation in the government's plans and programs. It will
accelerate the rate of growth of the economy. Planners and leaders should, of course, remember that the
majority of the people whose support for economic
progress is most needed are in agriculture and the
rural villages. If most of the increase in national
income goes to those who have already a high living
standard, the over-all effect on economic progress, as
well as the effect on political stability, is much
less favorable than if most of the increase goes to
those who have not enough for increasing their productive capacity and achieving a decent living.

The second way to counteract the disadvantages
of a widening income gap consists of the rich countries making available out of their production increases the capital goods so urgently needed by the
developing countries for accelerating their progress.

This should be done preferably in the form of
long-term, low-interest loans repayable out of the
increased future output, rather than in the form of
grants. This is merely an application to the international scene of the age-old practice whereby the
have's save and make capital available for investment
to the have-nots who gain from the resulting production increases enough to better themselves as well as
repay the loans. A well-functioning international
credit and capital market is just as essential to
world economic development as to the progress of an
individual nation, rich or poor. We shall return to
this issue later (see Chapter 14).

The point here is that this widening of the income gap places the rich countries under political
and economic obligation to make sufficient development capital available to the poor countries at
terms acceptable to them. The international credit
market for capital investment is at present pitifully
underdeveloped, most haphazard, and in volume as well
as in terms of repayment conditions woefully

inadequate. The challenge to the high-income countries is to create an international capital market
designed to meet the needs of developing countries,
and to work out corollary trade and payment arrangements enabling them to meet their debt obligations.

NOTES TO CHAPTER 2

1. For a clear exposition of the problems of
food requirements and population growth, see P. V.
Sukhatme, "The World's Hunger and Future Needs in
Food Supplies," Journal of Royal Statistical Society,
Series A, Vol. 124, Part 4 (1961), pp. 463-525; and
Willard W. Cochrane, "The World Food Budget: A For-
ward Look to 2000 and Beyond," World Food Forum
(Washington, D.C.: U.S. Department of Agriculture,
January 1963), pp. 86-95. The world population pro-
jections for 2000 made by the United Nations in 1963
range from a high estimate of 7 billion to a low one
of 5.4 billion, with a medium variant of 6.1 billion.
The 1965 population was 3.3 billion. See United Na-
tions, World Population Prospects as Assessed in 1963
(New York: U.N., 1963).

2. See Simon Kuznets, "Quantitative Aspects of
the Economic Growth of Nations," Economic Development
and Cultural Change, Part II, Vol. V, No. 4 (July
1957).

3. Kuznets, op. cit., Part I, Vol. V, No. 1
(October 1956), p. 15.

4. Hoffman, op. cit., p. 18. Apart from the
very shaky statistical data on which they are based,
they vary widely in the number of items included in
the national account statistics, in the completeness
of coverage of these items, and in the composition of
the national product they represent. On top of these
sources of non-comparability come the distortions involved in converting the many national currencies to
a common monetary unit. All these shortcomings severely impair the reliability of intercountry comparison of national income per head, and particularly
its interpretation in terms of living levels. The

national income data, however, are somewhat more reliable for international comparison of growth rates,
as long as the method of national income accounting
remains the same in each country.

CHAPTER **3** APPROACHES

TO PLANNING

The race against time does not permit the nations of today to let development processes take
their traditional courses. This would yield too slow
a rate of progress.

In the low-income countries, more effective
planning for increased production, for application of
modern technology is needed. Along with the planning
for technical innovations must go planning for economic and social innovations which generate the will
and create the ability of farmers to produce more efficiently. Here the government has a key role to
play.

In the high-income countries, the accent must be
placed on improving and reorienting international capital and commodity markets, trade arrangements and international finance, credit and money transactions.
Such international organizations as the United Nations,
the FAO, the World Bank (IBRD), the International Monetary fund, GATT, various commodity agreements, and
several regional agencies like the European Common
Market (EEC) and the Central American Integration
Scheme are very new intergovernmental planning ven-
tures, and none of them have really grown up yet to
maturity with respect to their indispensable role and
effective functioning required for the years ahead.

In all countries, more planning efforts must be
directed at reducing hunger and poverty, at expanding
the opportunities for the individual's human, social,
and economic growth, for his participation in public
affairs, his responsibility to this community and his
fellowmen, for his freedom and dignity.[1] This holds
for small and large nations, of whatever political

system; it calls for the forging of rules of individual and group conduct, enforceable by responsible
leadership from the village to the city, from the nation to the world.

It is in this broad context of goals and measures that economic development planning needs to be
formulated and implemented. The United Nations and
its Food and Agriculture Organization (FAO), for example, are furthering these efforts through such programs as the "Development Decade" of the U.N., the
"Freedom from Hunger Campaign" of the FAO.

PLANNING: DAYDREAMING OR ACTION?

Everyone is planning. The farmer is planning
his crop rotations, the storekeeper his window dis-
plays. The board of directors is planning investments in factories, space agencies are planning trips
to the moon, and burglars their bank robberies. Everyone who wants to do something must plan, must make
up his mind what he wants to do, and must figure out
how he can accomplish it. Formulating objectives
without working out ways and means to reach them is
daydreaming or playful speculation, but is not planning. Plans must prescribe effective means for
achieving the objectives--lest they be merely shop-
ping lists for things someone feels would be nice to
have.

We are dealing here with government planning.
Government plans affect all the people, directly or
indirectly. Hence, every citizen has a real stake in
the planning carried out by his government.

Planning is as much an art as it is a science.
If art stands for doing, and science for knowing,
planners must not only know what ought to be, but
must also have a realistic sense of what can be done,
and how it can be done. Plans which only deal with a
description of the present situation and a list of
broad goals and global production targets are nice to
talk about, publish and put on bookshelves, but are
not getting something done. For this reason, specific

goals must be selected and so grouped in a plan that
they complement each other, and must be translated
into detailed projects which will make their implementation feasible. This, indeed, is a phase in the
planning process which is as yet little understood
and much neglected.

If goals are stated very broadly, they give no
indication of what lines of action are needed. For
instance, stating the goal of "improving the nutrition of people" gives no indication of what must be
done. This broad goal must be broken down into a set
of specific "program objectives" indicating lines of
action, such as (a) increasing the production of food
most needed for health and work capacity such as
meat, milk, eggs, vegetables, and fruit; (b) education of consumers about what a good diet requires;
(c) enabling consumers to obtain the right kind and
amounts of foods. These are goals of a concrete nature which are operationally useful in designing a
set of practical programs each centered around one of
these "program objectives."

A development plan, therefore, consists of an
integrated set of concrete program objectives, each
with a clearly defined focus, and of specific program
measures required to achieve these objectives. Each
program must be administratively manageable and adequately staffed and financed to assure success. Programs and projects are the operating parts of the
plan, the avenues along which action is taken such as
employing people to do specific jobs, investing capital and manpower in building roads, irrigation systems, etc. Progress in the field and people's homes
depends upon the practical feasibility of these programs. Regardless of how logically beautiful the en-
semble of input and output targets is in an over-all
plan, it will not become useful until the plan is
broken down into operationally feasible projects.[2]

A realistic assessment of political and administrative feasibility of these projects is even more
important for the realization of the plan than the
strict internal consistency of quantitative investment and output targets with which planning economists

tend to be unduly concerned. If the targets for food
crops, for instance, are underfulfilled and those for
industrial export crops are overfulfilled as a result
of some projects working better than expected, and
others worse, the originally delicately planned balance between the inputs (e.g., fertilizers) for various production lines is upset, and a new balance is
found, usually by quite indelicate means of budgetary
controls and transfers of resources from projects
with unexpended funds to projects short of funds.
This happens all the time, in both private and public
sectors, with and without central planning. It would
be sheer folly to cut off a successful project when
its allocation is used up faster than planned, and
keep unused funds indefinitely idle in projects that
do not get off the ground. A rigorous central planning system is very susceptible, indeed, to succumb-
ing to this folly. It has taken the U.S.S.R. several
decades to face up to this problem and begin to solve
it by decentralization of many production decisions
and providing flexibility in resource allocation--
which means losing some of the power of central control over the economy, but gaining efficiency by
stimulating producers' incentives and ingenuity.
Perhaps the most constructive role of decentralization is, in fact, to provide such flexibility and local initiative.

A complete national plan, internally consistent
in its input and output targets and adding up nicely
to a predetermined over-all goal of a 6 per cent
growth rate is great fun to work out; it is an es-
thetic pleasure. But it is like a gorgeous, fully
rigged schooner without wind in its sails, beautiful
to look at but getting nowhere. There are national
development plans that come close to these characteristics.

INSTITUTIONAL INERTIA

It is the implementation aspect of planning
which demands much more effort, much more detailed
attention to practical means for stimulating the motivations of people upon whose work the success of

the plan depends. The most elaborate plan that fails
to elicit the necessary productive efforts of individuals and to provide necessary flexibility to cope
with the vicissitudes of production processes is
bound to fall short of its goals. These problems require more imaginative approaches than have been be-
stowed upon them in the past.[3]

Let us examine briefly how restrictive the lack
of capital is for achieving rapid growth in the developing countries. If we determine the capital requirements of all the developing countries for a 6
per cent annual growth rate of national income, there
can be little doubt that these capital goods could
become available from the combined sources of the
newly developing and the industrial countries without
reducing present living levels. Just consider the
amount of development capital that could become
available if a world disarmament program would release up to 10 per cent of the national income of industrial nations for peaceful developmental purposes.
Consider the additional steel, trucks, farm machinery,
and fertilizer that could be produced merely by running present plants at full capacity month after
month and year after year. Consider all the roads,
market facilities, schools, hospitals, and low-cost
houses in rural and urban areas of developing countries that could be built with local stone, clay,
lumber, and local labor. Soil scientists estimate
that the area under cultivation in the world could be
doubled, and crop yields per acre could be more than
tripled by the application of known techniques.

It is not the insufficient potential quantity of
material resources that is holding back progress; it
is our insufficient knowledge of how to organize ourselves, our wavering will to make the social changes
needed for economic progress that is holding us back.
It is institutional inertia rather than niggardliness
of nature or scarcity of resources that is holding
back progress.

DEFECTS IN THEORY OF PLANNING

Yet, we argue as if the only things that mattered in economic development were quantities of capital and finance, of fertilizer and machines and innumerable other modern inputs. Surely these things matter--but they obviously are not the limiting factors over the years ahead. We certainly know how to produce very much more of them. What we obviously do not know is how to shape institutional arrangements and administrative procedures to make full use of our technical knowledge and production capacity and to motivate people to do what is needed.

Our economic theories and development models are preoccupied with the allocation of materials for a narrowly conceived single goal of maximizing national income. The models do not deal explicitly and in detail with how to make people produce what the model wants, that is with the problems of incentives and organization, nor with who gets the income, that is with the problems of poverty, of bargaining power, and income distribution among different groups of people.

Our theories are not equipped to deal with three crucial sets of variables: (1) organizational aspects regarding how to get resources where they are most needed, and how to improve the organization of production processes; (2) motivational (or incentive) aspects regarding how to make people willing and able to modernize and expand production; and (3) welfare aspects regarding how to guide income distribution into a desirable pattern in which poverty is minimized. It is obviously inappropriate to leave the organizational aspects solely to an assumed competitive market, the motivational aspects solely to the individual profit motive, and to neglect poverty almost entirely, as we do in our planning models. These aspects must be studied in detail, facts about them must be gathered and analyzed, and they must be incorporated in our analysis as key variables rather than as ceteris paribus conditions or vague axiomatic assumptions.

What is needed is a different selection of aspects, factors, and data that must be gathered and interpreted. We must learn to manipulate a variety of incentives inducing people to produce more of high priority goods, to create various opportunities enabling people to produce more efficiently and by so doing achieve living levels well above hunger and poverty. We must drop the implicit assumption that poverty will be eliminated automatically by economic development, and instead introduce explicitly specific institutional arrangements and administrative techniques for reducing poverty, simply because poverty depresses production (both from the supply and the demand sides) and deprives people of human dignity and the exercise of citizenship (see pp. 47-48).

Supply, demand, prices, producer behavior and his alternative opportunities are deeply affected by relative bargaining positions of sellers and buyers, of small farmers and merchants, of laborers and employers, and by the organizational structure of production and distribution processes. New credit arrangements need to be developed giving farmers access to modern inputs where none exists now, and various institutional measures bringing about economies of scale in selling, buying and producing which can be made to work on small farms. All these aspects-- and there are many more--deal with behavioral characteristics of individuals and groups, with organizational aspects of marketing and production processes, and with the bargaining power of various groups such as landlords and tenants, merchants and farmers, employers and laborers.

Econometric analysis can be useful, if it is applied within the framework of an institutional economic model in which the production incentives and income opportunities, the bargaining power of various groups, the working conditions of laborers, and the socio-economic welfare and production aspects of income distribution are sufficiently specified to guide resource allocation and the composition of the national product in desirable directions.[4] The proposition that all that matters is "maximizing" the national income, and that once produced the income

increases will "trickle down" and eliminate poverty
automatically is obviously wrong. The riches from oil
and other mineral resources have not trickled through
to farmers and laborers in Saudi Arabia and Venezuela, in the Congo and Iran.

NATIONAL INCOME AND LEVELS OF LIVING

National income or the gross national product is
usually taken as the dominant indicator of national
welfare. The ultimate goal of development planning
is formulated as the maximization of national income,
of the sum of all goods and services produced. It
appears as the single-purpose goal of economic progress. National income is expressed in one single
figure, in terms of some monetary unit (dollars or
rupees or pesos, etc.), with all the different goods
and services valued at market prices, whatever they
happened to be at certain periods (or imputed prices
somehow derived from market prices). The national
income, this single figure, tells nothing about income distribution and the extent of poverty, composition of the national product, relative prices of the
component products, and many other aspects which
deeply affect the levels of living and the general
welfare of people, especially of those in the lower-
income groups.

A recent study illustrates clearly how misleading an exclusive preoccupation with "maximizing" national income can be in development planning. Table
5 shows great discrepancies between national income
per head and level of living. A well-conceived index of living levels has been worked out recently in
the United Nations Research Institute for Social Development.[5] This index consists of seven components:
nutrition, housing, health, education, leisure (or
recreation), security (personal safety, insurance
against losses from unemployment, illness, death,
and old-age pension), and "higher needs and comforts"
(surplus over the basic necessities of living). For
combining these seven components into a composite
level of living index, the weights assigned to the
first six components (reflecting the basic needs of

TABLE 5

National Income Per Head and Level of Living Index

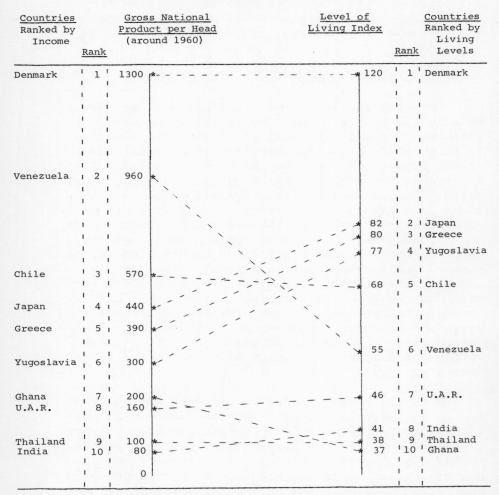

Countries Ranked by Income	Rank	Gross National Product per Head (around 1960)	Level of Living Index		Rank	Countries Ranked by Living Levels
Denmark	1	1300		120	1	Denmark
Venezuela	2	960				
				82	2	Japan
				80	3	Greece
				77	4	Yugoslavia
Chile	3	570		68	5	Chile
Japan	4	440				
Greece	5	390				
				55	6	Venezuela
Yugoslavia	6	300				
Ghana	7	200		46	7	U.A.R.
U.A.R.	8	160				
				41	8	India
Thailand	9	100		38	9	Thailand
India	10	80		37	10	Ghana
		0				

Source: Jan Drewnowski and Wolf Scott, The Level of Living Index, U.N. Research Institute for Social Development, Report No. 4 (Geneva: U.N. Research Institute for Social Development, September 1966), p. 71; income based on official exchange rates; index based on sliding weights.

34

(people) are increased according to their deficiency
from the adequacy norm of the respective performance.
For instance, if the norm for adequate nutrition is
100, and the average component index of nutrition in
a country is found to be 50, the weight given to the
component is 2 (100:50); if the component is 100, its
weight is 1 (100:100); if it is 130, its weight is
0.8 (100:130). This pulls the composite level of
living index down as the deficiencies of basic needs
grow. Hence, the index reflects, at least to some
extent, the lack of basic necessities, the degree of
poverty.

Take, for example, Venezuela in Table 5. It
ranks second in income per head, with by far the
highest income of the nine developing countries represented, but drops to sixth place on the level of
living scale, because it is much more deficient in
some or all of the basic needs than the four other
developing countries, despite the fact that these
have a much lower income per head than Venezuela.
One of the reasons for this may be that its high oil
production and export boost its national income, but
very little of it benefits the great masses of farmers and workers throughout the country.

On the other side, take Japan. It ranks fourth
in income per head, but second in level of living,
with the highest index among the developing countries. This means, that although Japan has a per
capita income of less than one-half of that of Venezuela, its people are very much better supplied with
the necessities of life and suffer much less from poverty.

In the process of development planning, we can
very profitably place much greater emphasis on raising the level of living, and use it as a more reliable measure of economic development than the national
income (see Chapter 4).

ALLOCATIVE AND INSTITUTIONAL PLANNING

It is generally assumed that accelerating the
economic growth in developing countries requires more

comprehensive and centralized planning than has been
applied in the past. This creates a bit of a dilemma.
Some economic planners argue that an over-all, well-
balanced development plan (which logically implies
that it be centrally controlled and implemented)
promises a much more efficient use of scarce resources, while others argue that private enterprise with
a minimum of government interference is much more efficient in raising production. As often in doctrinal
arguments, the truth lies somewhere in between.

There are two types of planning:

1. Allocative planning deals with the direct
government allocation of capital, manpower, and land
resources to specific economic sectors and lines of
production;
2. Institutional framework planning deals with
establishing standards of behavior, "rules of the
game," inducements and deterrents, regulatory measures and similar institutional arrangements guiding
and circumscribing people's actions.

Allocative planning in Western economies per-
tains mainly to the public sector: The government
decides how much shall be invested in education,
roads, public health, military defense, etc. In the
private sector, government does not apply allocative
planning at all. How much should be invested in
textile, chemical, machine-tool, crop and livestock
production, and the various service trades is left to
private firms and the investors, to farmers and managers of factories.

Still, the government exercises strong influence
on the private sector through an institutional framework of laws and regulatory measures such as minimum
wages, standards of working conditions and collective
bargaining, support of farmers' cooperatives, low-cost
housing, etc., and specific inducement measures such
as fiscal policy, social security measures, subsidies, and loan guaranties designed to guide resources
or income streams into certain directions, in the interest of the country and its people as a whole.

From this, it should be clear that in non-Communist countries, over-all allocative planning is
much less important than institutional framework
planning, since allocative planning applies only to
a small public sector, while institutional framework
planning applies to the large private sector which
comprises 80 to 90 per cent of the total economy.
The proportion of government expenditures (including
military) in the national income is rarely above 20
per cent and usually well below that level in most
non-Communist countries.[6]

National development planning promises to become
much more effective if institutional framework planning is given the dominant role in the planning procedure. Allocative planning, of course, retains a
crucially important function even if it is given a
supporting role limited mainly to the public sector
and to a few key aspects of fiscal, monetary, and
foreign trade controls needed to assure a quantitative
balance in aggregate input-output relationships, investment and consumption rates, and foreign trade.

This shift in the approach to planning, from the
excessive preoccupation with allocative planning so
characteristic of econometric development models, to
a realistic assessment of the need for institutional
framework planning, is bound to make development planning much more effective in accelerating the rate of
economic progress.

If private incentives are properly guided by effective institutional frameworks, by inducements to
produce in the interest of the people's welfare, and
by deterrents to its detriment, the over-all results
in aggregate output and economic growth are likely to
be better, especially in the long run, than the results of detailed allocative planning under a centrally controlled economy.

The duplication or waste of resources that often
does result from spontaneous development in the private sector can be more than offset by (1) the more
efficient and flexible use of the resources under the

stimulus of individual motivations, and (2) by institutional and regulatory government measures inducing
desirable and restraining undesirable production and
other business activities.

In a slightly facetious vein, I submit that institutional framework planning serves the function
which Adam Smith attributed to the "invisible hand"
which leads the individual to promote the nation's
welfare by pursuing his own self-interest.

TOWARD A SYNTHESIS OF PLANNED
AND SPONTANEOUS ECONOMIC ACTIVITIES

Theoretically, we can conceive of a national
economy which is minutely controlled by central planning. This would be the "pure case" of a socialist
state enterprise economy. In reality, no such state
exists, nor ever will exist. A recent study estimates, for instance, that about 50 per cent of total
milk and meat production, over 60 per cent of pota-
toes and over 80 per cent of egg production in the
U.S.S.R. originated in the private sector.[7] Moreover, some production decisions even within the public
sector are left to managers of industrial concerns,
individual factories, and collective farms; these
managers are making decisions and operate in a way
quite similar to private producers.

Since the 1950's, the trend in Communist countries has been in the direction of expanding opportunities for individual initiative and income incentives on the production side, and greater choice in
goods and services on the consumer side. This trend
was seen first in agriculture, the most difficult
sector to plan centrally, as we shall see later.
Yugoslavia, Poland, the U.S.S.R., and even Mainland
China have recently made changes in their agriculture
in the direction of decentralizing planning and control. The U.S.S.R. repeatedly loosened the central
planning reins on agriculture and gave more freedom
and responsibility to the collective farms and their
managers in the 1950's and 1960's. Recently, the
same trend is evident in industry, by the reduction

in the central allocative control of supplies to individual factories, by giving managers more freedom
to purchase their supplies in the market and to gear
their production more closely to the demand and preferences of consumers. Along with this liberalization, new production incentives in the form of higher
income rewards are offered to individual factories
and workers.[8] These trends are clearly reflected in
the 1966-70 Five-Year Plan of the U.S.S.R.

Alternatively, we can conceive of a national
economy wherein the government does not interfere in
private production decisions of entrepreneurs and in
the market price system. Again, this "pure case" of
a "laissez-faire" private enterprise system does not,
nor ever will, exist. Even during the last half of
the nineteenth century up to World War I, when the
Western countries developed under an avowed laissez-
faire policy, government played an active regulatory
and institutional framework planning role in many
fields of activities.[9] It controlled prices of various public utilities like electricity and rail transport, subsidized shipping, licensed various professions and services, gave import duty protection to
certain industries, supported agricultural settlement, and improved tenure conditions of farmers, to
mention just a few regulatory functions of government.

Since that time, the role of government has
greatly expanded. Institutional framework planning
leads to government measures of improving the bargaining position and economic opportunities of workers and farmers, the income distribution through progressive income taxes and a series of social security
and welfare programs providing for unemployment compensation, old-age pensions, medical care, etc. Contrary to the prophecies of ardent free enterprisers,[10]
all these government interventions did not impair the
initiative, efficiency, and justifiable income rewards
of private producers, as can be seen from the remarkable increase in production and per capita income in
the Western countries since the 1940's.

In fact, the result of these government functions in promoting economic welfare, in equalizing

opportunities and bargaining strength between the weak and the strong, the poor and the rich, has been the distribution of mass purchasing power over larger and larger portions of the population. This created a buoyant demand and stimulated production and economic growth. Instead of sapping the vigor of private enterprise, these government welfare policies have expanded its markets and guided its activities in more desirable directions than would have been the case otherwise. The modern private enterprise system bears little resemblance to the "capitalism" which Karl Marx knew a century ago. It is evolving into a "mixed economy," in which private enterprise thrives under the guidance, stimulation, and restraints of government plans and programs. Even the most serious imperfection in the modern Western mixed economies, the persistence of large poverty groups in the midst of affluent societies, could be corrected by institutional framework planning within the mixed economy system. All this can be achieved by keeping allocative planning limited primarily to the public sector, to infrastructural investments, and various government services which, of course, need to expand also in support of general economic growth.

Clearly, the directions in which the Communist and non-Communist economic systems move are converging. The orthodox system of state enterprise is moving from a rigorously planned central government control of both production and consumption toward decentralization, toward greater flexibility and freedom of individual enterprises, and wider choices for consumers.[11] The orthodox nineteenth century capitalist system of private enterprise is moving from a laissez-faire policy of uncontrolled spontaneous economic activities toward greater social responsibility, toward government planning and guiding private activities in the interest of national welfare, and of abolishing poverty. Both systems converge toward a "mixed economy," a new synthesis of government planning and spontaneous individual activities, through policies and institutional arrangements which offer the individual ample leeway for private initiative, adequate but not excessive income rewards, and choices among opportunities for producing and consuming.

At the same time these government planning functions protect the common good, restrain the strong
from abusing their power, stimulate the weak for developing their capacities. This promising convergence of the two economic systems is proof of the
basic similarity of the ideological forces motivating people in the Communist and non-Communist countries: People on both sides of the curtain share
the fundamental humanist belief in the equality of
man and human dignity.

NOTES TO CHAPTER 3

1. This is not my subjective value judgement,
but is the objectively observable value judgement
achieving dominance in modern society, and as such
constitutes a datum for economists and other social
scientists. For a thought-provoking discussion of
this issue see Robert Theobald, The Rich and the
Poor (New York: New American Library, Inc., 1960),
especially Part One, pp. 11-74.

2. Albert Waterston, Development Planning:
Lessons of Experience (Baltimore, Md.: Johns
Hopkins Press, 1965), pp. 293-370.

3. See, for instance, an interesting review of
planning procedures by Clair Wilcox, The Planning
and Execution of Economic Development in Southeast
Asia, Occasional Papers in International Affairs,
No. 10 (Cambridge, Mass.: Center for International
Affairs, Harvard University, January 1965).

4. For a penetrating discussion of the importance of "non-economic" variables and constraints in
economic planning, see B. S. Yamey, "The Study of
Peasant Economic Systems: Some Concluding Comments
and Questions," Saving and Credit in Peasant Societies, Firth and Yamey, eds., (Chicago, Ill.: Aldine
Publishing Co., 1964), pp. 376-86.

5. See Jan Drewnowski and Wolf Scott, The Level
of Living Index, U.N. Research Institute for Social

Development, Report No. 4 (Geneva: U.N. Research Institute for Social Development, September 1966).

6. For instance, in 1964, government consumption expenditures in per cent of the gross national
product amounted to 18 per cent in the U.S.A., 17 per
cent in the U.K., 13 per cent in France, 14 per cent
in Brazil, 10 per cent in Japan, and 6 per cent in
Mexico--to mention just a few of the major countries.
The public sector in most of the non-Communist nations
accounts for 10-15 per cent of the GNP. This includes government expenditures on contracts to private firms, e.g., for armaments and construction of
roads, schools, etc., but does not include government
subsidies and transfers to households and private non-
profit institutions. See United Nations, Yearbook of
National Accounts Statistics, 1965 (New York: U.N.,
1965), p. 454.

7. A. N. Sakoff, "The Private Sector in Soviet
Agriculture," Monthly Bulletin of Agricultural Economics and Statistics, Vol. 11, No. 9 (September 1962),
pp. 1-12.

8. See Jerzy F. Karcz, "The New Soviet Agricultural Programme," Soviet Studies, Vol. XVII, No. 2
(October 1965).

9. See Edward S. Mason, Economic Planning in
Underdeveloped Areas: Government and Business (New
York: Fordham University Press, 1958), pp. 21-40.

10. See, for instance, Friedrich A. Hayek, The
Road to Serfdom (Chicago, Ill.: University of Chicago Press, 1944).

11. For an excellent discussion of this trend,
see Rudolf Bicanic, "Economics of Socialism in a Developed Country," Foreign Affairs, Vol. 44, No. 4
(July 1966), pp. 633-50. This article deals primarily
with recent shifts in government policy in Yugoslavia. As to the U.S.S.R., see Peter Wiles, "Convergence: Possibility and Probability," Planning and
the Market in the USSR: The 1960's (New Brunswick,
N.J.: Rutgers University Press, 1967), pp. 89-118.

CHAPTER **4** GOALS OF DEVELOPMENT
PLANNING: INCREASE
PRODUCTION AND REDUCE POVERTY

Clearly, a determined effort in economic planning is required to accelerate the rate of progress.
The question is: What is the most effective way to
do it?

We have seen earlier that most national development plans deal predominantly with the allocation of
resources for the purpose of maximizing national income, and that this exclusive preoccupation with production for its own sake is not enough to sustain a
vigorous rate of economic progress (see pp. 32-33).

POVERTY--AN OBSTACLE TO PROGRESS

The most pervasive obstacle to economic progress
is poverty. More than a billion farmers who produce
the bulk of the world's food have been living in an
environment of severe poverty for centuries, and many
of these environmental conditions have become so in-
stitutionalized that they function as formidable obstacles to agricultural production expansion, to the
emancipation of the peasant, and to economic progress
in general. They are so deeply embedded in the local
economic system and power structure that farmers cannot overcome them by their individual effort. The
same holds for the millions of poor workers in the
cities. We cannot eliminate these obstacles unless
we deal with them specifically in our development
plans, unless we study them and formulate effective
programs to overcome them.

First, let us look at the progress-retarding effect of poverty from the production side. Poverty

creates many severe obstacles to increasing production. Hunger and malnutrition reduces man's health and physical energy, his work capacity, and even his mental alertness. Lack of education keeps him ignorant and in a weak position vis-à-vis employer, landlord, creditor, and merchant, which discourages him from taking initiative in technological innovations. He feels that he would get little, if anything, from the increased production because of his weak bargaining position. His low income does not permit purchase of modern inputs for productive investment in his farm or workshop, which means he has no access to the new types of inputs. His living at the margin of bare subsistence makes him highly vulnerable to risk losses involved in innovations, such as loss of his fertilizer investment due to drought or pests, or in some cases even loss of his livelihood, his occupancy on the land, if he joins a cooperative against the wish of his landlord or loses his land through foreclosure to a moneylender. Poverty not only saps people's will and ability to produce, but also holds down the productive effort of the well-to-do worker, industrialist, and investor by depressing the demand for goods and services.

This leads us to the second progress-retarding effect of poverty: It reduces the market demand for consumption and production goods, and hence reduces investment opportunities, and hence capital formation for output expansion. This chain of events has been demonstrated dramatically by every major business depression, but it exists in a chronic and submerged way in low-income countries with its hidden effect of disappointingly low rates of progress. This holds particularly for industrial development, because it does not take much industry to saturate the demand for the necessities of life of the small high-income group, and most luxuries such as cars, air conditioners, and whisky cannot be produced at home, but must be imported. Domestic industrial development in low-income countries depends primarily upon production of necessities of life, of food, clothing, shoes, housing, furniture, education, health, and many other goods and services, to meet the needs of the vast majority of people. If this is to be accomplished mainly under a private enterprise system,[1] it is essential that the effective market demand for these goods and services increase sufficiently to meet the needs. This increased demand can come only from the large masses of poor people, by reducing their poverty and increasing their purchasing power.

Economic progress, and especially industrialization, under modern technological and economic conditions depends heavily upon a wide distribution of purchasing power throughout the masses of consumers--and this means that economic progress in modern times depends upon reduction of poverty.

PRIORITY FOR NECESSITIES OF LIFE

It becomes clear that development planning designed to maximize national income mainly for reducing poverty and distributing purchasing power widely throughout the population is bound to be more effective, more dynamic in promoting a high rate of self-sustaining growth, than planning for production per se.

For instance, increasing production for reducing poverty would call for more farm-to-market roads, schools and hospitals, more low-cost housing and clothing, more protective foods such as meat, eggs, milk, vegetables, fruits, more trucks and tractors and small cars. It would call for relatively (though perhaps not absolutely) less luxury apartments and hotels, less sumptuous bank, insurance, business, and government administration buildings, less air conditioners and other imported symbols of affluence.

There are great differences in consumers' needs and preferences between various groups of the population, according to income, age, sex, occupation, and cultural traits. A certain size and composition of the national income favors one of these groups more than another. A national income which includes more fur coats and _filets mignon_ favors the rich; one that includes more jewelry favors the women; one with more

GOSHEN COLLEGE LIBRARY
GOSHEN, INDIANA 46526

bars favors the men; one with more old-age homes favors the old. What weights should be assigned to the
needs and preferences of these various groups? The
weighting of these various consumer preferences in
conventional development plans is mainly by market
prices. This means, in effect, by personal income,
by purchasing power, since prices and quantities of
goods in the market reflect consumers' ability to
pay. Hence, the consumer preferences of the rich are
given a much greater weight than the needs of the
poor.

For instance, a recent survey in Chile revealed
that the top 10 per cent of the families received 43
per cent of the national income.[2] In India, the top
25 per cent received about 50 per cent of the national income.[3] It is therefore inevitable that
planning targets based on market demand and prices
cater to the consumer preferences of the rich, and
discriminate against the needs of the poor. Families
who lack the money to buy even the bare necessities
of life are out of the market. Their demand is not
effective, is not registered in market prices, does
not bring forth the supplies of the things they need.
Hence, market prices steer investment and production
away from the necessities of life rather than toward
them.[4]

There is ample historical evidence of this fact.
During the early stages of the Western Industrial Revolution, national income increased but so did abject
poverty among millions of workers in "sweatshops" of
factories and in mines and in agricultural plantations. The increased wealth trickled down from the
top slowly and rarely beyond the middle class of
technicians, factory "bosses" and managers, businessmen and professionals. Income distribution was left
entirely to the market forces, with the result that
poverty remained much longer and more widespread than
the rising wealth of the country warranted. This, in
turn, led to much human suffering, unemployment and
depressions, strife and political unrest. The newly
developing countries can avoid this unhappy phase of
early Western industrialization.

In economic planning, the consumer needs of the poor must be given a higher priority, instead of a lower one, relative to the consumer preferences of the rich. This is not a personal value judgement that you or I may or may not hold. It is a basic socio-economic value held by modern democratic societies throughout the world, and hence has to be treated by the economist as a datum, as a socio-political condition to which economic growth must be accommodated.

All modern societies, regardless of culture and political system, give evidence of people's belief that meeting the needs for the necessities of life should have some degree of precedence over meeting the demand for comforts and luxuries. The whole concept of economic welfare in private enterprise countries as well as in Communist countries is based upon this belief. Its roots reach deep into the ideology of humanist democracy, of the freedom and dignity of the individual, very much deeper than the belief in the justice of the free marketplace.[5]

Economic planning, therefore, must be oriented toward steering more resources into the production of necessities of life, and toward measures making these necessities accessible to the poor. This holds with particular force for the developing countries where poverty is so widespread and where a self-sustaining and rapid rate of economic development depends so heavily upon the creation of mass purchasing power and a buoyant domestic demand for the products of modernized agriculture and many new industries, trades, and services.

Raising the productivity of the masses of farmers and workers is essential both for economic growth and for reducing poverty. It surely is not enough to depend only on the top 10 per cent of present producers --although one may be tempted to do so because they are usually better educated, control more resources per person and are (perhaps often wrongly) considered more receptive to technical innovations for output expansion. They alone will not be able to sustain

economic growth because there will not be the necessary concomitant expansion of demand for the increasing output, nor will the rest of the people acquiesce
to being left out of the benefits of progress. A development plan providing education and access to capital, production incentives, and income opportunities
to low-income producers, as well as encouraging the
higher-income producers, will bring forth much higher
production increases and a much more widely distributed purchasing power to sustain a buoyant demand.
This holds at least in the longer run. Whatever head
start might be gained by an initial dependence on a
small producer elite is fraught with social and political dangers and economic setbacks. Unless the great
majority of people feel they are partners in progress
and noticeably benefiting from it, the economy will
soon run into trouble.

     The problem is to channel additional investments
into products benefiting the poor, making them more
efficient as producers and better customers as consumers. This requires that additional income is being channeled to low-income groups at a relatively
higher rate than to high-income groups.

     This can be done without "soaking the rich,"
without transferring present income from the rich to
the poor. Conventional thought is still caught in
the experience of past centuries where economies
were static and no one could get richer without someone getting poorer. Today, reducing poverty is no
longer such a "zero-sum game" wherein the sum of all
gains and losses is zero. Instead, as long as national income grows faster than population, it is
possible for the poor to become richer without the
rich becoming poorer.

     Some people might ask why a redistribution of
some present income from the rich to the poor would
not be justified. Under certain conditions such a
transfer of income might indeed help to reduce poverty and at the same time increase total production.
For instance, this might be possible where agricultural areas are owned by a few large landowners who
show no interest in developing modern agriculture and

in letting their tenants and workers reap the reward
from increased productivity of their labor. In fact,
this transfer of income happens in revolutions when
landlords have their land expropriated without compensation. However, unless such a land redistribution is immediately accompanied by effective extension services, cooperatives, credit, and supplies of
fertilizer and other modern inputs, production will
not increase and may actually decline for some years
or even a decade or more. This happened in Mexico
following the 1910 revolution, in the U.S.S.R. during
the 1920's.

The point to be stressed here is that government
measures to reduce poverty need not and should not
depress production and national income, and, indeed,
should contribute to its increase, and that these
measures can be so designed that the knowledge and
the organizational experience of producers in the
higher-income groups are not lost to the national effort of accelerating economic progress.

HOW TO MEASURE POVERTY

The terms "rich" and "poor" are used here for
brevity's sake and do not divide a country's population into such distinct groups. In advanced industrial countries, for instance, the majority of people
are neither rich nor poor in the colloquial sense of
the term, but fall in a middle-income group stretch-
ing from a minimum adequate living standard called
the "poverty line" up to an income level called the
"affluence line" beyond which a family cannot spend
its income on normal consumption without indulging in
spending habits considered extravagant by most people.
The term "poor" refers to families living below the
poverty line, and the term "rich" to families living
safely above that line, that is, the "non-poor" whose
access to the necessities of life is well assured.

A clear-cut distinction between the "poor" and
the "rich" (or the "non-poor") segments of the population is neither required nor desirable. It is sufficient to determine the extent of the unfulfilled

needs for living essentials of the low-income groups, to plan for a larger rate of increase of these needed goods than the market forces would bring forth, and to provide for measures which make these living essentials accessible to low-income families through increasing their productivity and income, through concessional prices of selected goods, free public services, and other measures. For establishing standards which can be applied in such programs, the consumption patterns of families just clearly above the "poverty line" can be used.

The extent of poverty can best be measured by two criteria:

(1) The <u>poverty rate</u> which is the proportion of the people falling below the "poverty line";

(2) The <u>poverty income gap</u> which is the income it would take to bring all the poor up to the poverty line.

For instance, the U.S.A. launched an antipoverty program in recent years. In 1963, nearly 20 per cent of the American families fell below the poverty line which was determined to be around $3,000 for a family of four, or $750 per person per year. Hence, the "poverty rate" in the U.S.A. at that time was 20 per cent. To bring these 9 million families up to the poverty line it would take $12 billion, or 2 per cent of the national income.[6] This means that the "poverty income gap" was 2 per cent of the national income. With an annual growth rate of 3 per cent per capita, it would be theoretically possible to keep per capita consumption of all families above the poverty line stable or even allowing a small raise, and allocate resources for that year in such a way as to produce $12 billion worth of necessities, and to channel them to the 9 million families below the poverty line most urgently in need. In practice this is, of course, not possible in a literal sense. But the general principle and a feasible approximation to its achievement is sound and in line with economic progress and social welfare.

To put this principle in more concrete terms:
Assume that a developing country in Asia has a per
capita national income of $100 and a population of
10 million. Estimates are made of the extent of poverty, i.e., of the number of families with a real income below the poverty line or a "minimum adequate
living standard," and of the poverty income gap (see
Table 6 below).

The approximate number of people below the poverty line and their average income can be estimated.
A high degree of accuracy for such estimates is not
needed, since the policy measures for reducing poverty are necessarily selective, dealing only with a
few key necessities in a rather flexible way. What
is important is that they work in the right direction, and that the planners have some idea of the
order of magnitude of poverty in relation to national
income and population. These are considerations that
belong in any growth model, in any national development plan, and that do not require an elaborate set
of quantitative production targets for the economy as
a whole. Instead, they require a few critical standards of consumption for a few selected necessities
of life, and a few administratively feasible institutional and regulatory policy measures which modify
only slightly, but importantly, the workings of the
production and market forces in both the private and
public sectors of the economy.

The "poverty line" can only be determined by a
consensus of planners, civic and government leaders,
based on considerations of present incomes and their
distribution among the population, of priority of
needs of the low-income group in view of their own
aspirations, and of certain standards for education,
health and housing considered desirable and within
reach over a five-to ten-year period of development.
In our example in Table 6, the poverty line is around
80 per cent of the average income level, and 50 per
cent of the population live below that level. This
level is very low compared to industrialized countries, but is still higher than that achieved by 50

TABLE 6

Estimates of Magnitude of Poverty
in a Country[1]
(Hypothetical Example)

(1)	Population	10 million
(2)	National income	$1,000 million
(3)	Per capita income	$100
(4)	Poverty line determined by socio-economic consensus (80 per cent of average per capita income)	$80
(5)	Estimated number of people below poverty line (50 per cent)	5 million
(6)	Estimated average per capita income of the poor	$55
(7)	Total income of the poor (55 times 5 million people)	$275 million
(8)	<u>Deficit from poverty line (80-55) times 5 million poor people</u>	$125 million
(9)	Poverty deficit in per cent of national income	12.5%

---

1. All estimates derived from the income distri-
    bution, i.e., items (5), (6) and (7), are
    based upon the actual income distribution in
    India, reported by P. D. Ojha and V. V.
    Bhatt, "Pattern of Income Distribution in an
    Underdeveloped Economy: A Case Study of In-
    dia," <u>American Economic Review</u>, Vol. 54, No.
    5 (September 1964), pp. 711-20.

per cent of the people, and hence can serve as a target which might be brought within reach for perhaps
two thirds of the poor over a five- to ten-year period.
As the country develops, this poverty line will rise
along with the national income. For planning purposes, the poverty line, i.e., the minimum adequate
living standard, might best be redetermined every
five years, or at least every ten years.[7]

In our example, the poverty income gap is around
12 per cent of the national income. Theoretically,
this "income deficit" could be wiped out in four
years, if the country maintains a 3 per cent rate of
growth in per capita income and channels all the increase into the real income stream of the poor.
Practically, this is not possible--except, perhaps,
under a strict central distribution system of rationing and administrative certification of families
classed as "poor," a system which not even the highly
centralized Communist economies have ever applied.
The "poverty line" should never appear rigorously
drawn in actual life, and over a planning period a
number of the poor families will move above the poverty line well before all the rest of the poor will
have reached it. Some families have lower aspirations and cling to their traditional consumption habits longer than others who are more eager to progress
and would be thwarted by the lack of production incentives under an inflexible rationing system.

PROGRAMS FOR REDUCING POVERTY

This over-all measure of poverty does not indicate what specific goods and services are most urgently needed to raise low incomes to an acceptable
level of living. There are two basic types of necessities of life distinguished by the way they become
accessible to people:

(1) Those people can receive through <u>public
services</u> free of charge, such as elementary education, roads, public health services, and sanitary water supplies;
(2) Those which people must buy out of their

own personal income or _family budget_, such as food, clothing, household goods, and housing.

This is not the place to go into the details of antipoverty programs. I shall only highlight some critical aspects.

For the _public-service type of necessities_, the formulation of planning targets is comparatively simple. Minimum standards for education, health, and roads can be made accessible to everyone without cumbersome administrative machinery. Feasible minimum standards have to be worked out, and financial allocations have to be made for meeting these standards in low-income areas, and especially in rural areas that are often seriously deficient in these necessities.[8] (See Chapter 7.) With respect to economic development, a significant part of the poverty income gap can be closed by reducing the deficiencies of poor people and many rural areas in these basic necessities directly affecting the productivity of people and their access to markets.

For the _family-budget type of necessities_, the implementation of adequate minimum standards is more difficult to achieve. Production, distribution, and consumption of these goods are left to the workings of the market forces, except in emergencies such as wars and famines when government establishes rationing programs, at least for some goods, out of sheer necessity to prevent riots and wholesale starvation.

Yet, the lack of adequate kinds and amounts of food is often the most debilitating aspect of poverty. Hunger renders people physically unproductive, mentally indolent, emotionally despondent. Malnutrition produces a wide variety of malfunctioning of body and mind, and renders people vulnerable to many diseases. This holds particularly for children. Even the learning capacity of school children is severely reduced by malnutrition.[9]

Clothing is also a necessity of life which requires more attention in economic planning. Its deficiency is often closely related to certain diseases,

such as hookworms (through going barefoot), or res-
piratory diseases and chilblains (in cold and wet
climates), and hence to lower productive capacity.
With the conglomeration of people in fast-growing
cities, clothes become more important for health and
human dignity and vocational requirements. Gaining
a sense of self-respect is a fundamental necessity
for the poor in modern society. In fact, rags are
the most visible and degrading badge of poverty
throughout the world.

As in the case of food, various ways can be
worked out for making selected items of food and
clothing available to low-income people in local
stores at reasonable prices within their ability to
pay. For instance, in some countries school lunches
and standard clothes for pupils are provided free or
at a nominal charge. In general, perhaps the most
effective means for making sufficient food and clothing available to the poor is to establish ample production targets for low-cost food and clothing and
provide for marketing arrangements involving a minimum amount of service charges and perhaps supervision
of dealers' margins, so that adequate supplies become
available throughout rural villages and in low-income
areas in cities at prices people can afford to pay.

In principle, programs for reducing poverty con-
sist of three kinds:

(1) Making education, health, and other public
services available to the poor, free or at minimal
rates;
(2) Increasing the productivity of labor of the
poor and their income so that they can pay out of
their personal income for an adequate supply of the
necessities of life by giving them access to capital
and credit and strengthening their bargaining power
in the market;
(3) Providing for the necessities of life of
the non-employables, the sick and the old people, the
mothers and children of broken families, by effective
social security programs.

Only the last of these measures involves a "redistribution" of current national income without direct

effect upon labor productivity (except indirectly by supporting the demand for goods and services and by giving children a chance for a decent upbringing). The first two kinds of programs for reducing poverty contribute directly and strongly to the nation's productivity and economic progress.[10]

CONSUMPTION PATTERNS, EAST AND WEST

Comparison of consumption patterns in the U.S.S.R. and the United States reveals that although Russia has a per capita income much lower than the United States, the consumption rates of basic necessities are nearly as high or higher. This indicates that a high priority is given to the production of essential goods and services in the development planning, and a low priority to luxury goods.

For instance, in 1958, the per capita consumption of low-cost food items, of wool and cotton fabrics, of bicycles and sewing machines, of urban housing with electricity, of education, books, pamphlets and movies, in the U.S.S.R. was nearly as high or higher than in the United States. Medical doctors per 10,000 population were 30 per cent higher, and hospital beds only 20 per cent lower. In contrast, per capita consumption of automobiles, TV sets, refrigerators, telephones, and other high-cost durable consumption goods was less than 15 per cent of the United States[11] (see Table 7).

This means that with respect to low-cost food, clothing, durable consumer goods, education, and medical services, the average Russian is about as adequately supplied as the average American, despite the fact that his income is probably less than half as high. These low-cost goods and services may give the family consumption pattern a rather dull and somewhat dreary look, but they are essential for a normal family to live in health and decency and to contribute its productive effort and active participation to the community's economic development.

TABLE 7

Differences in Consumption Patterns,
U.S.S.R. and U.S.A., 1958[1]

Per Capita Consumer Income
33% of U.S.A.

Per Capita Consumption Rates,
U.S.S.R. in Per Cent of U.S.A.
(U.S.A. = 100)

	Living Essentials (High Priority Items, over 60% of U.S.A.)		Luxury Goods (Low Priority Items, under 15% of U.S.A.)	
Food:	Potatoes	314		
	Flour	274		
	Fish	117		
	Milk	71		
Clothing:	Wool fabrics	107		
	Cotton fabrics	60		
Consumer Durables:	Motorcycles	850	Cars	12
	Sewing machines	108	TV sets	14
	Bicycles	89	Washing machines	11
			Refrigerators	9
			Vacuum cleaners	6
Housing, Utilities:	Electricity in urban housing	96	Central heating in urban housing	7
			Telephones	3
Education, Publications:	School enrollment	80[2]		
	Books and Pamphlets	83	Periodicals	7
	Movies attended	107		
Medical Care:	Doctors	130		
	Hospital beds	79		

1. Based on data in Abram Bergson and Simon Kuznets, eds., Economic Trends in the Soviet Union (Cambridge, Mass.: Harvard University Press, 1963), pp. 252-53. The figures represent U.S.S.R. physical consumption rates per capita in per cent of U.S.A. "High and low priority" refers to the issue of reducing poverty.
2. Source: United Nations, Statistical Yearbook, 1963 (New York: 1963). Per cent of population attending school was 26.7 per cent in the U.S.A. and 21.4 per cent in the U.S.S.R.

Another good example for the emphasis on necessities for modern life in the state enterprise economies is the priority given to education. Comparing Eastern European Communist countries with Southern non-Communist countries of similar income levels, we find that in the Soviet Union, Czechoslovakia, Hungary, Rumania, and Poland about 20-22 per cent of the population attend school, while in Spain, Portugal, and Greece only 13-15 per cent do.[12]

But man does not live by bread alone. Many luxury goods and services are still essential for the cultural enrichment of life. They are the source of enjoyment of a great variety of activities and experiences, many of which affect human productivity favorably. Developing countries will certainly aim at raising their production of both necessities and luxury goods. In practical terms, giving higher priority to the necessities simply means that as long as many people live in acute poverty, the rate of increase in the production of necessities is to be kept greater than that of luxury goods.

A REORIENTED NATIONAL DEVELOPMENT PLAN

It is quite possible to take account of these considerations within the general economic development plan. Such a reoriented plan would have the following characteristics distinguishing it from the conventional or "classical" planning model:

(1) A specific allocation of resources is made for increases in the production of necessities of life at a rate substantially greater than the average planned growth rate of the national income. If the national growth rate is planned for 6 per cent per year, production in each of the major categories of living essentials is planned for well above those rates (say 7 to 10 per cent) while the targets for other products such as refrigerators and luxury apartments and golden bedsteads may be correspondingly reduced (say to 1 or 2 per cent);

(2) Production goals are set with reference to standard minimum targets for selected items of prime

necessities to which a priority is assigned, such as
education, health, housing, food, and such goods as
low-cost clothing, cooking stoves, indoor water supply, toilet and heating facilities (in cold climates).
The quantitative targets for these selected necessities are derived not from market demand estimates,
but from minimum adequate consumption rates as determined by physiological and social need according to
a consensus of the community through discussion, negotiation, and legislative or administrative decision. The main constraints placed upon setting minimum adequate standards come from realistic estimates
of what the economy could accomplish under favorable
circumstances over a five- to ten-year period, i.e.,
within the planning horizon;

(3) The plan must also provide for program measures which will channel the increase in necessities
to the families who need them most. The production
targets do not do this nor do the free market forces.
Without specific distributive programs the market
will continue to favor the rich and discriminate
against the poor. Appropriate programs vary between
types of necessities and between countries. Some of
them have been briefly outlined earlier (see pp. 53-56);

(4) These additional quantities of necessities,
planned for the specific purpose of reducing poverty
and establishing certain minimum standards of decency,
can be added to the targets derived from the conventional development plan based upon market demand estimates. If comprehensive input-output matrices
should indicate that some of the resources will not
be sufficient to achieve these higher production targets for necessities, adjustments can be made to reduce the targets of less essential goods and shift
the resources thus released to the necessities of
life.[13]

What is proposed here is a deliberate specifica-
tion of quantitative and institutional administrative
detail in the development plan for raising the consumption of key necessities and meeting basic physical and cultural needs of low-income families. Such
a development policy, if competently planned and implemented, is bound to boost the rate of economic
progress rather than depress it.

CLASSICAL AND MODERN DEVELOPMENT PLANS

The nature of this reorientation in development planning can be illustrated by a hypothetical example.

Take the country shown in Table 6. The per capita income of $100 and the income distribution corresponds roughly to that of India. The lower half of the people falls below the poverty line of $80 per head. The Planning Board works out two alternative development plans, both designed to double per capita income during the planning period of about 20 years, i.e., at an annual rate of 3.5 per cent per year, as shown in Table 8. We shall disregard population increase to show the effect of the two plans more clearly. Since the growth target is stated in terms of a per capita rate of increase of 3.5 per cent, a population growth of 2 per cent would call for a growth rate of the total national income of about 5.5 per cent per year.[14] This is an order of magnitude which actually has been achieved by several developing countries over the last ten to fifteen years (see Table 4, p. 21).

Plan A follows the "classical" approach of maximizing production for its own sake by a laissez-faire policy of private capital investment and free market forces without specific measures for reducing poverty.

Plan B follows the "modern" approach of maximizing production and of reducing poverty by a policy of raising the productivity of the poor, and of guiding sufficient new private and public investment into production of necessities of life to meet the needs of the poor more adequately.

The results of both plans are compared in Table 8, and depicted in Chart 1.

Under the Classical Plan A, only one out of five poor families move above the poverty line, while under the Modern Plan B, four out of five escape from poverty. Hence, Plan B is much more effective in

TABLE 8

Classical and Modern Development Plans

(A hypothetical example based on Table 6)

		Present Position	End of Plan Period			
			Plan A		Plan B	
				Per Cent Change		Per Cent Change
Total National Income	million $	1,000	2,000	+100	2,000	+100
Income per capita	$	100	200	+100	200	+100
The Poor Group:						
Population below poverty line[1]	million	5	4	- 20	1	- 80
Income per capita of present poor group	$	55	66	+ 20	120	+120
Total income of same group	million $	275	330	+ 20	600	+120
Market demand for necessities	million $	275	315	+ 15	550	+100
Savings	million $	---	15	---	50	---
The Non-Poor Group:						
Population above poverty line	million	5	6	+ 20	9	+ 80
Income per capita of present non-poor group	$	145	334	+130	280	+ 93
Total income of same group	million $	725	1,670	+130	1,400	+ 93
Savings	million $	110	400	260	310	180
Total Savings (of poor and non-poor)	million $	110	415		360	
Per cent of national income	%	11	21		18	

1. The poverty line is assumed to be $80 per capita, hence representing the upper-income limit of the present poor group, and the lower limit of the present non-poor groups. During the plan period, the identity of these two present groups is preserved; and for the poor group, it is assumed that as many people fall above as below the group average and that the upper limit of its income ($80 at present) increases at the same rate as its average (see Chart 1).

reducing poverty than Plan A.

Under Plan A, the additional demand for the necessities of life of the poor half of the population
increases only by 15 per cent, while under Plan B,
it increases 100 per cent, since the bulk of the increased income of the poor group will be used for
these necessities. For the non-poor group a good
part of the increased income will go for luxury goods
and services. Therefore, Plan B creates a much more
rapidly expanding market for domestic industries than
does Plan A, since most of the necessities must come
from domestic industries, and most of the modern luxury goods must be imported. The Classical Plan A
places the country's scarce foreign exchange resources under severe pressure of using them for luxury
consumption rather than for productive investment,
and encourages imports of luxuries at the expense of
capital goods needed for developing domestic industries. An initial spurt in economic development may
often be followed by a period of stagnation, of idle
factories and increased unemployment, because there
is not enough purchasing power generated among the
masses of lower-income people to sustain the demand
for factory output and employment.

Under Modern Plan B, the savings rate might be
somewhat lower than under A--but probably not significantly so because the income of the non-poor
group that does most of the saving is also increasing strongly, by 93 per cent, as seen in Table
8. Since under Plan B the rich are getting richer along with the poor the rate of saving will
increase in both groups substantially above the
level of the beginning of the plan period. The savings rate might be expected to increase from 11 per
cent of the national income at the beginning to 21
per cent under Plan A, but still be 18 per cent under
Plan B, that is, only slightly lower. Under either
Plan the savings rate should be ample to support the
investment rate necessary for sustained economic
growth.[15] Moreover, under Plan B, there will be a
comparative lack of luxury goods which will tend to
increase the savings of the rich and bring the absolute amount of savings potentially available for

CHART 1

Poverty Under Classical and
Modern Development Plans

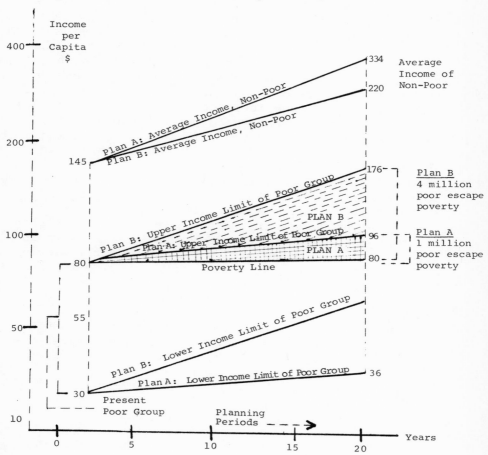

productive investment very close to the level of Plan
A. On the other hand, the somewhat higher savings
rate under Plan A will meet with unattractive or
lacking investment opportunities, which is a perfect
condition for economic depression and stagnation.

As to production incentives, Plan B will prove
distinctly superior to Plan A, because in most newly
developing countries the bulk of the poor live on
farms and in rural villages and produce most of the
food and much of the necessities of life. To change
traditional production techniques to modern methods
requires strong production incentives for these rural
producers. An income increase of 20 per cent for the
poor group over a twenty-year period under Plan A,
which is 1 per cent per year, is certainly not sufficient to induce the needed modernization, while an
income increase of 120 per cent, or 4 per cent per
year under Plan B, offers a potent incentive and en-
ables farmers to meet the increased input costs and
risks involved in the modernization process. At the
same time, producers in the non-poor group under Plan
B should also find ample production incentives in an
annual income increase of 3.0 per cent, particularly
if we keep in mind that this percentage rate is applied to an average level of income three times as
high as that of the poor group.

On balance, the poverty-reducing Modern Plan B
is likely to be much superior to the poverty-preserv-
ing Classical Plan A with respect to achieving high
rates of self-sustaining growth.

POLITICAL ASCENDANCY OF THE POOR

We need to realize, perhaps more clearly than we
often do, that the poor people throughout the world
are in rapid political ascendancy. The horizon of
their economic and social aspirations is widening.
In planning economic development, it appears imperative that governments apply their policies more explicitly to the problems of reducing poverty, along
with those of increasing production. We tend to
greatly exaggerate the conflict between increasing

"production" and "social justice." Basically, these
two goals are complementary rather than competitive,
as the history of economic development clearly demonstrates. It surely is not enough to raise production per se. Production must be increased selective-
ly at different rates, and most in those goods which
are most urgently needed to reduce poverty. This, in
the developing countries, demands a much greater emphasis on agriculture and the rural areas than governments have hitherto been inclined to give them.

Raising the income and living level of low-
income families is as urgent for increasing their
production capacity and incentives as it is for reasons of social justice. Programs must be so designed
that they will increase people's health, energy,
knowledge, and motivations to produce more and thereby rise above poverty, in their own interest as well
as that of the nation. Poor families are awakening
to these opportunities and to the role they can play
in the development process.

This emphasis on the role of urban and rural
workers and their families in national development
and recognition of their political ascendancy are
clearly reflected in the "social standards" adopted
in 1966 by the Council of the Organization of American States:

Article 1: The member states, convinced
that man can only achieve his full realization within a just social order, along
with economic development and true peace,
agree to dedicate every effort to the application of the following principles and
mechanisms:

a. All human beings, without distinction as to race, sex, nationality,
creed or social condition, have a
right to material well-being and
to their spiritual development under circumstances of liberty, dignity, equality of opportunity, and
economic security;

b. Work is a right and a social duty,
    it gives dignity to the one who
    performs it, and it should be per-
    formed under conditions, including
    a system of fair wages, that en-
    sure life, health, and a decent
    standard of living for the worker
    and his family, both during his
    working years and his old age, or
    when any circumstance deprives him
    of the possibility of working;

c. Employers and workers, both rural
    and urban, have the right to asso-
    ciate themselves freely for the
    defense and promotion of their in-
    terests, including the right to
    collective bargaining and the
    workers' right to strike, recogni-
    tion of the juridical personality
    of associations and the protection
    of their freedom and independence,
    all in accordance with applicable
    laws;...[16]

The basic issue is to devise an institutional framework, to modify the market organization, to expand
the economic opportunities and strengthen the bargaining position of the disadvantaged groups in such a
way that those families who are now poor will be able
to work more efficiently and receive, as a reward for
their productive effort, a sufficient income to provide the necessities, at least, for a modest, adequate level of living, as citizens with self-respect
and dignity.

This is, in essence, the charge that the multi-
tudes of poor people in all regions of the world, of
all races and creeds and political convictions, are
giving their politicians and governments, their planners and economists.[17] A difficult task, but a fundamental and imperative one.

NOTES TO CHAPTER 4

1.   In Communist countries under a centralized state enterprise system, this can be accomplished more or less effectively through direct allocative planning on the production side, and through rationing according to need on the distribution side.

2.   See Andrew Pearse, "Agrarian Change Trends in Latin America," Latin American Research Review, Vol. I, No. 3 (Summer 1966), p. 53. See also comment by R. P. Dore in Pearse, ibid., pp. 70-74.

3.   P. D. Ojha and V. V. Bhatt, "Pattern of Income Distribution in an Underdeveloped Economy: A Case Study of India," American Economic Review, Vol. 54, No. 5 (September 1964), pp. 711-20.

4.   See Jan Tinbergen, Design of Development (Baltimore, Md.: Johns Hopkins Press, 1958), p. 40: "We have to accept, therefore, in a number of underdeveloped countries that the market price structure is not the correct guide for making decisions," and Gunnar Myrdal, Economic Theory and Underdeveloped Regions (London: Methuen and Co., 1957), p. 89: "The price system does not give rational criteria for economic planning." This issue of the socio-economic "justice" of free market prices is related to the neo-classical argument that there is no "objective" proof that an additional dollar means more satisfaction ("utility") to a poor than to a rich man. But this argument is irrelevant to the problem of economic planning, because people observe and feel, individually and collectively, that an additional dollar does, in fact, mean a lot more to the poor than to the rich family, and that poverty is, indeed, a socio-economic evil that must be combated.

5.   See John Kenneth Galbraith, Economic Development in Perspective (Cambridge, Mass.: Harvard University Press, 1962), pp. 43-45. He urges that "prime attention must be accorded goods that are within the range of the modal income. Above all, nothing is so important as abundant and efficiently

produced food, clothing, and shelter, for these are the most universal of requirements.

6. See Robert J. Lampman, "Approaches to the Reduction of Poverty," American Economic Review, Vol. 55, No. 2 (May 1965), p. 523. These figures are not based upon per capita gross national product, but upon personal family income. The general method for estimating the magnitude of poverty, however, can also be applied to more readily available gross national product data. In fact, the latter has the advantage of including all those items of real income which people receive from public services and facilities, such as education, public health, etc., not paid for directly out of their personal income.

7. For practical purposes, a rough guide for determining the poverty line for a five-year period might be the consideration that the poverty income gap should not exceed 20 per cent of the gross national product, since it would take too long a time and too large a portion of the annual increment (e.g., the full annual increment of a 3 per cent growth rate of per capita income over seven years which is practically not possible) to wipe out poverty. In reality, perhaps only one half or two thirds of this increment could be channeled into the real income stream of the poor. But even this would represent a great advance as compared to what the market forces alone would do, which may often channel hardly more than one tenth of the increment to the poor.

8. See United Nations Economic Commission for Asia and the Far East, Problems of Social Development Planning. Report of a group of experts, Development Programming Techniques Series No. 4 (E/CN.11/663) (New York: United Nations, 1964). Chapters on planning for the educational, health, housing, and social welfare sectors contain some promising proposals for the planning and implementation of programs in these fields.

9. See World Health Organization, Malnutrition and Disease, Freedom from Hunger Campaign Basic Study No. 12 (Geneva: FFHC, 1963).

10. In affluent industrial countries, where capital accumulation and automation may eventually lead
to a degree of labor productivity so high that even
a much-reduced workday and number of workdays per
year may not provide employment opportunities for all,
a "guaranteed income" could be made available to
everyone out of tax revenues or some national income
pool. See Robert Theobald, ed., The Guaranteed Income (New York: Doubleday & Co., 1965).

11. In Russia's 1966-70 Plan, the 1970 targets
call for quadrupling passenger cars, trebling refrigerators, and doubling TV sets (The New York Times, Feb.
20, 1966). This means that for the first time in
any of the eight Development Plans adopted since the
first one in 1929 has there been a strong increase in
luxury goods, and that the planners feel such increases justified at the present time to make life more
interesting and colorful and convenient and to provide production incentives to individuals and families. This occurred only after thirty-five years of
detailed allocative planning indicating the strong
priority assigned to the necessities of life.

12. See United Nations, Statistical Yearbook,
1963 (New York: United Nations, 1963). Per cent of
population attending school was 26.7 per cent in the
U.S.A., and 21.4 per cent in the U.S.S.R.

13. The supplies of some of the necessities
needed on top of the estimated prospective market demand might be ordered by the government for sale at
concessional prices to low-income families, e.g.,
through "fair price stores" or cooperatives or schools
(in the case of school uniforms and school lunches),
or to workers on public works projects such as the
building of roads, irrigation systems, power plants,
etc. Educational campaigns and promotion for increasing the consumption of certain important goods
such as protective foods, shoes and clothes, kerosene
cooking stoves and lamps, can also improve consumption habits and raise living levels in low-income
areas.

14. It is easy to adjust these models of the two plans for the effect of population increase. If population growth is 2 per cent per year, total population will be 50 per cent greater after twenty years. This means that the total national income shown in Table 8 at the end of the plan period must be $3 billion instead of $2 billion. This represents an annual growth rate of the total national product of 5.5 per cent--which is well within practical reach of a number of the developing countries, including India.

15. Savings actually available for productive investment are usually considerably below the total savings, since some savings are used for non-productive investment (real estate and commodity speculation, hoarding in various farms, etc). A development plan can be designed to minimize such unproductive uses of savings (see pp. 84-86). Moreover, private savings can be supplemented by appropriate taxation in order to raise the rate of productive investment.

16. Pan American Union, The OAS Chronicle, Vol. II, No. 1 (August 1966), pp. 28 and 29.

17. For a revealing study of how political leaders size up their own public future in light of the attitudes and aspirations of their local constituents, see Charles C. Moskos and Wendell Bell, "Some Implications of Equality for Political, Economic and Social Development," International Review of Community Development, Nos. 13-14 (1965), pp. 219-46.

PART II

MOBILIZING AGRICULTURE

FOR ECONOMIC DEVELOPMENT

CHAPTER **5** BLEEDING AGRICULTURE?
--THE QUESTION OF
CAPITAL FORMATION

The conventional argument is simple: (1) Capital formation depends on savings; (2) The majority of people in developing countries are in agriculture; (3) Hence, a major part of capital for industrialization must come from more savings in agriculture.

The simplicity of this argument, however, does not make it valid. It may lead to costly mistakes in economic policies, as it did, for instance, in Russia where at the beginning of the Communist regime agriculture was bled for the purpose of boosting industrialization; and in Japan during the late 1800's and early 1900's; and in England and other Western countries during earlier stages of their industrial development. Partly as a consequence, agriculture lagged much behind industry in the development process as well as in per capita income, and thereby acted as a brake on the over-all rate of economic development.

Industrialization has, in fact, depended a good deal upon transfers of "savings" (i.e., nonconsumed past income) from the agricultural sector to industrial investments in many countries.[1] These transfers often came about more by the traditional workings of institutional arrangements such as land tenure systems and market forces than by deliberate government policy aimed at industrialization. These historical facts, however, do not prove that it should and must be that way. Indeed, they suggest that the siphoning off of savings from agriculture into industry may easily be overdone and retard agricultural development in the first instance, and industrial development in the second instance, as compared to what it would have been if capital formation and the adoption of scientific techniques in agriculture had proceeded more in step with industry and other sectors of the economy.

This issue is of strategic importance for the economic planning in developing countries. It is so easy to exploit agriculture for industrial development, because farmers are politically the least articulate and least organized group, have a very weak and vulnerable bargaining position in the market and vis-à-vis landlords, moneylenders, traders, businessmen, and the government itself. Taxes on land and its products are easy to collect. Moreover, policymakers and the educated group in general are oriented toward the city and toward industry and trade and are biased against agriculture as an occupation and a way of life. There are clear indications that the resulting neglect of the capital requirements for agricultural progress threatens to retard development not only in the agricultural sector, but in the industrial and trade sectors as well.

Let us examine the validity of the argument for increasing the rate of savings in agriculture for the purpose of transferring such savings to industrial capital formation.

AGRICULTURE AND INDUSTRY

Many people fail to realize how much agriculture has been and continues to be a blood donor to the industrial and service sectors of the economy. A large part of the savings arising from the agricultural sector in many countries is already being transferred elsewhere through the workings of the land tenure system with its rent charges and taxes, the credit system with its interest rates, and the market system allotting farmers a very weak bargaining position and often unduly low prices for their products. The almost universal income disparity between farm and nonfarm population resulting from these conditions represents an income transfer in the sense that what farmers lose by a low level of food prices, city people gain by the corresponding reduction in their food expenditure, which benefits industrialization at the expense of agriculture.

What happens as to savings is that of all the
rent received by the landlords--the interest payments
to the creditors, the land and farm product taxes or
export duties collected by the government, and the
savings of large land or plantation owners--of all
these incomes originating in agriculture, only a
small part is reinvested in agriculture while by far
the largest part is transferred to investments and
other uses elsewhere. For instance, many countries
levy heavy export taxes on farm products which often
constitute the major source of government revenues.
This makes farmers the heaviest taxpayers.[2]

It is well known that the typical large land or
plantation owner in Latin America invests his savings
mainly in industry, trade, urban real estate speculation, and the stock market. The same holds true for
landlords in Asia and Africa. The same holds true
for many merchants and traders and moneylenders in
rural areas. In many cases, it holds even for the
government when it collects more in land and other
agricultural taxes than it spends in the agricultural
sector--which has been and is true in some countries
as a deliberate policy of financing industrial development, but also applies to many other countries not
pursuing such a deliberate policy.

In addition to these direct and indirect transfers of income from agriculture to industry, farmers
make another major contribution to industrialization
by carrying the burden of rearing the surplus farm
population that enters the industrial labor force after reaching a productive age.

We can safely conclude that for most developing
countries, a deliberate policy of forcing agriculture
to increase its income transfers to industry above
what it is already, is very likely to further retard
agricultural progress, and by this very token general
economic progress as well.

THE NEED FOR CAPITAL IN AGRICULTURE

There are several reasons why agriculture is much less adequately supplied with capital than industry and trade.

In the first place, the great masses of small farmers live so close to a bare subsistence level that their low rate of savings from their own net income (after rent, interest, and taxes) is barely sufficient to replace their few traditional tools, implements, and draft animals.[3] It usually is not sufficient to obtain new production factors such as fertilizer, machinery, and other modern inputs needed for raising production. Hence, whatever small increase in their rate of saving can be achieved is desperately needed for investment in modernizing production, that is, in fertilizer, machinery, land improvement, etc.

Secondly, agriculture is more starved for capital than industry and trade. Already now, a large part of the savings of landlords and rural traders derived from agricultural rents, the employment of cheap farm labor, and the purchase of farm products at low prices, is being transferred to industrial and other sectors. A policy of pushing industrial development at the expense of an already disadvantaged agriculture is bound to be self-defeating.

Thirdly, access to credit for industry and trade is much easier and better organized than it is for agriculture. The prosperous savers do reinvest in industry and trade, with hardly any transfers to the agricultural sector. Moreover, the whole banking and credit system is geared to fit the needs of commerce and industry, and is typically not adapted to meet the needs of millions of small farmers. For instance, corporate financing methods through the issuance of stocks and bonds provide an enormous source of investment funds and credit for industry, but cannot do so for agriculture. Commercial banks are organized to make large loans to industrial and trading firms

at terms adjusted to the needs of industry and trade,
but they are not organized to make millions of small
loans to farmers at terms adjusted to the needs of
agriculture.

Industrialization, of course, also requires much
capital. The question is where to look for sources
of additional investment. As we shall see presently,
there are several sources much more promising and
without the inevitable progress-retarding repercus-
sions which attend a policy of bleeding agriculture.

In principle, there may be one situation in
which industrialization might depend heavily upon
transfers of income out of agriculture: if the agricultural sector is almost completely of a subsistence
nature and is producing 70 or 80 per cent of the
gross national product, and if no development credit
for industrial capital formation is available from
the outside. At present, none of the developing
countries meet these conditions. In most of them,
agriculture produces between 20-40 per cent of the
gross national product, with 40-70 per cent of the
population.[4] Under these conditions, there is no
reason why the poorest sector, whose population con-
tributes only one-half of its proportion to the national product, should be further depressed by income
transfers to non-agricultural sectors, where the population receives twice its proportion of the national
income, hence can be expected to increase its savings
for capital formation much more readily. This is an
important fact which is often overlooked.

In conclusion: Agriculture is already a heavy
contributor to industrial development in the form of
rental and interest payments, various taxes and
low-food prices, and in the form of farm-to-city migrants increasing the industrial labor supply. Instead of forcing a further increase of income transfers from agriculture to industry, balanced economic
development and a sustained rate of industrial progress are better served by:

(1) Increasing productive investment out of
present agricultural savings in agriculture for the

specific purpose of raising farm productivity;

(2) Doing the same with industrial and trade
savings for productive investment in industry and
trade;

(3) Improving agriculture's access to production credit, to marketing facilities, roads, schools,
health services, and other infrastructural facilities
more nearly in line with conditions in cities and
towns--regardless of where the savings and credit
funds and taxes required originated from in the first
place.

This means that for a balanced rate of development in
the agricultural and industrial sectors a high rate
of capital formation is required in both, and investment allocations should be guided by the respective
needs of the sectors, not by sectoral origins of the
savings.

Capital formation in the rural sector usually
represents also a direct contribution to industrialization, as, for instance, in the case of roads,
transport, and marketing facilities; conversely, a
good part of capital formation in industry benefits
the agricultural sector. There is no reason for a
separate accounting of the origins of savings, or for
an a priori judgement that each sector must generate
its own investment funds, or that income must be
transferred from agriculture to industry for capital
formation, or vice versa.

HOW TO INCREASE CAPITAL FORMATION

The rate of development capital formation, of
course, must be increased well over present levels.
But it is much too simple and misleading to argue
that the only way this can be done is by increasing
the rate of savings out of present incomes in agriculture. Let us examine some of these other ways.[5]

1. Increasing investment in productive development capital by shifting the use of savings away from

unproductive investment is one very effective way.
Even in countries where capital is extremely scarce,
a substantial part of savings is used for such unproductive purposes as (a) real estate and commodity
speculation; (b) sumptuous elaborate office buildings
for banks, insurance companies, commercial and industrial firms, and government agencies; (c) fancy hotels and apartment houses, suburban and country res-
idences; (d) hedging against inflation by acquiring
gold, jewelry, old paintings, and sculpture; (e)
hoarding money; and (f) investments abroad in foreign
stocks, bonds and real estate--all these unproductive
uses of savings are lost to the development process.
Note that of these six unproductive uses of savings,
only one, i.e., that of hoarding money, and in some
places women's jewelry, is practiced to any significant extent by small farmers.

We unwittingly apply a double standard to capital investments in agriculture and industry. In agriculture we apply rigorous benefit-cost, or "efficiency," standards to its roads, cooperative facilities, and irrigation systems; to individual housing
and farm buildings; and to farm machinery and equipment, always keeping in mind the question: Is this
investment absolutely necessary? In industry, our
standards are greatly relaxed, and we nod approvingly
at the palatial filling stations, office buildings,
superhighways, etc., because whoever built them apparently can "afford" them. It would be interesting
to subject some of these conspicuously sumptuous capital investments to efficiency tests as rigorously as
we do it in agriculture. Perhaps we have come to
look at these administration buildings and market
outlets of business firms as ceremonial symbols of
culture, like the royal palaces, pyramids, and tem-
ples of earlier periods. As long as the firms can
"afford" them, we tend to consider them "justified,"
whether or not they are economically necessary for
efficient operations. Yet, the "firms-can-afford"
principle is not a valid criterion for capital allocation in the interest of economic development.

The rate of capital formation, even with present
savings, could be much increased in critical,

high-priority fields, such as factories for fertilizers and machinery production, processing plants for agricultural, forestry, and fishery products, for textiles and other necessities of life, low-cost housing, etc., if unproductive uses of savings and conspicuous consumption expenditures could be redirected into these high-priority development investments.

For instance, several recent studies in Chile indicated that large landowners spend an exceptionally large portion of their income on luxury consumption. Nicholas Kaldor estimated that if the large property owners in Chile would reduce their consumption expenditures to the corresponding level of that found among large property owners in Great Britain (i.e., to 30 per cent of gross income from property), "the personal consumption expenditures of this group would fall from 21.1 to 10.3 per cent of the national income. The freed resources would be more than sufficient to double the country's investment in fixed capital and inventories. This means that, according to official estimates, net investment would increase from 2 to 14 per cent of net national income."[6]

Policy measures for suppressing such unproductive uses of savings and extravagant consumption, and channeling them into developmental capital formation, are fairly well known and can be improved and adapted to the peculiar conditions of the various countries.[7] This should be an important part of any economic development plan.

2. Mobilization of underemployed labor and unutilized local materials offers another way to increase capital formation without reducing present consumption. Some of the most strategic types of development capital, such as roads, school buildings, and storehouses, can be created with the use of locally available building materials and underemployed manpower. The developing countries have not seized upon these opportunities for capital formation with the decisive and systematic efforts they deserve, although some countries have made a promising start in this direction. The potential contribution of this

source of capital formation is greatly underrated.
The difficulties lie mainly in the organizational and
administrative aspects of mobilizing these underemployed labor resources, of motivating people and offering incentives in whatever form may be needed to
get the job done.

3. Credit is still another way by which capital
can be formed without reducing the borrower's present
consumption level. He repays the loan out of future
savings that come from an increased future income resulting from the new capital resources placed at the
borrower's disposal by the loan. This means that a
poor producer with insufficient savings--and, for
that matter, a poor country--can use future savings
for present capital formation, without reducing his
present consumption. Credit does to capital formation what it does to money supply: it increases money supply well above the amount of the currency stock
in circulation; and, consequently, it can increase
capital formation well above what it would be without
it, i.e., if each individual could invest only his
own savings into his own farm or producing unit.
Hence, credit functions as a source of capital formation. It allows a producer to order and get capital
goods now which he will pay for later out of his increased future income.[8]

This credit function in capital formation works
also in the international context and is particularly
important for developing countries. They can obtain
from industrialized countries, through foreign credit,
more capital goods strategic for development than they
could buy with their current foreign exchange earnings, and can do so without increasing their present
savings, thereby lowering their own present consumption level.

Most of the developing countries start from such
a low income and consumption level that a policy of
increasing capital formation mainly by reducing current consumption still further below the prevailing
low level would be self-defeating. Such a policy
would reduce demand and production incentives, and
investment opportunities, all of which must be

increased rather than reduced during the early stages
of development. This holds particularly for the
great masses of farmers and laborers who cannot be
expected to want to work harder and produce more unless this increases their income, that is, their demand for things. This provides production incentives
and investment opportunities, without which there
will be no capital formation of a sustained and pro-
gress-generating nature.[9]

On the side of the highly industrialized countries, the situation is very different. Here, the
high-savings rate tends to outrun the investment opportunities, and capital formation for development
could be greatly increased by shifting a larger part
of the savings into high-priority investments abroad.
This could be done without reducing the prevailing
high-consumption levels noticeably. In this important respect, the rich and the poor countries complement each other--if we only could find practical ways
to capitalize upon this complementary relationship of
mutual interest.

4. Reducing luxury consumption is another effective way for increasing capital formation. In
contrast to the other ways mentioned so far, this one
does involve an increase in saving, but in a way
which will not reduce consumption of necessities of
life. If these savings are directed into capital
goods for development, they create production incentives for farmers, industrial and commercial entrepreneurs and laborers, and productive investment opportunities for savers at home and abroad.

For instance, a developing country can prohibit
the importation of Rolls Royce cars and other luxuries, and use the "saved" foreign exchange to buy
textile machinery, a fertilizer plant, and some vege-
table-processing plants. It is obvious that such an
increase in "savings" from the income of the rich
does not reduce the demand for necessities of life on
the part of the poor. At the same time, the increased capital formation for development purposes
makes available: modern inputs to farmers; employment and more of the necessities of life to workers;

and more attractive investment opportunities in high-
priority capital goods to local entrepreneurs and to
the very persons whose luxury consumption has been
curtailed.

To put such a policy into effect, the government might severely discourage consumption of selected luxury goods by import duties, quotas and foreign
exchange controls, and, at the same time, offer
stocks and bonds of development-oriented industries
to the wealthy for purchase, with an appeal to their
long-term interest in the nation's economic progress
--a policy which Mexico, for instance, has adopted in
recent years with remarkable success.[10]

5. At this point, the role which taxation plays
in capital formation deserves some comment. Apart
from the growing service functions of modern governments, a large part of the capital formation for infrastructural development is the government's responsibility. Tax revenues spent on capital formation
represent "forced savings" from the income of the
taxpayers. Requirements for capital formation in the
public sector are usually met by these tax revenues.
If, however, the investment rate required for developmental capital in the private sector is not forthcoming from voluntary savings, taxation can be used
to increase capital investment for development purposes in various ways. For instance, the government
can use tax revenues (preferably collected from high-
income people) to build a fertilizer or textile
plant, sell stock shares to private investors (mainly
to high-income taxpayers), and may turn it over to
joint or full private ownership and management, as
mentioned above.

In state enterprise economies, the rate of investment for capital formation is primarily determined by government through taxation, often in the
form of deliveries of a certain share of the output
(in kind or in money) to the state. For instance,
Russia financed a good part of the rapid industrialization process since the 1930's through heavy tax
collections in the form of food and fibers from agriculture, with the result that investment in agriculture

was badly neglected. Since 1956, and especially in
the current Five-Year Plan of 1966-70, capital investment in agriculture has been increased greatly,
while taxation in terms of farm output has been reduced to make it possible for agriculture to catch up
with industrial development.

REDIRECTING SAVINGS, INVESTMENT, AND CREDIT FOR DEVELOPMENT

In summary, the simple prescription to increase
capital formation by reducing consumption and increasing savings, especially in the agricultural sector for transfer to industrial investments, is dan-
gerously misleading. It is bound to inhibit general
economic development in the longer run. Industry
needs agricultural progress for providing more and
better food for the growing urban population, and
needs a farm population with rising incomes as a market for its goods. Agriculture needs industry for
providing modern production goods to raise its output
of food and fiber, and needs industrial employment
opportunities for its surplus population.

Industry and agriculture depend upon each other
for their economic progress. Development planning
requires that the allocation of investment for capital formation in both sectors be determined by their
respective needs within the over-all developmental
process, regardless of where the savings originate.

Agriculture is more starved for capital than industry and trade, and has less ready access to the
capital market. These are handicaps which must be
overcome by deliberate government policies. Moreover, agriculture is already now contributing to industrial capital formation at a higher rate than is
commonly recognized. Increasing the present rate of
saving is not the only, and often not even the most
important, source of capital formation for economic
development.

There are three sources of capital formation
which do not require reduction in the present rate of

consumption:

(1) Redirecting present savings into more productive developmental investments, e.g., from real
estate speculation and sumptuous office buildings into fertilizer and other industrial plants;

(2) Mobilization of underemployed labor and unutilized local materials for the construction of
roads, schools, storehouses, irrigation schemes, rural processing plants for agricultural products, etc.;

(3) Credit systems geared to channel domestic as
well as foreign savings into high-priority development investment, and to make much larger amounts of
foreign investment funds available to the developing
countries. A vigorous expansion of foreign credit
and improvement in the international capital market
are desperately needed.

There is a fourth source of capital formation
which involves a special kind of increase in savings
but avoids the progress-retarding effect of lowering
the consumption level of the poor: shifting expenditures from luxury consumption to development investment.

In the agricultural sector, mobilization of underemployed labor and expansion of purpose-directed
credit are by far the most important sources of capital formation. These two sources can achieve a very
high effectiveness, especially when they complement
each other. For instance, a small injection of foreign capital in the form of bulldozers can mobilize
seasonally underemployed manpower in road construction; metal tubes and pumps combined with local labor
can bring large areas of land under irrigation.
There are many opportunities in agriculture where
small injections of scarce capital goods have an un-
usually high-leverage effect upon capital formation
and the productivity of the new capital created. Unfortunately, this aspect of capital formation in agriculture is too often overlooked in economic development planning and deserves much more attention.

In industry as well as in agriculture, the rate of economic development can be accelerated by guiding investment funds into more productive and development-oriented channels; by improving the organization of production processes yielding a higher output per unit of input; and by producing more necessities of life to reduce poverty than unregulated market forces would do.

In contrast, measures which would further reduce current consumption from already-low levels for the sake of increasing capital formation should be avoided (except for reduction in luxury consumption), because in the first place, they are bound to backfire through progress-retarding side effects, and in the second place, they are not necessary as long as the opportunities outlined in this chapter have not been fully exhausted. This holds particularly for agriculture whose contributions to other sectors through income transfers is already high, and whose population is poorer than that in other sectors of the economy.

NOTES TO CHAPTER 5

1. See W. Arthur Lewis, Theory of Economic Growth (London: George Allen & Unwin, 1955), pp. 225-44.

2. See. W. Arthur Lewis, "Aspects of Economic Development," Africa: Progress Through Cooperation, John Karefa-Smart, ed. (New York: Dodd, Mead & Co., 1966), pp. 115-30.

3. For instance, in Orissa State, India, 50-60 per cent of total outstanding farm loans were used for consumption. See B. Misra, et al., "Possibilities of Capital Formation in Agriculture in Cuttack (Orissa)," Indian Journal of Agricultural Economics, Vol. XX, No. 1 (January-March 1965), p. 213. See also Tara Shukla, Capital Formation in Indian Agriculture (Bombay: Vora and Co., 1965), p. 224.

4. Of the eighty-seven nations with available data, only five reported agricultural production in excess of 50 per cent of the national produce in the early 1960's (The Sudan with 51 per cent, Tanzania 57 per cent, Togo 59 per cent, Uganda 61 per cent, and Nigeria 65 per cent). See United Nations, Yearbook of National Accounts Statistics, 1965, op. cit., p. 457.

5. For a stimulating discussion of problems of capital formation, see Lauchlin Currie, "The Capital Formation Approach," Accelerating Development: The Necessity and the Means (New York: McGraw-Hill Book Co., 1966), pp. 121-39.

6. See Nicholas Kaldor, "Problemas Economicas de Chile," El Trimestre Economico (April-June 1959), p. 196; and Solon L. Barraclough and Arthur L. Domike, "Agrarian Structure in Seven Latin American Countries," Land Economics, Vol. XLII, No. 4 (November 1966), p. 405.
For a very thought-provoking discussion of this issue in broad terms of economic development, see Joan Robinson, Economic Philosophy (Chicago, Ill.: Aldine Publishing Co., 1962), pp. 116-23.

7. These measures range from steeply graduated income taxes to embargoes or prohibitive duties on luxury imports; from government guarantees and interest-subsidies on loans for low-income houses to high-capital-gains taxes on real estate transfers; from foreign exchange control to attractive public bond issues to finance developmental capital formation, etc.

8. Provisions for especially attractive credit terms restricted to high-priority types of capital formation can be very effective in directing savings into more productive investments than would otherwise occur, by raising the demand for these urgently needed capital goods. For instance, if farmers could not get production credit for buying fertilizer and machinery, these capital goods would not be demanded, hence, not

be produced, and savings would be diverted into much
less urgently needed goods or into speculative uses
and conspicuous consumption. There is ample room
for this kind of credit policy in many countries, for
expanding it and adapting it to urgent development
needs. For an excellent exposition of this issue and
the fallacies to which classical theory can lead,
see Clyde Mitchell, "Credit in an Expanding Economy,"
Land Economics, Vol. 32, No. 4 (November 1956), pp.
326-33.

    9. See W. Arthur Lewis, Africa: Progress
Through Cooperation, op. cit., p. 125: "The most
that is practicable is to have consumption grow less
rapidly than output."

    10. For stimulating and penetrating studies of
these issues, see Raymond Vernon, ed., Public Policy
and Private Enterprise in Mexico (Cambridge, Mass.:
Harvard University Press, 1964), and Raymond Vernon,
The Dilemma of Mexico's Development: The Roles of
the Private and Public Sectors (Cambridge, Mass.:
Harvard University Press, 1965). These two books
furnish a wealth of empirical data of "social science
laboratory experience," and of insight into process
of policy formulation which is deeply relevant to
the current and future development process in most of
the other low-income countries.

CHAPTER 6

THE IMAGES OF INDUS-TRY AND AGRICULTURE --AND THE FACTS

In the minds of many people, industry stands for progress, agriculture for stagnation. Industry is the paragon of science and technology, the herald of the modern world, of power over matter and space, over machines and men. Agriculture is the repository of primitive life, of superstition and witchcraft, of fearful subjugation to the capricious forces of nature. The ways of industry lead to individual wealth and national power; the ways of agriculture lead to individual poverty and national subservience. In broad strokes, these are the world images of industry and agriculture for many people in all walks of life.

In the minds of the educated, these images become a little more refined, but hardly lose their essential features. Around industry are grouped the trades and the learned professions as complementary occupations which, along with the landed gentry, furnish the core of modern entrepreneurial and political leadership. Around agriculture are grouped small village craftsmen and a great mass of casual, unskilled, and manual laborers who, along with the peasants, furnish the bulk of the inarticulate and subservient labor force.

Such images are oversimplified and exaggerated concepts of certain aspects of things which catch people's imagination and impart to them emotional values of an attractive or repulsive nature. They become stereotyped prejudices for or against their substance and govern people's attitudes and behavior. The prejudices for industry and against agriculture in the developing regions are reflected in many ways which endanger economic development or at least retard progress.

AGRICULTURE--A POOR RELATION

Few of the sons of the educated choose agricultural subjects in their university studies. The image of agriculture gives them a lower cultural status
and intellectual respect at home than students in the
humanities, pure sciences, and engineering. For instance, of all the fellowships requested by developing countries under the United Nations Technical
Assistance Programme, which by its nature has a
strong bias toward technology, only 11 per cent were
in agriculture. Industry and trade lead with 28 per
cent, and public health, labor relations and general
education are all ahead of agriculture, as shown in
Table 9.[1] What rational justification is there for
this?

In government service, the ministry of agriculture tends to rank lower, and its salary scale tends
to be lower also than in ministries of finance, public works, health, and education. Why should this be
so?

A recent survey among students in Nigeria revealed the respect in which various occupations were
held by them, as shown in Table 10. If we group the
ratings by the amount of formal education required
for the occupations, it appears quite clearly how
these ratings reflect the educational level of the
occupations. Those requiring some academic training
range between the ratings of 3.2 to 4.7, those with
no formal training between 0.5 and 2.5, and those
with secondary and vocational training fall between
these groups. Of course, they reflect income levels,
too. But it is interesting to note that the only agricultural occupation requiring some academic training is agricultural officer, the lowest in this
group except for the secondary schoolteacher, but
just barely below the lawyer and pharmacist, while
the cash-crop farmer (probably referring to the cocoa
farmer) ranks highest in the "no formal training"
group, and, in fact, a bit higher than the public
health inspector, the hospital laboratory technician,
and the male hospital nurse of the intermediate group.

TABLE 9

United Nations Fellowships
Awarded under Expanded
Technical Assistance Programme
by Major Fields of Study, 1951-64

	Total Number
Fellowships Awarded by All U.N. Agencies	31,538

- -

Distribution by Major Fields		Per Cent of Total Fellowships %
U.N.	Industry, Trade, Communications, Economics	28
WHO	Public Health, Sanitation, Malaria Control	20
ILO	Labor Organization and Legislation, Employment, Wages, Working Conditions	19
UNESCO	Education, Sciences, Humanities	12
FAO	Agriculture, Forestry, Fisheries	11
ICAO	Civil Aviation	4
WMO	Meteorology (2%)	
IAEA	Atomic Energy (2%)	
ITU	Telecommunication (1.5%)	
UPU	Postal Service (0.2%)	6

Source: United Nations, Technical Assistance News
Letter, Vol. III, No. 4 (June-July 1965), p. 6.

91

The food-crop farmer is on par with the craftsman, but a bit below the clerk, driver, policeman, and primary schoolteacher. It might be a good idea to keep track of how these various occupations rank in the minds of the young generation as they are bound to influence development. For instance, the spectrum of ratings suggests that the respect for food-crop farmers and schoolteachers needs a good boosting, and that an agricultural officer might well outrank an accountant.

Opportunities for advancement in agricultural careers within and outside the government are judged to be much more restricted than in industry and commerce. This may have been so in the past, but does it have to stay so in the future?

It is true, of course, that agriculture is rooted in the soil, and soil gets feet and hands dirty. But oil, mineral ores, and cement can get the hands of an engineer dirty, too, and even blood, the hands of a surgeon. Dirt alone cannot explain the whole story.

Perhaps the most important fact that militates against agriculture as a professional career is the cultural bleakness of the rural countryside with respect to schools, communications, home conveniences, and intellectual stimulation. But it is precisely this bleakness, this lack of living, working, and thinking conditions in rural villages, which must be overcome in order to get competent trained people to live and work with farmers and people in the villages, and to open new opportunities for rural people in education, production, and the cultural aspects of life. Getting rural areas out of this economic and cultural isolation is one of the key necessities of progress.

The upshot of these handicaps under which agriculture is smarting is that in the council of ministers, in economic planning circles, in the teaching from primary schools to universities, in board meetings of banks and caucuses of political parties, the needs of agriculture get neglected.

TABLE 10

Occupational Prestige Ratings by Nigerian Students

Occupations	Academic Training (or equiv.)	Requiring: Secondary or Vocational Training	No Formal Training
		Average Scores	
Government Service			
Minister	4.39		
Permanent Secretary	4.10		
*Agricultural Officer	*3.19		
Accountant		3.84	
Army Officer		3.47	
Clerk, Driver, Policeman		1.66	
Medicine and Science			
Medical Doctor	4.25		
Physicist	3.71		
Pharmacist	3.27		
Inspector, Technician, Nurse		2.41	
Herbalist			0.95
Law and Religion			
High-Court Judge	4.27		
Lawyer	3.27		
Bishop (Cath. or Prot.)	3.53		
Oba, Emir, Obi		3.48	
Diviner			1.23
Teachers			
University	4.66		
Secondary School	2.63		
Primary School		1.62	
Private Entrepreneurs			
Firm or Mine Owner		3.82	
Artist or Writer		2.61	
*Cash-Crop Farmer			*2.51
Artisan			2.13
Trader (owns store)			1.71
Gold- or Blacksmith			1.43
Weaver or Tailor			1.32
*Food-Crop Farmer			*1.31
Barber			0.84
Hired Workers			
Coal Miner			1.08
Road Construction Worker			0.85
*Palm-Wine Tapper			*0.62
Steward			0.53

Source: Robert W. Morgan, Jr., "Occupational Prestige Ratings by Nigerian Students," The Nigerian Journal of Economic and Social Studies, Vol. 7, No. 3 (November 1965), p. 329. The scores ranged from 5 (excellent) to 0 (poor); 41 different occupations were rated by 63 economic students. Agricultural occupations marked by *.

The tragedy, however, is that the task of solving the problems of agriculture, of modernizing its production processes and institutional environment, is more difficult to accomplish and requires more complex administrative and organizational innovations, and hence a larger corps of well-trained and highly motivated persons, than is the case for industry, as we shall see presently.

There are signs that agriculture's role in economic development is gaining more recognition. Over the last ten years, planned public investment in agriculture increased 6-fold in the Sudan and Ghana, and doubled in Malaysia and Iran. But the prevailing level in most developing countries is still very low, considering how dependent the agricultural sector is upon public investment in view of the notorious lack of interest of private investors. In forty-two out of seventy-one developing countries for which recent data were obtainable, planned public investment in agriculture was less than 20 per cent of total public investment, and in only seven countries was it over 30 per cent.[2]

There is still far too little recognition of the strategic role which culture must play in economic development and industrialization, and too little comprehension of the peculiarities which render it different, but not inferior, to industry in offering scope for talent, creative energy, and intelligence on the part of farmers as well as professionals in agricultural technology, economics, rural sociology, and education.

Even those who believe that industrialization must be the dominant approach to economic development cannot get around the hard fact that industrialization requires an increasing labor force the bulk of which must come from the rural areas. This means that productivity per man and per acre must increase in order to provide food for the growing number of industrial workers, that one farm family must produce enough to feed itself and four or six additional families in industry, and feed all of them better than they are fed at present.

Much has been made of the fact that economic development leads to a decline in the percentage of the
population in agriculture. But is this a reason for
dubbing agriculture a "declining industry" with the
implication of sickness and obsolescence? On the
contrary, in the Western industrialized countries,
the increase in productivity per man in agriculture
in recent years has exceeded that in industry, and
the actual living level of farmers has been approaching that of city people. Why don't we call transportation and public utilities a "declining industry"?
In the U.S.A., its labor force declined from 12.5
per cent in 1929 to 6.6 per cent in 1965, but its
wage rates rose steadily, relative to those in manufacturing industries, and are now among the highest.[3]

Past experience has been that once economic development gets started, the absolute number of the
farm population can remain fairly constant or even
increase over a long time, although its percentage in
the total declines steadily. It is only at a very
high stage of industrialization that the farm population actually declines in numbers. For instance, in
the U.S.A., farm population remained constant from
1900 to 1940 at around 31 million, declined slowly to
26 million in 1947, and only then dropped sharply to
12 million in 1965. Especially since 1940, productivity per man in agriculture rose much faster than
in industry (see p. 115).

How this process is likely to unfold in the newly developing world between now and the year 2000 is
illustrated by a hypothetical example in Table 11.
Assume a developing country with a population of 100
million, of which 60 per cent now live on farms. By
the year 2000, its population will double and agriculture will produce enough to feed the people at
either of two dietary levels, one at the present inadequate one, and the other at an adequate nutritional level about 35 per cent higher.

In the first case, we assume a moderate rate of
industrialization and little emphasis on reducing
poverty, which will retard industrial labor demand,
will barely absorb the surplus farm population, and

TABLE 11

Population Increase and Required Farmer Productivity,
1965 to 2000

(Hypothetical Example)

		1965	2000 Present Diet Level	2000 Adequate Diet Level
Total Population	millions	100	200	200
In agriculture	millions	60	60	50
In industry	millions	40	140	150
Agricultural Production				
Total	1965 = 100	100	200	270
Per capita in agriculture	1965 = 100	100	200	325
Annual Rate of Increase (compound)				
Total agricultural production	%	---	2.0	3.0
Per capita agricultural production	%	---	2.0	3.5
Number of families fed by one farm family		1.7	3.4	4.0

Assumptions:

1. A developing country with a total population of 100 million in 1965, and 200 million in 2000.

2. In 2000, under "present diet level," farm population remains the same in number, but declines from 60 per cent to 30 per cent of total population; under "adequate diet level," it declines by 10 million in number, and from 60 per cent to 25 per cent of total population.

3. The "adequate diet level" assumes that an increase of 35 per cent in per capita food production (weighted by value) over present levels would be required to assure every family an adequate diet.

4. Food imports are offset by agricultural exports.

will fail to create markets for the protective foods
needed for an adequate diet; even so, perhaps not
many of the countries will manage to absorb the total
farm population surplus in industry and trade and reduce farm population from 60 to 30 per cent of the
total in 35 years.

In the second case, we assume a more vigorous
rate of industrialization and stronger measures for
reducing poverty, resulting in an increased non-farm
labor demand, leaving only 25 per cent of the people
in agriculture, and creating markets for a substantial increase in protective foods. Perhaps fewer
countries will be able to achieve this within 35
years. The annual rate of increase in agricultural
production required, however, is not beyond reach as
several countries have increased farm production per
capita by 2 to 4 per cent per year in recent years.
There are also several countries whose farm population has not increased much or has slightly declined
recently.[4]

Our example in Table 11, therefore, is based on
reasonable assumptions and reflects the general pattern observed earlier in the Western world and recently in some of the developing countries. But it does
not represent an estimate of what most countries will
be able to achieve in the next 35 years: Some might
well require a longer time; others might do it faster;
in still others where population growth is high and
the industrialization process has barely begun, as in
a number of African countries, an increase in the
farm population is likely to occur for a considerable
time. An estimate for Nigeria indicates that the
farm population might increase from about 40 million
in 1965 to 55 million in 1980, simply because industry is now on such a low level that even if it expands at a high percentage rate, it will be some time
before it can absorb the total farm population surplus.[5]

What increase in agricultural productivity will
be necessary to accomplish this? For the present
dietary level, output per agricultural worker must
increase 100 per cent over 1965, at an annual rate of

2 per cent. For the <u>adequate dietary level</u>, the increase must be 225 per cent, that is, at a rate of
3.5 per cent per year; chances are that the farm population will remain around 60 million or may even increase during the first twenty years, and that an
absolute decline in the farm population will occur
only during the last ten years—between 1990 and 2000.
Although the percentage of the farm population will
have dropped from 60 per cent in 1965 to 25 per cent
in 2000, the absolute number will drop by only 17 per
cent, from 60 to 50 million.

     This is the general pattern that can be expected
to unfold in the newly developing countries concerning the agricultural population and its productivity
per man. There will be many variations between countries, especially concerning the time period by which
industry will be able to absorb the total farm population surplus, and then the time by which farm population will actually decline in number. When that
happens, productivity per man in agriculture will begin to rise sharply, as it is only then that labor-
saving machinery can have its real impact on average
productivity per man. When this time will come for
any particular country depends mainly on the people's
will and capacity for progressive change in organization and production techniques. We do know that comparable rates of growth in agricultural productivity
have been achieved by some countries in recent times,
and that mankind has not very much time left for accomplishing a development rate of this general order
of magnitude if major catastrophes are to be avoided.

     To achieve the needed increase in agricultural
productivity will require trained manpower as competent, respected, and well rewarded as their counter-
parts in the cities. It will require capital investment in education, public health, housing, marketing
facilities, and other services comparable to those in
the city. Without such parallel progress in agriculture, the newly developing industries will suffer
from lack of markets and demand for their products,
from a progress-retarding diversion of foreign exchange for food imports instead of for industrial
capital goods, and from lack of literate,

well-motivated rural migrants to boost the industrial
labor force.

THE PRODUCTION PROCESS
ON FARMS AND IN FACTORIES

Part of the imagery of agriculture and industry
stems from the vision of a small peasant family on a
few acres--with no machinery and other capital--as
the typical producer, in contrast to the large-scale
highly mechanized factory with thousands of workers
and a lot of capital. How can such old-fashioned,
small-family enterprises compete with modern big industrial plants in efficiency and productivity? The
clue for the answer lies in the contrast between old-
fashioned and modern, rather than in the contrast between small and big. It is perfectly true that old-
fashioned traditional farming cannot produce the food
for the rapidly growing population; it is not true,
however, that big agricultural factories in the field
organized along industrial lines are necessarily the
best and the only appropriate answer.

There are several reasons for this fallacy which
are too often overlooked.

Agriculture depends on biological growth processes, while industry depends on the transformation of
inanimate materials from one form into another.
Plant growth depends on soil and climate, on the seasonality of seeding and harvesting, on the vagaries
of weather and temperature changes, on many different
natural forces beyond human control. Industry does
not depend upon these natural forces, or can control
them through heating or air conditioning, humidify-
ing, artificial lighting, and other devices. As a
result, agriculture has a much less direct and less
accurate control over its output, and is of necessity
much more widely dispersed over space than industry.
These two facts have far-reaching implications for
the structure of the production process.

In the first place, specialization of labor, labor division, and assembly-line techniques are much

less applicable in agriculture than in industry. Even on a large-scale collective farm, it is not possible to employ a crew of hundreds of workers specially trained to plow and do nothing else--or weed, or thresh, or spray pesticides--because this can be done only during a few days or weeks in a year, due to the seasonality of biological growth.

In the second place, these tasks are spread over wide areas, and on each particular spot only a few people can work at the same task at the same time. Hence, the supervision of the amount and quality of the work done is much more difficult to perform than in a factory. This combination of seasonality and spatial dispersion alone severely limits labor division, specialization, and work supervision in agriculture. As a result of these physical peculiarities of agriculture, it is necessary, for high-production efficiency, to decentralize many management functions and to offer to the farm labor force individual incentives for efficient work which require a strong element of rewards for entrepreneurial initiative and responsibility. But there are other peculiarities which work in the same direction.

To utilize the permanent labor force and the land as efficiently as possible throughout the year, considerable diversification is required. On one farm, a number of different crops and kinds of livestock are often needed to make full use of the land and labor resources. This further limits labor division, specialization, and routinization of tasks in the production process as compared with industry. Most crops are grown more efficiently in rotation with other crops than as a monoculture year after year on the same field.[6]

This means that specialized machinery (e.g., a combine harvester, or pesticide sprayer, etc.) for any one task or crop can be utilized only a few weeks in the year, regardless of how large the farm is. Their operators must be trained to handle a complex set of farm machinery, and, in addition, must learn various other skilled tasks if they are to be employed the year round. This can be done, but it is

not the typical industrial way, and can be done more
readily in the context of a small and medium farm-
size pattern.

The seasonality of biological growth, the dispersion of agriculture over space, the dependence upon natural soil, climate, and weather conditions
highly variable even within small areas and largely
beyond human control--these are the main peculiar
characteristics of the agricultural production process which are in striking contrast to industry.
These characteristics are vaguely known to everybody,
but their economic and technological implications regarding the organization of efficient production processes are too often neglected or ignored by economists, planners, and government leaders.

Throughout the Communist world and in many influential quarters in private enterprise economies,
the belief prevails that what is good for industry is
good for agriculture. Industry has achieved its dramatic success through large-scale organization based
on labor division and minute specialization in
skills; on routinizing work along assembly-line principles; on centralized supervision and management of
large numbers of employees by a small group of technical experts and managerial executives. Hence, the
argument is: Agriculture must use the same methods
to achieve comparable success.

There is ample evidence that this argument is
fallacious. The dogmatic application of these industrial methods to agricultural collectivization in some
of the Communist countries resulted in production declines, or in retarding production expansion from
what it might have been under methods better adapted
to the nature of agriculture. This experience has
led to a reversal toward more decentralization and
smaller production units, under pressure from the innate characteristics of agriculture as well as from
human frustrations and socio-political tensions created by such wholesale collectivization in the industrial image.

We conclude with a warning against blindly imitating industrial methods in modernizing agriculture. The basic physical and human production conditions are too different in these two fields. Effective application of modern technology to agriculture must find its own organizational forms adapted to the peculiar characteristic of the agricultural production process.

This means, in principle, that because of the dominance of biological growth and the spatial dispersion of agricultural production, the individual responsibility for many operational decisions will always be much greater and critically important than in industry, and that management functions must be much more decentralized. To bring just one example: Seeding wheat in semi-arid areas by a few days earlier or later than the best date can result in a 20-30 per cent reduction in yield, and the best date can never be set by the calendar, but can only be determined by keen observation, local experience, and intuition based upon both--concerning in this case mainly--the present and expected moisture conditions of the soil.

Limits of economies of scale are reached much sooner than in industry, so that increasing a farm beyond a rather moderate size brings no further advantages and may result in serious losses in efficiency. This holds particularly where large-scale organization entails an impersonalization of relationships between the farm worker and the end product of plant and animal growth, and between him and his employer or supervisor. Routinization of work and its supervision and central managerial control all along the production process, so effective in industry, have much less scope in agriculture.

PATHS TO MODERNIZATION OF AGRICULTURE

The task of teaching millions of individual peasants modern farming methods appears so staggering that the industrial way of putting a few trained experts and executive managers in charge of thousands of farm workers is indeed appealing as an alternative. We have just seen why this alternative is not very promising of success. But what else is there to do?

Let us look at some of the other things that would have to be done under any program of agricultural development, whether farm collectivization is involved or not.

Large amounts of capital have to be made available in the form of fertilizer, improved seeds, pesticides, farm machinery, and equipment. Without these, collectivization could only disrupt present farming methods without modernizing them, and would result in lower production. This, indeed, has been the effect where collectivization proceeded faster than these modern inputs became available.[7] Hence, agricultural development plans should provide, in any case, for rapid increases in the supply of these inputs. Recent studies have shown that under traditional farming methods without the modern inputs the peasants are often remarkably efficient and could not do much better than they are doing.[8]

As these modern inputs become available, the government can guide their introduction into the production process through various types of programs, such as experiment station research, trials and demonstrations on cultivators' fields for fertilizer, better seed, and pesticides. Many of these inputs can be as effective on small as on large farms.

For tractors and other farm machinery, which cannot pay for themselves on a single small farm, these inputs can be used jointly by a group of farmers through cooperatives, through private machinery operators doing customwork on farms for hire, or through government tractor stations. And under some conditions, the government can establish several state or collective farms in carefully chosen areas where these new inputs and production methods are tried out under local conditions and demonstrated to farmers, and where improved seed and animal breeding stock can be multiplied for use by the farmers in the region. Every one of these different forms of introducing new production techniques might have a constructive place somewhere in every country.

It is equally important to train a large number of technical experts, agricultural economists, and administrative officers for cooperative and government services to agriculture. Without these, progress will be much too slow. Lack of trained personnel retards progress on small farms as much as on large-scale farms. For both types of production organization, there is special need for many field-level workers trained in simple but locally important skills for providing an effective linkage between the highly trained experts and the farmers. These field-level workers are best recruited from the local farm population and trained on the job and in short courses and evening meetings in their respective regions. They must be guided by more highly trained technical experts and given administrative and moral support by regional and national officers. This, again, holds equally for modernizing production on individual family farms and on large collective farms.

We might look at it this way: The introduction of modern production methods requires a number of specialized technicians. While in industry such a group of technicians can be assigned to one large factory employing thousands of workers, in agriculture it must be assigned to work with a few hundred individual farmers, through farmers' cooperatives, through government services (or with agricultural workers on large-scale private collective or state farms), through supervisors and technical-administrative staff. We must recognize that due to the spatial dispersion and limited routinization of the agricultural production process, a considerably smaller number of workers in the labor force can be served effectively by such a group of technicians than in industry. This holds for private or collective large-scale farming as well as for individual family-scale farming, which is too easily overlooked in the planning and operation of large-scale farms.

FAMILY-TYPE FARMS
OR FACTORIES IN THE FIELD

The argument for "factories in the field," that is, for large-scale state, collective, or private farming in which the farm worker is <u>de facto</u> a wage earner, works under the supervision of a foreman and has an employee-relationship to management similar to that of an industrial factory worker, runs as follows:

(1) Modern production techniques can be introduced much faster than in family-type farms because of centralized management. Instead of training millions of individual farmers in scientific farming, only some thousand managers have to be trained;

(2) Large-scale farming is more efficient because full advantage can be taken of mechanization;

(3) Capital and credit are more accessible at more favorable terms because of the larger size of the farm unit;

(4) Marketing and quality control of farm products can be achieved more efficiently;

(5) Planning of agricultural production in line with national requirements can be more effectively implemented through the control over relatively few large farming units.

These aspects have a strong appeal to governments bent upon accelerating agricultural progress and increasing food production rapidly. But actual experience with collective farming has not lived up to these expectations. For instance, after the collectivization process in Russia, it took a long time until the rate of production increase was comparable to that achieved under individual family-type farming in many other countries--even allowing for the severe

drop in production in the wake of the revolution.   It
took large capital inputs in fertilizer and machinery,
in opening vast new land areas for cultivation and
irrigation, and in training large numbers of technicians and managers, before the growth rate in farm
production rose enough to exceed population growth
significantly.   Even since about 1953, when Khrushchev
began to place higher priority on supplying agriculture with capital, the agricultural growth rate remained (as it had been before) consistently well below
the planned targets, and has not exceeded the growth
rates achieved by many other countries under the small
family-farm type of agriculture.   Between 1952 and
1964, the rate of increase in farm production is estimated at 4-5 per cent per year,[9] which is reasonably good, but still below that achieved by a good
many family-type farming countries, as can be seen
from Table 2, p. 16.   This is all the more disconcerting as the U.S.S.R. has had thirty-five years experience with collective farming; with exercising direct centralized control over the agricultural production process; with training and building up a
large administrative staff and cadre of technicians;
and still, the economic performance of collective
farming has been far from spectacular, in fact, has
not been better and has not brought quicker progress
than that of the middle group of family-type farming
countries, and has lagged behind quite a number of
the more successful ones, such as Taiwan, Malaysia,
Mexico, Venezuela, and several others.

The Indian Government has promoted "cooperative
farming" through voluntary action since independence,
with but little demonstrable success.[10] Wherever the
political events in Communist countries permitted it,
decollectivization has occurred, as in Yugoslavia and
Poland, as a result of disappointing results and of
farmers' deep-seated preference for family-type farming.   Nevertheless, where governments have land available for new agricultural development, they often
lean toward large-scale collective, or state or private
estate farming as in some countries in Asia, Africa,
and Latin America.

The argument for small-scale, family-type farming, where most of the labor is provided by the farm
family and the family head is an entrepreneur in
charge of the production process, runs as follows:

(1) Family-type farming can become highly efficient if farmers are trained in modern production
techniques and can obtain the needed inputs at prices
profitable to them, because economies of scale in the
agricultural production process are very limited, and
individual incentives to produce and to make management decisions on the spot when they are needed can
be more effectively mobilized than in large-scale
units;

(2) Adoption of modern production techniques by
individual farmers can be accelerated by training
farm advisors and organizing an efficient extension
service;

(3) Capital and credit needed for modern farming
can be made available through government farm-credit
programs and cooperative credit. Also, the use of
tractors and specialized machinery on family-type
farms can be organized by hire-service through government, cooperative or private agencies;

(4) Marketing and quality control of farm products and other external economies of scale can be
achieved for family-type farms under cooperative or
government organization.

These aspects have a strong appeal to farmers
and to civic leaders placing a high value on the human and social role of the individual in community
life. At the same time, these aspects also make it
possible for family-type farming to exceed factory-
type farming in efficiency of production.[11] Japan
is an outstanding example of agricultural achievement
of family-type farming, as are Taiwan and many of the
Western countries. Family-type farming in many different areas of the world has demonstrated that productivity per man can be higher than on large-scale

collective, state or private farms.

The proponents of large-scale collective farming are prone to underestimate the demands on education, technical knowledge, organizational and administrative skill, and leadership qualities of the management and technical officers on the one hand, and the difficulties in obtaining from the workers the necessary quality of performance, attitude or personal care for plants and animals, and incentives to work on the other. There is ample evidence that these are the weak points of large-scale farming, as compared to family-type farming.

For instance, 11 per cent of the labor force in collective farms in the U.S.S.R. is managerial and administrative.[12]   This means that one person for every eight field workers has to be specially trained for managerial, administrative, and supervisory functions (including paper work of which there is plenty on a collective farm). This places a heavy burden on the specialized educational and training resources of the country, much heavier than even the most elaborate extension service would do under a family-type farming system. Farming advice and assistance in intensive settlement or other pilot projects requires one field extension worker for every 80-100 farmers (representing about 160-200 worker equivalents), and in some highly advanced countries one extension worker covers about 400-600 farms. It is all too often overlooked that collective farming puts a much higher strain on highly trained and specialized manpower resources than does family-type farming where most of the managerial and administrative work is carried out by the farmer himself, and where his production incentives can be so strong and direct that he responds to the extension worker's advice and assistance more effectively with voluntary cooperation than the worker on the collective farm responds to central direction and supervision. Hence, the common notion that collective farming inherently requires less educational effort and time to increase agricultural productivity than family-type farming is not borne out by facts.

Another example: Ghana established a "State
Farms Corporation" to demonstrate the advantages of
large-scale mechanized farming. In 1964, the Corporation had 16,420 employees and officers on its pay-
roll, operating 60,000 acres on 90 farms (average 670
acres per farm). This labor force comes to 183 employees and officers per farm, averaging 3.7 acres
per worker, with a rather low output per worker.[13]
This experience illustrates the serious difficulties
in organizing the staffing of large-scale farms so
that they become efficient units of production in a
short time. There certainly is no magic in large-
scale farming which can raise production efficiency
quickly and easily.

There is no question that starting from a very
low level of agricultural technology, production efficiency can be increased through large-scale farming
if incentive conditions are worked out that will so-
licit genuine interest in the work on the part of the
farm worker, if competent technicians and managers
are available, and if modern capital inputs are provided. The question is, however, whether production
efficiency cannot be increased as well or better
through family-type farming if equivalent incentives,
technical assistance, and capital are provided to the
farmers. In fact, the latter alternative may accomplish a rise in efficiency and income of farmers as
rapidly and in a more desirable way, from the viewpoint of the nature of the agricultural production
process and of the aspirations of farm people.

To put the issue in a nutshell: Agricultural
progress in any case needs more trained people and
more capital. The question is: How can agricultural
officers be used more effectively--by running large-
scale farms as managers with farm workers as employees, or by giving technical assistance to family
farmers through extension services and vocational
training? To make such a comparison meaningful, a-
vailability of capital and credit, common use of machinery, marketing services, and number of farm workers per technical officer must be roughly the same in

both systems.

We lack research findings to answer this question. So far, we can only speculate from informal
observations. It seems quite obvious that many advantages of large-scale farming, for instance enforcing the use of fertilizers and better seeds and
machinery through central management, are often offset by the workers' lack of incentives to carry
through all the various improved practices so as to
get maximum results. Under family-type farming, incentives are much stronger, and farmers develop managerial skills and responsibilities of their own which
enable them to control the production processes of
the farm as an organic whole in close adaptation to
the requirements of biological growth of plants and
animals and to local soil, climate and weather conditions. These are the great advantages of decentralized management in agriculture.

For instance, it is not likely that over-all
production efficiency in Japanese agriculture would
be higher today if agriculture had been collectivized
after the war. It might, indeed, have been lower.
On the other hand, many advantages of family-type
farming are often offset by the difficulties in establishing the required institutional arrangements that
bring forth the production incentives and enable farmers to adopt modern farming methods, such as extension
services, cooperatives, land reforms, and production
credit. These difficulties, however, can hardly be
considered greater than those involved in a sweeping,
technically and economically successful collectivization of agriculture.

A general transformation of family-type farms
into large-scale state or collective farming will
rarely be possible through voluntary means but requires coercive measures of one form or another.
Since the newly developing countries are typically
agrarian, and their governments must rely more and
more upon majority support of the people at large,
the search for tenure and credit arrangements, and
incentives which will accelerate progress without
eliminating the basic nature of family-type farming

becomes a key issue in agricultural development policy.

This is an interpretation of factual evidence
based upon observations and many discussions I have
had with government officials, peasants, and large
and small landowners throughout the developing world.
It is evident that the decisions between collective
and family-type farming in every case will be made on
political rather than economic grounds; that the potential production efficiency of both systems is much
higher than that of traditional farming; and that the
overwhelming majority of farmers have a strong preference for family-type farming.

A sweeping national policy of rapid collectivization of agriculture, however, offers the government
a source of revenue through compulsory deliveries of
grains and other agricultural products, which can
easily be collected and whose quantity can be readily
controlled. This has been an effective device used
by most Communist countries for transferring savings
and income from the agricultural sector into industrial capital formation. But it is not the only nor
the best device for boosting industrialization, as
we have seen earlier. It requires stern coercive
measures and brings the danger of severe setbacks in
production, and of socio-political tension.

The crux of the matter is this: In industry,
modern technology requires a high degree of labor
division and specialization and separation of labor
and management; in agriculture, it does not. Modern
technology can be efficiently applied within small-
scale, family-type farms and through cooperative arrangements between such farms. In fact, chances are
that the race of food with population, the battle for
freedom from hunger, can be won more readily by modernizing family-type farming than by collectivizing
agriculture.

NEW FORMS OF ORGANIZING PRODUCTION: SUDAN'S GEZIRA SCHEME

The wondrous ways of life are such that where
the theorist constructs dichotomies of mutually

exclusive types, people often find ways to synthesize
elements of the one and the other into a new type
that combines good features of both. A very promising
prototype of such a synthesis is the Gezira Scheme in
the Sudan. Although it is unique in several aspects,
and has, after thirty-five years, not yet found its
final shape nor reached its full potential performance, it is a grand experiment with far-reaching
significance throughout the developing world.

Farm families in the Gezira produce cotton under
large-scale farming conditions under central management and supervision, but produce forage crops, maize,
vegetables, and animal products on the two thirds or
three quarters of the tenant's farm not in cotton under family-type farming conditions. Since cotton is
grown under a three- or four-year rotation, the tenant
uses the remaining land under his own management for
his own purposes.[14]

What gives the Gezira Scheme its world-wide importance is the novel approach of settling peasants
in a large-scale modern farming enterprise as family-
type farmers instead of hired workers. The centralized management of the production of one basic cash
crop on the tenant's holding, through well-trained
technicians and administrators, introduces a modicum
of economic and technical efficiency; produces a dependable core of income to tenants and the government; and provides a practical means for educating
the farmers in the ways of scientific farming and
commercial market transactions. The family-type
farming aspect offers individual farmers wide areas
of opportunities for developing managerial skills,
initiative, and responsibility, and a number of supplemental sources of income from crop and livestock
production on his holding.[15]

A NEW IMAGE OF AGRICULTURE:
FARMERS AS ENTREPRENEURS

The facts about agriculture in the industrial
West, particularly the United States, Canada, and the
Scandinavian countries, have changed so much in the

last twenty years that they hardly resemble at all
the features of the old image. Agriculture has been
far from stagnant and farmers are far from leading a
primitive life. Farmers have found their own ways
of adapting their production processes to take full
advantage of modern technology on their family-type
farms. They have been strongly supported in this
task by government policies. The result was high increases in productivity comparable with those achieved
in industry, yet brought about without imitating industrial methods of organizing production along
large-scale collective or plantation-type "factories
in the field." Instead, these scientific achievements in agriculture occurred on family-type farms,
were made by small individual farmers as entrepreneurs with their families furnishing the main labor
force.

   More recently, the same has been true in Japan
and Taiwan, where the government promoted agricultural development by strong general education programs in rural areas, by agricultural research and
extension services, by production credit and price-
support programs, by land reforms and various other
measures. Farmers found it possible and profitable
to adopt modern techniques, and they responded remarkably well with increased productivity. Such positive responses to new opportunities for increased
production and income have also been obtained from
farmers in specific development projects in many developing countries. Where farmers failed to respond,
one could usually find that something was wrong with
the project rather than with the farmers.

   The potential managerial capacity of the peasant
is a crucial issue in major agricultural development
policies. There is evidence that this potential capacity of the small farmer is greatly underrated by
planners and the urban intelligentsia, because they
fail to realize the managerial nature of a peasant's
tasks. Whatever the size of his farm and the degree
of his literacy, he does not receive his income in
the form of wages, and there is no employer to tell
him every day when to show up for work, what he
should do in the morning, and what in the afternoon.

He receives his income basically from his managerial function of combining whatever resources he has available into a production process, and from the work of himself and his family members which he controls and directs.

Even under traditional farming conditions, the peasant is not a hired worker. He is an entrepreneur who makes many managerial decisions and carries the burden of risk. He decides when to plant which crop and when and how often to weed it; what crop rotations to follow; how many of what kinds of animals to feed; how much of what to sell, when and to whom; how much to retain for family use and seed for next year; and how much of what inputs to buy where, and makes many other decisions throughout the production process during the year. All these managerial decisions affect his production and income. It is fallacious to believe that these decisions are all routinized by tradition, that they are easy because the farm is small and he has little to sell and to buy. Within whatever traditional farming system, tenure conditions, and environmental limitations he operates, there is a considerable range of choices he must make, and he knows from bitter and from sweet experiences that much of his survival and success depends on what choices he makes--that is, on his entrepreneurship. Recent studies have shown that given the limitations of the traditional farming systems, the average peasant is performing his managerial role with a remarkable degree of efficiency.[16]

These managerial capabilities of millions of small farmers are a most valuable economic asset of the farm population. Planners and policy-makers must realize that this asset is not only eminently worth preserving, but promises high economic returns to investment in its development in the form of extension and cooperative services, land tenure improvements, and various other institutional arrangements which offer to farmers incentives, access to modern farm inputs, and expanding opportunities for adopting technological innovations and increasing their output and income. Under a rapid and centrally controlled farm collectivization program there is grave danger that

this precious entrepreneurial asset of the farm population is squandered away, is lost to the agricultural
production process. It has been proven very difficult
and time consuming to replace this asset by competent
centralized management from above.

That the peculiar characteristics of the agricultural production process and the dispersal of entrepreneurship among millions of individual farmers do
not necessarily hinder the application of science and
technology is seen in Table 12. Over the fourteen-
year period of 1950-64, the productivity per man-hour
in American agriculture increased 110 per cent, that
is, more than doubled, while in industry it increased
only by 43 per cent. In terms of annual rate of
growth, output per man-hour increased at an average
rate of 7.9 per cent per year in agriculture as compared to only 3.1 per cent in industry. This remarkable increase in agricultural labor productivity took
place mainly on family-type farms; 74 per cent of the
agricultural labor force are family workers, and of
the 26 per cent hired workers a substantial proportion are seasonal workers on family-type farms hired
only for a short time during the peak periods of farm
work.

Table 13 shows the extraordinary importance of
modern inputs and production methods in bringing about
this increase in agricultural productivity. Fertilizer use in the United States since 1940 had trebled by 1955 and quintupled by 1964, machinery use increased about 2.5 times, and feed, seed, and livestock purchases doubled by 1955 and nearly trebled by
1964. During this same period, farm labor declined
by one third in 1955, and by over one half in 1964.
This strong increase in purchased farm inputs, accompanied by a decrease in the farm labor force, accounts
for much of the impressive rise in productivity per
man-hour and for the fact that less than half of the
farmers produced nearly 60 per cent more in 1964 than
in 1940.

This increase in agricultural productivity was
accomplished predominantly on individual family-type
farms. On an annual man-equivalent basis, well over

TABLE 12

Labor Productivity Increases
in Agriculture and Industry, 1950-64,
in the United States

Index of Output per Man-hour
(1950 = 100)

	Agriculture	Non-agricultural Industry
1950	100	100
1960	168	128
1964	210	143

Average Annual Rate of Increase

1950-64 (14 years)	7.9%	3.1%

Source: U.S. Bureau of the Census, Statistical Ab-
          stract of the United States, 1965 (Washing-
          ton, D.C.: U.S. Department of Commerce,
          Bureau of the Census, 1965), p. 236.

three fourths of the total farm work is done by the
farmer and his family, although that farm might be
quite large compared with Asian, African, and Latin
American family-type farms.

    These facts contradict the widely held belief
that American agriculture is predominantly of the
large-scale, industrial-factory type; in reality, it
is mainly of the individual-family type, where the
bulk of labor is furnished by the family members.

    Compared with industry, the individual farm in
the U.S.A. represents a small production unit. It
is, however, well supplied with capital. The total

TABLE 13

Changes in Farm Output and Inputs
in the United States,
1940-64

	Index (1940 = 100)	
	1955	1964
Total Output	137	158
Total Inputs	105	106
Inputs by Classes		
Fertilizers	331	490
Mechanical Power and Machinery	235	240
Feed, Seed, Livestock Purchases	191	273
Farm Labor	63	42
Farm Real Estate	108	111
Miscellaneous	129	233

Hired Workers
In per cent of total
farm employment

1940	25.5%
1955	24.3%
1964	26.2%

Source: Economic Report of the President Transmitted to the Congress January 1965 (Washington, D.C.: U.S. Government Printing Office, 1965), pp. 279-80.

TABLE 14

Investment per Worker in Agriculture
and Industry, 1960,
in the United States

	Total Assets per Worker $
Agriculture[1]	21,500
Industry[2]	
Average, 500 Largest Corporations	15,500
Textiles, Autos, Aircraft, Shipbuilding, Rubber	11,000
Metal Manufacturing and Chemicals	21,500
Petroleum Refining	70,000

1. U.S. Department of Agriculture, Agricultural
    Statistics, 1965 (Washington, D.C.: U.S.
    Government Printing Office, 1965), p. 439.
    "Production Assets" include real estate,
    less value of operators' dwellings. This
    figure is roughly comparable to that of "as-
    sets per employee" in industry.
2. U.S. Bureau of the Census, Statistical Ab-
    stract of the United States, 1962 (Washing-
    ton, D.C.: U.S. Department of Commerce,
    Bureau of the Census, 1962), p. 236.

investment (including land but not farm dwellings)
per agricultural worker averaged $21,500 in 1960.
This amount is similar to the investment per worker
in the 500 largest industrial corporations which averaged $15,500 and ranged from $11,000 to $70,000 in
the various types of industries, as shown in Table
14.

This capacity of the small-scale family farm to absorb about the same amount of capital investment per worker as large-scale industry, and to do so on millions of individual family-type farms with about the same degree of production efficiency, is a fact which is not sufficiently recognized. This capacity of striking productivity increases achieved by individual farmers is not at all limited to the United States, but has been demonstrated in Western European countries such as Denmark, Sweden, and the Netherlands, and in some areas in Asia, Africa, and Latin America where effective development programs and institutional reforms actually offered farmers practical opportunities and incentives for adopting modern farming methods and becoming efficient producers.

To avoid misunderstanding: We have discussed the adaptability, in principle, of family-type farms to modern farming technology in the developing countries. This adaptability, however, requires that the farmer has a farm large enough to introduce modern practices, and that he has access to the various inputs, fertilizer, machinery, and other supplies and equipment he needs for utilizing his land and labor fully and efficiently. There are many farms which are too small for going far in this direction. An agricultural development program, therefore, must arrange for a gradual enlargement of such dwarf farms, and for creating new settlement opportunities by breaking up large land holdings and by developing new land. In such farm-settlement projects, the minimum farm size should be determined mainly by the acreage needed to utilize the labor force of a farm family, complemented by a full set of farm supplies, equipment and cooperative services, and yielding an income comparable to that received by non-farm families.

This problem of undersized farms and underemployment of the agricultural labor force cannot be solved by farm collectivization or large private farm enterprises, since the present farm population would be even more underemployed than it is on small farms now. The rate at which the farm population can be reduced without creating city slums depends on the

rate of industrialization and the demand for non-
agricultural labor. Industry will do very well indeed if it grows fast enough to absorb the present
population surplus of the agricultural sector. In
many countries there is little prospect for that during the next few decades. Although the percentage of
the population in agriculture has been declining almost everywhere in recent years, it will be some time
yet before the absolute number of farm people will
decline.

TWO STRATEGIES FOR PROGRESS:
FOR THE FEW--OR FOR THE MANY

Some planners believe that the easiest and
quickest way to increase production is to help the
top 5 per cent of the farmers--the large-scale producers who now contribute 40 or 50 per cent of the
output in some Latin American countries, for instance.
They are better educated, have more capital, and could
adopt modern technology faster than the small farmers.

One might ask, why don't they produce more now?
The output per hectare on these large-scale farms is
usually not higher, but lower than on the small
farms.[17] The planners say that these large farmers
need cheaper credit, better farm prices, and lower
input prices for fertilizers and machinery as incentives to produce more. One might argue that such incentives would also motivate the smaller farmers to
produce more. But it might be true in some areas
that more extension services and other kinds of assistance would be required, and that would take more
time and cost more money. In general, however, this
is questionable. To introduce modern techniques, it
is primarily the farmer and farm laborer who actually
work in the fields who need to be trained in the use
of modern inputs. The large estate owner, or his administrator, does not apply fertilizer himself, does
not plant crops, does not weed and spray pesticides,
does not operate a tractor. He must hire technicians
and foremen to demonstrate and teach these skills to
farmers. I seriously doubt that the real cost of
technical personnel and training of farm laborers

required to modernize large-scale farming is lower
than that required for modernizing small-scale,
family-type farming. In fact, what little evidence
we have indicates a higher input of technical and supervisory personnel per worker on large-scale than
under family-type farming for comparable levels of
productivity under modern production processes.

Let us compare two alternative development plans.

Plan A is "classical," disregards poverty as an
obstacle, and focuses exclusively on encouraging the
few large-scale farmers to increase production. Let
us assume that this plan is properly implemented and
succeeds in raising total agricultural production and
income in a certain area by 60 per cent over a ten-
year period, and that all the smaller farmers will
not be affected by this plan, nor will the agricultural workers on the large-scale farms benefit as
their wages will remain the same.

Plan B is "modern," deals with overcoming institutional obstacles, and focuses on raising production
and reducing poverty at the same time, as complementary, mutually reinforcing goals, as we have outlined
earlier. The plan does not aim only at the top 5 per
cent of the large producers; it aims at a sizeable
proportion of the masses of small farmers as well.
In addition to some of the policy measures under Plan
A, Plan B makes cheap-production credit available to
small farmers; provides extension service assisting
them in adopting modern inputs and techniques; encourages marketing cooperatives to bring more favorable product prices and input costs to farmers; and
helps agricultural workers to earn better incomes in
line with their increasing productivity through minimum wage laws, collective bargaining, and minimum
standards for housing and working conditions. Let us
assume that this plan also is properly implemented
and succeeds in raising production by 60 per cent over
a ten-year period.

This assumption is, in principle, as realistic
as that under Plan A. Remarkable production increases
have, in fact, been obtained in some countries under

TABLE 15

Agricultural Development Plans: Classical and Modern
(Hypothetical Example)
"Present Position" based on 1960 conditions in Chile

Classes of Farm Families		Present[1] Position (1960)	Plan A (Classical)[2] 10 Years Later	Per Cent Change %	Plan B (Modern) 10 Years Later	Per Cent Change %
Small Farmers and Workers (71% of families)						
Average family income	$	636	636	---	1,200	+ 90
Total family income	million $	155	155	---	293	+ 90
Expenditures:						
Necessities[3]	million $	155	155	---	281	+ 80
Luxuries[4]	million $	---	---	---	---	---
Savings	million $	---	---	---	12	---
Family-Scale Farmers (20% of families)						
Average family income	$	1,000	1,000	---	1,570	+ 57
Total family income	million $	68	68	---	107	+ 57
Expenditures:						
Necessities	million $	65	65	---	103	+ 58
Luxuries	million $	---	---	---	---	---
Savings	million $	3	3	---	4	+ 33
Medium-Scale Farmers (6% of families)						
Average family income	$	3,202	4,600	+ 50	4,600	+ 50
Total family income	million $	71	106	+ 50	106	+ 50
Expenditures:						
Necessities	million $	46	46	---	46	---
Luxuries	million $	16	46	+188	46	+188
Savings	million $	9	14	+ 55	14	+ 55

Large-Scale Farmers
(3% of families)

Average family income	$	16,582	42,100	+145	24,400	+ 43
Total family income	million $	171	421	+145	244	+ 43
Expenditures:						
Necessities	million $	20	20	---	20	---
Luxuries	million $	117	294	+150	175	+ 50
Savings	million $	34	107	+215	49	+ 44

All Farmers
(100% of families)

Average family income	$	1,348	2,180	+ 60	2,180	+ 60
Total family income	million $	465	750	+ 60	750	+ 60
Expenditures:						
Necessities	million $	286	286	---	450	+ 57
Luxuries	million $	133	340	+156	221	+ 66
Savings	million $	46	124	+170	79	+ 72

1. See Solon L. Barraclough and Arthur L. Domike, "Agrarian Structure in Seven Latin American Countries," Land Economics, Vol. XLII, No. 4 (November 1966), p. 407. "Family-scale farmers" operate 5-20 hectares, and "supervisory personnel" on large-scale farms are included because of their similar income; "medium-scale farmers" employ 4-12 workers; and "large-scale farmers" employ over 12 workers.

2. Plan A: Government assists only large- and medium-scale farmers, with loans and price incentives; agricultural wages and small farmers' production and income remain unaffected. Plan B: Government provides assistance to all farmers, through loans, price incentives, and extension service, etc.; agricultural wages reflect workers' increasing productivity. Under Plan B, the goal is to reduce poverty by enabling small farmers to raise their family income to $1,200, and family-scale farmers to $1,500, which is still below the minimum requirement of $2,000 per family to meet an acceptable living standard. Both plans assume an increase in total production (and income) of 60 per cent over a ten-year period.

3. Consumer expenditures cover necessities of life up to $2,000 per family, which is assumed to meet the requirement for living essentials of a typical family; expenditures beyond this "poverty line" are designated as "luxuries." (See discussion of this issue in Chapter 4 above.) This also corresponds to the concept of "surplus" over basic needs discussed above.

4. Savings and personal taxes are assumed to be around 4 per cent in the second, 13 per cent in the third, and 20 per cent in the fourth class of farmers. The last rate is low for the respective income range, but has been reported in a recent study of large-scale farms (ibid., p. 406); for Plan A, a savings rate of 25 per cent is assumed.

the modern type B approach, as, for instance, in Taiwan under the land reform and farmers' associations
scheme. Plans A and B are presented, in simplified
form, in Table 15. Although this is a hypothetical
example, the data regarding present income distribution by classes of farm families is based upon actual
conditions in Chile in 1960; so is the investment-
and-savings rate of the large-scale farmers.

Now let us ask ourselves: How do the prospects
for continued self-sustaining growth compare at the
end of these two plans?

Note that under Plan A, 90 per cent of the farm
families have not benefited from the increase of 60
per cent in agricultural production, while the income
of the large-scale producers (3 per cent of the families) has increased by 145 per cent, which is 2.5
times higher than before. The medium-scale farmers
(6 per cent of the families) show a moderate increase
of around 50 per cent, largely because their access
to capital and to adequate supplies of modern inputs
is more limited than for large-scale farmers. Total
consumer expenditures for necessities of life, that
is for the food, clothing, household goods, housing,
etc., considered necessary for a minimum adequate
level of living (assumed to be $2,000 per family) are
the same as before, while expenditures on luxury
goods have increased about 2.5 times. This classical
Plan A characterizes tha main features of agricultural
development which were prevalent under colonial rule.

Under Plan B, all classes of farmers contribute
to, and benefit from, the production increase. Family income of small farmers and workers rise 90 per
cent; of family-scale farmers 60 per cent; of medium-
scale farmers 50 per cent; and of large-scale farmers
only 45 per cent, because profit incentives for the
large-scale farmers are less than under Plan A, due
to minimum-wage laws and other measures for permitting workers to share in the higher productivity.
What is most important for economic progress, however,
is that total consumer expenditures for necessities
increase by about 60 per cent, from $286 million un-
der Plan A to $450 million under Plan B, which is a

tremendous boost for industrial progress, particularly for domestic food and manufactured products because living essentials usually have a much lower foreign exchange component than luxury goods which depend heavily upon highly capital-intensive industries and, hence, need to be imported for the most part. This modern Plan B characterizes the main features of agricultural development in Japan since the end of World War II, to mention just one concrete example.

Under Plan A, poverty is not reduced, while the demand for luxury goods increases much more than agricultural production, namely by nearly 160 per cent. This creates a real pressure for unproductive uses of scarce foreign exchange since much of the consumption of wealthy families in developing countries consists of imported goods and travel abroad. Under Plan B, the demand for luxury goods is much lower than under Plan A, but is still over 60 per cent higher than in 1960, which should provide adequate production incentives for the large-scale farmers. Note that no "redistribution" of the 1960 level of income has taken place under Plan B; each class of farmer is substantially better off than in 1960. Yet, poverty has been reduced markedly; the poorest 70 per cent of all farm families doubled their income through increasing their production rather than through shifting income from the rich to the poor (see Chapter 4).

Savings are higher under Plan A. With a stagnant domestic demand for necessities, however, there is great danger that these savings will be used for investment abroad or for real estate speculation rather than for the development of the domestic economy. Under Plan B savings are still 70 per cent higher than in 1960; if they should prove too low, they could be doubled and brought up to the Plan A level by channeling an additional $45 million from luxury consumption into domestic developmental investment, which would still allow the rich to increase their luxury consumption by 10-15 per cent. This might be achieved by appropriate restrictions on foreign exchange; by government guarantees for investments in certain domestic industries; by attractive

government-bond issues, and various other means on
which they would earn a reasonable annual return to
add to their income.

Both plans assume that adequate amounts of modern inputs, of fertilizer, improved seeds, etc., are
made available to farmers in quantities and in time
and locations required to bring about the output increase. With appropriate institutional and organizational arrangements, these inputs can be applied on
family-scale farms as effectively as on large-scale
farms. This holds even for farm machinery if various
joint-use measures (on a cooperative or custom-hire
basis) are worked out. In most countries, however,
one might best start the program by allocating the
scarce inputs on soils and on farms, large and small,
where their output response is high, and assign high
priority to making supplies available fully as fast
as farmers are ready to use them, and do so at favorable prices and credit terms to create the needed incentives. There is ample evidence in most parts of
the world that under such conditions producers on
family-scale farms adopt modern practices quite readily, as soon as their beneficial effects have been
demonstrated on cultivators' fields. Even if Plan B
should require initially heavier public investments
in extension services and infrastructural facilities,
their returns are bound to be high in the longer run.
In fact, without them, sustained agricultural progress is not possible.

I have deliberately presented these two alternative plans in sharp contrast in order to highlight
the principal difference in approach. Whenever we
deal with complex issues such as development planning
and policy measures, real life rarely permits clear-
cut alternatives of an either/or nature, but works
out to some of both, to more or less of the one and
the other. Initially, a country might put major emphasis on Plan A, but if it does not soon shift emphasis toward Plan B by increasing farm laborers'
wages and living conditions, and opening up opportunities for the masses of small farmers to increase
their output and income too, progress will suffer.
Domestic demand will lag; undiminished poverty will

retard the rise in productivity of small farmers and
agricultural workers, and will engender mounting dis-
content and social unrest. Under Plan A, profit incentives for large-scale farmers tend to be much
higher than needed for bringing about the desired
production response on the part of a small number of
producers, such as returns on investment of 100 per
cent or more where 20 per cent should provide ample
incentives to investors. But what is more important
for economic progress is that these high incomes to a
few large-scale producers do not "trickle down" to
the small farmers and poor laborers, and hence, do
not provide income incentives for them, nor an expanding demand for domestic industries. To provide
a broad base for making modern technology available
to all farmers with favorable prices and credit terms
as production incentives, and to distribute the resulting income increase widely to bolster the demand
for domestic industry--these are the dynamic characteristics of the modern Plan B.

It is, of course, conceivable that sustained agricultural development can take place under large-
scale farming systems by modernizing not only the
technical production process, but also the conditions
under which farm workers are employed. If farm workers get the full benefit of their increased productivity in the form of higher wages, better housing,
education, training, and working conditions, and if
they have some voice in management which will give
them a feeling of partnership in the enterprise,
large-scale farming can maintain a good growth rate
in production and provide an expanding market for
the country's industrial output. In many countries,
however, it might be much more difficult to achieve
sustained progress along this plan than by modernizing a strong majority of the present family-scale
farms.

The same principle applies in the industrial and
service sectors of the economy, especially where these
sectors comprise a substantial proportion of the labor
force. In Chile, for instance, the urban population
in 1960 accounted for 68 per cent of the total.
Hence, if industrial production increases without

corresponding income increases for the masses of
workers, there soon will be no demand for further output expansion, progress will slow down, and social
unrest will grow. This was experienced during the
Industrial Revolution in Europe and the U.S.A. in the
nineteenth century, as dramatically manifested in the
"sweatshop" system--an institutional disease to
which many developing countries are far from being
immune. Where it still exists today it continues to
foster revolutions. In the twentieth century, a poor
peasantry and a poor urban proletariat do not make
for economic progress and political stability. Economic planning for production expansion without specific measures for poverty reduction prepares the
ground for social unrest and political upheavals.

FACTORIES IN VILLAGES:
THE ROLE OF RURAL INDUSTRIES

Agricultural development will not get very far
without the opening of new employment opportunities
for farm people in industry and other non-agricultural
activities. These two economic sectors must support,
not fight, each other in their struggle for development, and must get closer together. Since farms cannot be brought to the cities, let us bring certain
types of industrial plants to the rural villages.

Instead of trying to make farms over into factories, let farms develop their own modern production
organizations suited to the biological growth process
and its seasonality, and bring some industrial factories into villages and closer to the farms. Such a
selective rural industry program has much to commend
itself as a strategic factor in mobilizing agriculture as well as accelerating industrial development.[18]

Many farm products are bulky and perishable.
Transporting unprocessed, bulky raw materials is
wasteful; the processed, concentrated end product is
much more cheaply transported to market. Most vegetables and fruits contain over 80 per cent water and
are perishable. For distant markets they must be
processed, dried, canned or frozen, to reduce bulk

and perishability. This processing is best done as close as possible to the farms producing them. Rural processing plants open up sources of much valuable food that could not be produced profitably before.

There is the problem of farm population surplus. At present, farm-to-city migrants converge upon urban centers faster than urban industries can absorb them. The growing city slums of uprooted, casual, and un-skilled workers from the countryside create frustra-tion, health and moral hazards, starvation, and po-litical tension. A good part of these premature rural migrants can be given more steady and produc-tive employment in neighboring rural industries where they can learn industrial skills and work dis-cipline without being separated from their families and uprooted from their environment. After several years, and as industrial labor demand grows in the cities, they can move to urban industries as semi-skilled or skilled workers with much better prospects for steady and more remunerative employment. In the meantime, their employment in rural processing plants gives them a wage income, and new experiences and at-titudes toward work. Part of these are transferred to farm families, and help to create a new approach to farming and to marketing as well.

There is the effect such processing plants can have on local farming methods. Sugar refineries, ve-getable, fruit, and other processing plants can re-quire farmers to grow improved crop varieties and to use fertilizers and pesticides, and arrange for making these supplies available at favorable credit terms and with technical advice on how to apply them. Plant managers can set up a grading system, pay high-er prices for better grades, and encourage higher quality of farm products. Similar effects are crea-ted by processing plants for milk, meat, hides and skins, fish, and other animal products.

The Food and Agriculture Organization of the United Nations has carried out very successful tech-nical assistance projects of this nature where their progress-accelerating effects have been clearly dem-onstrated.[19]

There are many other opportunities for rural industries using locally available raw materials for
producing crates and boxes for packaging and furniture, bricks and other building materials, shoes and
other leather products, and a large number of other
manufactured goods not related to agriculture at all.
Modern technology has made it possible to operate
such processing and manufacturing plants efficiently
on a relatively small or medium-sized scale, employing anywhere between 50 to 200 workers and located in
villages and small farms throughout rural areas.

In any development plan, rural industries deserve a strategic role in the interest of both agricultural and industrial progress. Developing countries are very short of managerial skills and opportunities for entrepreneurship outside the agricultural
and trade sectors. Promoting carefully selected and
well-located, small- and medium-sized industries
opens such opportunities to local people with talent
and drive, and will in future decades become one of
the most dependable sources of manpower for industrial leadership in the technical as well as managerial and business functions throughout the industry
of the country.

Take the example of Japan. Her industry is more
decentralized than the industry of most other countries. Yet it is expanding vigorously and competing
successfully in world markets. In the early 1950's,
almost 60 per cent of the total labor force in manufacturing was employed in factories with less than
100 workers, while in West Germany and the U.S.A.
that percentage was 27 and 25 per cent, respectively.
In fabricated metal products, Japan had 80 per cent,
West Germany 35 per cent of the total labor force in
small factories; in apparel and related products,
such as clothing, shoes, etc., Japan had 84 per cent,
West Germany 42 per cent in small factories.[20]   Many
of these small factories are distributed throughout
rural areas and provide employment opportunities for
millions of farm people. This explains in part, the
curious fact, that only about one fourth of Japanese
farm families derive their income solely from their
farms; apparently the majority of the farmers live

close enough to factories to find industrial employment for some of the family members. This greatly
reduces the income-depressing effect of the many undersized farms in Japanese agriculture.

The Western industrial countries are now paying
a rapidly rising price for the failure of not having
planned a more decentralized pattern of industrialization and urbanization. The congestion of population in the industrial areas and large cities on the
northern Atlantic coast, around Chicago, and in California in the United States; in the Ruhr-area in
Germany; and in England, has gotten to a point of
creating most serious problems of water and air pol-
lution, of tremendous waste in commuting time and
cost to and from work, of traffic and transport, of
most unfavorable environment for family life and
raising children. Statesmen and planners in the
newly developing countries can earn the everlasting
gratitude of future generations by a judicious and
systematic planning and effective implementation of
industrial decentralization.

NOTES TO CHAPTER 6

1. These data probably reflect the preferences
and the relative strength of the various ministries
and planners more than those of the students. Still,
one could reasonably expect, for instance, that fellowships in agriculture would outrank those in labor
organization by two to one, instead of the reverse,
since farm population in most of the developing countries constitutes a much larger proportion than urban
labor, and since governments are beginning to realize
how important increased production in agriculture is
to general economic development.

2. The Food and Agriculture Organization of
the United Nations, The State of Food and Agriculture, 1966, (Rome: FAO, 1966), p. 118.

3. See U.S. Government Printing Office, Economic Report of the President Transmitted to the Congress January 1966 (Washington, D.C.: U.S.

Government Printing Office, 1966), pp. 238-241.

4. For instance, the agricultural labor force in Japan declined by 9 per cent between 1950 and 1960, according to Takekazu Ogura, ed., <u>Agricultural Development in Modern Japan</u> (Tokyo: Japan FAO Association, 1963), p. 683. Agricultural employment in Taiwan increased only by 0.3 per cent per year from 1956 to 1960, while total employment increased 1.5 per cent, according to S. C. Hsieh and T. H. Lee, <u>Agricultural Development and Its Contributions to Economic Growth in Taiwan</u>, Chinese-American Joint Commission on Rural Reconstruction Economic Digest Series No. 17 (Taipei: JCRR, April 1966), p. 95. From 1966 to 1970, rural population is expected to remain about the same in Venezuela, Chile, Argentina, and increase only slightly in Mexico and Colombia, according to projections presented in <u>Socio-Economic Progress in Latin America</u>, 6th Annual Report, 1966, Inter-American Development Bank, Washington, D.C.

5. See Food and Agriculture Organization, <u>Agricultural Development in Nigeria, 1965-1980</u> (Rome: FAO, 1966), p. 302; and Bruce F. Johnson, "Agriculture and Economic Development: The Relevance of the Japanese Experience," Food Research Institute Studies, Vol. VI, No. 3 (1966), pp. 267-273.

6. This holds for the bulk of agricultural products. The exceptions are limited mainly to tropical "plantation crops," such as rubber, coffee, tea, cocoa, sisal, sugar cane, and a few others. Even for some of these crops, land and labor can be more fully utilized by interplanting with other crops during the first three or four years after planting, which means diversification. There are areas where rice is grown on the same field indefinitely; but here, again, the typical rice farmer in Thailand, Japan, and Indonesia has some plots where rice cannot be grown but which he must use for vegetables, fruits or forage in order to better utilize his labor and land. The same holds where there is rain enough for only one rice crop, and where dry-season crops must be grown on the same land. All these natural and economic conditions require some degree of diversification which in turn

calls for decentralization of decision-making and
management on the one hand, and limits labor specialization on the other.

7. See Harry E. Walters, "New Soviet Plan Implies Major Farm Policy Switch," Foreign Agriculture,
Vol. IV, No. 12 (March 21, 1966), p. 4.

8. See John W. Mellor, The Economics of Agricultural Development (Ithaca, N.Y.: Cornell University Press, 1966), p. 135; and Theodore W. Schultz,
Transforming Traditional Agriculture (New Haven,
Conn.: Yale University Press, 1964), pp. 36-52.

9. See Karcz, op. cit., p. 161.

10. See N. S. Randhawa, "Returns to Scale and
Cooperative Farming," Indian Journal of Agricultural
Economics, Vol. 15, No. 3 (July-September 1960), pp.
22-23.

11. For an excellent discussion of this issue,
see John M. Brewster, "The Machine Process in Agriculture and Industry," Journal of Farm Economics,
Vol. 32, No. 1 (February 1950), pp. 69-81.

12. A. N. Sakoff, "Rural Population and Agricultural Labor Forces in the U.S.S.R.," Monthly Bulletin
of Agricultural Economics and Statistics, Vol. 15,
Nos. 7 and 8 (July-August 1966), pp. 1-10.

13. U.N./FAO/International Labor Organization,
Progress in Land Reform, Fourth Report (New York:
United Nations, 1966), p. 74.

14. See Arthur Gaitskell, Gezira; A Story of
Development in the Sudan (London: Faber & Faber,
1959). See also Peter F. M. McLoughlin, "The Sudan's
Gezira Scheme: An Economic Profile," Social and Economic Studies, Vol. 12, No. 2 (June 1963), pp. 179-99.

15. A similar production organization can be
found where farmers raise sugar cane on their land
under contract for a sugar refinery, as is being done
successfully in West Pakistan, Indonesia, and several

other countries.

16.   See Mellor, op. cit.

17.   See Barraclough and Domike, op. cit., p.
402; and Erven J. Long, "The Economic Basis of Land
Reform in Underdeveloped Countries," Land Economics,
Vol. 37, No. 2 (May 1961), pp. 117-19, referring to
India.

18.   For a most useful and penetrating study of
the issues involved, see Eugene Staley and R. Morse,
Modern Small Industry for Developing Countries, (New
York: McGraw-Hill Book Co., 1965).

19.   See the impressive series of "FAO Agricultural Development Papers" dealing with processing of
farm products such as hides and skins (Nos. 49, 68),
cassava (No. 54), olive oil (No. 58), copra (No. 63),
dates (No. 72), meat (No. 70), and animal by-prod-
ucts (No. 75).   Food and Agricultural Organization
of the United Nations, Rome, Italy.

20.   See Eugene Staley, Small Industry Development, Stanford Research Institute, Miscellaneous
Paper No. 1 (December 1958), pp. 7-8, and pp. 10-11
for an excellent summary of justifications for small
enterprises in many important products.

CHAPTER **7** PUBLIC INVESTMENT IN THE
RURAL SECTOR: CREATING THE
FOUNDATION FOR PROGRESS

It is not easy to achieve a good balance in developmental investment between the rural and the urban sectors. Leaders in government, business, labor organizations, and the professions are predominantly city oriented; private investors are mainly attracted to industry and trade and show very little interest in agriculture. The method of corporate finance, so eminently successful in industry, does not work in agriculture. The pressure on government for public investment in schools, hospitals, roads, electricity, housing, etc., is much stronger and more effectively applied by the urban interests than by farmers and rural villagers.

At the same time, agriculture depends much more on public investment and services than do industry and trade. Not only does agriculture fail to attract sufficient private investment, it also needs infrastructural investments with comparatively high per capita costs. Equivalent facilities for schools, roads, and communications, for instance, can be provided at a lower cost to city people than to the widely dispersed rural people. But this is no valid reason for depriving farmers of these facilities, particularly since they are essential for raising agricultural productivity. Without them, agriculture will not be able to pull its weight along with industry and trade in the troika of progress.

It becomes the government's task to provide for public investments in agriculture which will create a functional equivalence of developmental facilities between the rural and the urban sectors. This requires capital allocation and corollary services for compensating agriculture's handicap in geographic

dispersion, and in its peculiar biological nature of
the production process. It requires policy measures
which will more nearly equalize development opportunities, incentives, and income rewards between country
and city, between agriculture and industry.

This puts a heavy burden on enlightened leadership of statesmen and planners, because farmers and
rural villagers are generally less effectively organized and politically less articulate than are comparable interest groups in the cities. In modern times,
the mark of a statesman lies in his championship of
the inarticulate, the economically handicapped. Such
championship is not purely a labor of love; a statesman knows that by representing the interests of the
large masses of disadvantaged farmers and workers at
the council table he can count on the confidence and
support of these groups who are clearly in ascendancy
to political power.

ELEMENTARY EDUCATION:
A BASIC NECESSITY FOR PROGRESS

Nearly everywhere in the world, elementary education in rural areas is much inferior to that in urban areas. For instance, in most Latin American
countries around 1962, the rate of illiteracy was
three to four times higher in rural than in urban
areas (see Table 16). To some extent, this is due
to the higher cost per pupil resulting from the smaller density of population. But this higher cost is
not sufficient to explain the wide gap between countryside and city.

A more important reason for the gap may often be
a much more effective pressure for schools in the
city, where people may be more conscious of the value
of education and are closer to legislators and government leaders whose job it is to allocate funds.
The comparative lack of popular pressure for schools
in rural areas may be partly due to the many small
tasks children can do on the farm. Still, their
place in the labor force is not so indispensable as
to prevent farm children from going to school--as

TABLE 16

Illiteracy in Urban and Rural Areas in Latin American Countries[1]
(around 1962)

Country	All Areas	Urban Areas	Rural Areas	Rural Rate in Multiple of Urban (col.3 col.2)
	Illiteracy Rate Per Cent of Population 15 Years and Older			
	%	%	%	%
Panama[2]	21.7	6.1	35.4	5.8
Nicaragua[2]	50.0	20.4	80.4	4.0
Ecuador	32.5	11.9	44.5	3.7
Chile[3]	16.4	9.0	33.0	3.7
Costa Rica	16.0	6.1	22.0	3.6
Peru	38.9	17.7	59.4	3.4
Honduras[2]	53.0	23.0	62.0	2.7
Colombia	37.7	20.5	50.0	2.4
Brazil (1950)	50.0	27.0	66.0	2.4
El Salvador	56.0	27.0	64.0	2.4
Guatemala[4] (1950)	72.0	41.0	82.0	2.0

1. Source: Inter-American Development Bank, Social Progress Trust Fund; Fifth Annual Report, 1965, Washington, D.C. (February 28, 1966). See individual country sections.
2. Per cent of population ten years old and over.
3. Per cent of population six years old and over.
4. Per cent of total population.

can be seen where schools have become accessible to farm children.

What is a serious obstructive factor in some rural areas is the silent opposition of the rural elite, the landlords, estate managers, and merchants who feel that ignorant farmers are easier to deal with and keep in their subservient place as tenants, laborers, and borrowers. This obstacle is difficult to overcome, especially in areas where a quasi-feudal elite of large landowners wields power over small peasants and farm workers, as in much of Latin America. Here it can be met only by a strong government commitment to universal education on the one hand, and by enlightened local leadership on the other. To develop rural pressures for elementary schooling in opposition to a powerful rural elite requires a strong support by local organizations of small farmers, such as cooperatives, farmers' associations, and farm labor unions.[1]

This education issue is indeed a crucial one for development. Modern agricultural technology and group action for dealing with market forces and government services, with landlords and public officials, require literacy on the part of farmers, demand a facility to communicate, to articulate aspirations and complaints, to organize for specific tasks in production, marketing, and civic activities.

As a practical proposition, national development plans could make explicit and detailed provisions for narrowing the educational gap; for giving a relative priority to schools in rural areas for meeting a minimum standard of teachers and classrooms per 1,000 children; and for assuring their accessibility to all farm children.

To implement such a policy, various local measures can be used in rural areas, such as mobilization of local labor and materials for the building of schools, employing interim teachers with inadequate training but with talent and devotion for teaching until trained teachers become available, and providing some local tax base for collecting funds earmarked for local school improvements, to mention just a few which have proven highly effective in some areas. Such measures might not require extra appropriations from government revenues, but only enabling-legislation which empowers the government to support any initiative on the part of local communities along these lines and makes scarce public funds go farther. This type of policy measure that provides government support of a wide range of specific activities sponsored by local groups, and contributing to progress, is sorely neglected in most developing countries and could be applied much more widely and systematically. Large reserves of latent human and material resources could be mobilized and combined with the limited funds the government can provide. This would get local people involved and actively participating in school projects and other types of development projects.

Raising rural literacy is also a fundamental requirement for developing initiative, production incentives, managerial and organizational capacities.[2] For strengthening the social status of farmers vis-à-vis landlords, moneylenders, merchants, and local government officials, literacy is a potent asset, as it is for active citizenship in community affairs.

Better rural schooling is also in the interest of the urban sector, since a good proportion of the students later on will enter the industrial labor force at a higher level of skill and productive capacity. These are policy considerations deeply affecting the rate of economic growth in the various sectors, and their balance.

Finally, such a differential priority for primary education in rural areas is also needed for reducing poverty. Education is one of the strategic "necessities" of which an adequate minimum level should be placed within reach of everyone.

Most modern nations today are, in principle, committed to mandatory elementary schooling of children from six to twelve years of age. But many are still far from this goal, especially in rural areas.

How wide a gap between country and city does one dare
to permit for how long a time? The danger lies distinctly in permitting too wide a gap to occur over
too long a time. This holds particularly for those
Latin American and other countries where large landowners often oppose education of farmers and their
children.

Where countries have achieved a high enrollment
of children in elementary schools, the retention rate
for even a five-year schooling period is often very
low. Table 17 shows, for instance, that in the Philippines and Ceylon where 90 per cent of the children
enter first grade, nearly one half drop out before
they reach fifth grade. In Latin American countries,
these retention rates are usually much lower than
those for the majority of the Asian countries; of
twenty Latin American countries reporting, the highest retention rate was 48 per cent for Panama, and
most of them were between 10 and 25 per cent.[3] In
most African countries south of the Sahara, universal
elementary education has only begun in the 1960's.

The issues of primary education policy are of a
different nature than those of secondary and higher
education. Once elementary schooling has become universal, many of the students will remain in their locality, although some of the brighter and most of the
wealthier ones will leave for secondary education
elsewhere. Primary education, therefore, should be
oriented toward "home consumption," for becoming more
articulate, versatile, knowledgeable human beings
wherever they are and whatever they do, and for becoming more effective participants in community affairs, in business transactions, and social functions
--for becoming full-fledged citizens.[4]

In fact, the general outlook of students in primary schools might well be directed deliberately
toward this end by teaching children in rural areas
to understand the urgency for modernizing agriculture
and creating living conditions equivalent to urban
areas, rather than educating them away from their local environment toward an unrealistically glamorous
notion of city life. This, however, should not affect

TABLE 17

Enrollment of Children 6-12 Years of Age
at First Level of Education,
Asian Countries, 1962

Country	Percentage of Children Enrolled	Percentage of 1st Grade Students Reaching 5th Grade
	%	%
Below 40%		
Nepal	10	n.a.
Afghanistan	12	57
Laos	31	16
40-70%		
Pakistan	40	25
Iran	50	74
Vietnam	58	40
Cambodia	61	52
Indonesia	62	n.a.
Above 70%		
India	71	29
Burma	72	0
Thailand	75	0
Philippines	89	55
Malaysia	89	71
Mongolia	91	n.a.
Ceylon	91	57
Taiwan	92	92
Korea	95	88
Japan	100	99

Source: United Nations Children's Fund, Children and Youth in National Development in Asia. Report of Conference, March 8-15, 1966, Bangkok, Thailand (New York: United Nations Children's Fund, 1966), pp. 86-87.

the subject-matter core of the basic curriculum, which must remain the same for all children in cities and villages as a foundation of knowledge common to all, and which should include an appreciation of rural life by city people as well.[5]

For many years to come, only a minority of rural primary school students will be able to go on through secondary schools and to universities, or directly to clerical jobs in the city. It is useful to develop vocational courses for agricultural, mechanical, handicraft, and clerical skills in the rural areas where children are trained for two to four more years after they leave primary school at the age of twelve. These are important considerations for manpower planning which are as yet much neglected, especially in Africa where general primary education is new and school leavers with only six years or less of primary education drift off to cities in search of non-existing clerical jobs.

Secondary education for the ages of twelve to eighteen prepares students for occupations, most of which they must find outside their rural home community. Still, gifted children from rural areas deserve opportunities for higher education as much as urban children do. Since access to secondary education involves much heavier expenses to rural families as they have to send their children away from home, the government has an obligation to provide scholarships to compensate for the higher cost to rural families.

Secondary education raises the issue of whether employment opportunities will be sufficient and considered suitable by the school leavers for putting their advanced training to constructive uses, both from the national and individual points of view. Nigerian attempts to settle secondary school leavers as farmers have not been very promising. Perhaps they would contribute more to progress if they were trained as extension field officers to work with farmers on modern techniques, and as managers of cooperatives-- which also might fit better into their own conception of how to put their acquired knowledge to better use.

Twelve years of education is, indeed, potentially a very productive asset in developing countries. The graduates themselves sense it. We must not condone snobbish pretensions to desk jobs in the central government on the strength of a secondary school diploma; but we must realize that such a scarce educational asset demands to be fully utilized where it is most needed, and that the government cannot evade the responsibility of guiding school graduates into jobs or into further advanced training where their skills and knowledge are most productive. Where these jobs are not now available, they simply must be created, for instance, by developing large cadres of middle-echelon field workers to provide a working link between the highly trained technicians and administrative officers and the masses of farmers and village people. Otherwise, the waste of the educational asset becomes compounded with the school leaver's frustration. It is like building a dam for a water reservoir without building irrigation canals to bring the water to the fields.

"Intellectual unemployment" in developing countries does not indicate an excessive rate of education, but incompetence in planning and administering its use. Perhaps in many low-income countries we cannot afford the fortuitous and often ill-considered individual choice of subject-matter fields if too many students want to become lawyers, accountants, historians, and nuclear physicists, and not enough to become agricultural officers, hospital laboratory assistants, surveyors, and agricultural scientists. We may need to do some differential channeling of students into various occupations, at various levels, and in various regions of the country, not by coercion, but by inducements and opportunities offered. Many surveys of manpower needs are being conducted, but as in economic investment and production planning, we neglect to solve the implementation problems.

When a government builds an irrigation system, it commits funds, manpower, and materials ten or twenty years in advance. When it builds an

educational system, it might be wise to do likewise
--to establish a core of future jobs, announce them,
and guide students toward them, in their studies as
well as their attitudes and expectations. Promising
students jobs in major selected fields, after they
have completed their training creditably, at satisfactory salaries and prospects of promotion, is in
itself an effective measure for guiding them into desirable occupational channels. Within the framework
of a predominantly private enterprise economy, there
is little danger of exercising coercive pressure upon the student's choice; instead, such a policy would
expand employment opportunities in fields where there
is a known future scarcity of trained workers. In
agriculture, this scarcity is largely the result of
social prejudice, of lack of appreciation of the crucial function of professionally trained agricultur-
ists in field assignments.

This, indeed, represents an essential field for
economic development planning. Here, again, as in
production planning, the exact quantity targets
(though not their order of magnitude) are less important than the implementation measures for directing
whatever number of trained persons are brought forth
each year into productive employment where they are
most needed. Idle or misplaced trained people are
much worse than idle or misused machinery--they are
not only wasted, but they get demoralized and spread
corruption and sap the creative vigor of society.

We might conclude that universal primary schooling deserves high priority in education policy especially for the traditionally neglected rural sector,
at least until a six-year schooling level is in reach
of every child throughout the country. As this goal
is approached--but long before it is reached--empha-
sis shifts to a higher rate of expansion of secondary
education and to a general improvement of the quality of education and of the competence of teachers
throughout the primary and secondary school system.
At the same time, the substance of this higher education can be directed toward two complementary goals:
that of training the students toward meeting national
development needs; and that of molding their

motivations and instilling into their minds a sense of social responsibility to serve these needs.[6] This involves getting many of them, especially of those coming from rural areas, used to the prospect of spending a number of years after graduation in some field assignment away from the city. Westerners often scoff at the idea of "indoctrinating" students with social values, such as a sense of social responsibility, of duty to make one's individual contribution to the country's development in terms of some sort of service beyond his personal comfort and interest. In many developing countries, this idea is more readily acceptable since their cultures are not as extremely individualistic, utilitarian, and competitive as Western culture is.

In the rural areas, a much larger number of secondary school and college graduates will be needed, especially in primary school teaching, agriculture and many of the related biological and earth sciences, engineering, and economic and administrative services. Developing countries can ill afford to let educated people go unemployed or underutilized. A most obnoxious form of unemployment, or misuse of trained persons, is keeping them in cities waiting for "respectable" jobs to turn up, or in central government offices pushing papers up and down the echelons.

We have dealt briefly with lack of rural education as an almost universal obstacle to agricultural progress, and as a prototype of infrastructural deficiencies. What has been said of rural school problems applies, mutatis mutandis, to problems of bringing rural people up to par with urban people, regarding roads, transport and marketing facilities, hospitals and medical care, sanitary water supply, and electricity. These are all items in the national income of a country which need to be accessible to every family, at least up to a minimum acceptable standard--as a civic right as well as for mobilizing its latent productive capacities. They are instrumental for overcoming the obstacles of poverty whose incidence is peculiarly concentrated in rural areas, and hence, specifically impede agricultural progress.

Let us now turn to some of the other infrastructural deficiencies in the rural sector.

FARM-TO-MARKET ROADS:
OPENING THE DOOR TO RURAL PROGRESS

Mobility of goods and people heralds economic change. Roads and public transport, between the capital and the main cities and seaports, have already been developed to some extent by colonial administrations. Since independence, these facilities have been further expanded and modernized to suit the growing export and import trade. And what about the countryside? In many developing countries, roads, transport, and marketing facilities in rural areas have been badly neglected. As a result, the rate of progress is much slower than what it might be if a vigorous development plan in this field were adopted.

The transport situation in many rural areas is much worse than it might look at first sight. For millions and millions of acres of potentially highly productive farm lands, no farm-to-market roads exist on which the agricultural output could be transported by trucks, or even ox-carts.

A first principle of agricultural development is: Get the loads off people's backs onto wheels. Yet, at the present time, a major portion of the total farm produce brought to market is carried on the heads, shoulders, and backs of people. For instance, in an area including four villages in northern West Pakistan, there were still 84 per cent of the farmers who did not own even a bullock cart in 1963.[7] If we want farmers to double and triple their crop yields, we cannot expect them to carry a double or triple harvest load on their backs for miles to the nearest market, nor to carry large amounts of fertilizers to the fields. The implementation of this "first principle" is relatively easy in level, dry-land farming areas; it is much more difficult and costly in mountainous and in irrigated farming areas--but these areas include a large part of the most productive farming lands in Asia and the Far East, in Latin

America and Africa.

To indicate roughly the order of magnitude of
this problem: Around 1931, a survey of 131 farming
localities in 19 rural provinces in China revealed
that 53 per cent of these localities depended upon
men and women carrying loads to market; only 19 per
cent had market access by roads for animal-drawn
carts, and only 2 per cent by roads for trucks.[8] Of
course, there has been much road building in China
as well as elsewhere since 1931, but the farm-to-
market roads, almost everywhere in the developing
world, have been given much too small a share in the
transportation development.

In a recent study of transportation cost to market centers of agricultural produce in the Peruvian
Andes, the cost per ton-mile was calculated at 24
soles by mule, as compared to 1 sole by truck.[9] Mexico (around 1960) had a paved highway network of
36,000 km., but only 14,000 km. of farm-to-market
roads. Since then, Mexico has speeded up the program
of its "National Farm-to-Market Roads Commission"
("Comision Nacional de Caminos Vecinales," established in 1949 and expanded in 1956 and 1960), with a
strong emphasis on cooperation of private initiative
in road construction. Still, its current rate of
completing 1,500 km. per year is a rather modest one
in view of the task. Planners estimated that 200,000
km. are needed to bring every village within 5 km. of
a farm-to-market road. Every kilometer of a farm-to-
market road network in Mexico is expected to "permit
the utilization and incorporation into production and
the national economy of 250 additional hectares of
cultivated land." Moreover, it is estimated that the
annual planned addition of 1,500 km. of roads will
increase the income of the national economy by 170
million pesos each year through the benefits to the
construction, gasoline and oil, auto and tire indus-
tries--not including the benefits to farmers. The
annual allocation to finance the program of the National Farm-to-Market Road Commission was around 76
million pesos in 1960.[10]

These are just a few examples of the need for a
farm-to-market road network that will really do the
job of drawing agriculture's production potential into the national market economy.

Here, as in the case of schools, local communities are most keen on getting roads, and their people
often can be induced to make contributions in labor,
land, local raw materials like gravel, etc., which,
if properly organized, can substantially reduce the
financial burden on the government budget.

It is, of course, true that road building is
most popular in developing countries and with aid-
giving agencies. Many governments are allocating 20-
40 per cent of their public development capital into
transport facilities, and over the last fifteen
years, about 30 per cent of U.S. foreign economic
aid--and in 1960-61 about 50 per cent of the World
Bank loans--went to roads and transport facilities.[11]
But only a small part of this is used for farm-to-
market road networks. Instead, much of it goes into
fully paved multi-lane highways which for many years
to come will carry a traffic load much below their
capacity. One critic of such extravagance put it
this way:

> ...in the eyes of the aid advisers, (the
> roads) must be at least two lanes wide,
> surfaced with an all-weather dustless oil
> product and contain neither scratch nor
> wrinkle greater than that which a Detroit
> ensemble of five inches clearance can skim
> over without jar or quiver to a visiting
> VIP's wife's hips.[12]

The point is: Let us build quickly an extensive
farm-to-market road network at low cost, and with the
participation of local communities. Even for such
country roads, foreign financial aid can be made
available since it is easy to make a strong case for
the high priority which farm-to-market roads deserve.
They should, in most areas, be all-weather roads,
passable by trucks. A large proportion may carry for
some years a light traffic load, until production and

trade have expanded in response to the new access to markets. A gravel surface and, in difficult terrain, one lane with turn-outs will do the job in the beginning. As traffic does become heavier, the roads can be improved and enlarged as the need arises.

Don't listen to the engineer if he tells you that it is not very much more costly to build a paved double-lane road from the start, than to build a gravel single-lane road now and pave and broaden it a few years later. A wise strategy calls for opening the door to markets for all agricultural areas as quickly and as cheaply as possible, and then, in accordance with the actual response of any specific locality, for improving the roads as the traffic load rises. The nation can afford the additional cost of road improvement much better after production and trade have greatly expanded and where the traffic load has greatly increased, than before output expansion has taken place, and before it is known on which portions of the farm-to-market road network the traffic load will increase, how much and how fast.

This is one of many cases where overplanning in detail and setting overambitious standards of construction can easily lead to waste and costly errors, and thereby retard development from what it might have been had such waste been avoided.

MARKET HALLS, STOREHOUSES, AND MARKETING SERVICES

Following on the heels of farm-to-market roads, and wherever present local markets exist that assemble produce for shipping to ports and cities, there is great need for sanitary market halls; for warehouses equipped with protection against rodents and insects, and excessive moisture, heat, or cold; for supervision of sanitary conditions, honest weights and measures; enforcement of quality standards; public display of prices quoted at major market centers; assignment of market stalls to individuals or groups; and various others. The lack of these types of public service is severely retarding progress in

marketing. The results achieved by programs along
these lines in a number of countries have been most
promising indeed.[13]

Small farmers feel helpless and vulnerable in
face of the market forces. In their experience,
these inexorable forces have often frustrated their
hopes that a good crop and a special effort on their
part will get them out of debt and give them a start
toward a better living. Such experiences dampen the
farmer's incentives to produce, sell, and buy more
in the market, to get more deeply dependent upon the
market in his production and consumption. The government has a crucial obligation to create local market conditions in which the farmer can have confidence.

Public investments in local marketing facilities
is also of great benefit to the merchants. The increased volume and quality of produce will raise the
income of the middlemen as well as of the farmers.
Even the increase in prices actually received by farmers is in the middlemen's longer-term interest because of the increased volume of products generated
by the price incentive to farmers. Middlemen get
their income from marketing margins, and since the
volume is bound to increase more than the margins per
unit decline, their income will rise.

The need for these investments in marketing is
not confined to public market halls; it also holds
for farmers' cooperatives. Here, too, it is the government's function to initially finance such investment. Whether and to what extent the government
should require reimbursement depends mainly on the
local circumstances. It often might be wise to take
the position that the fixed capital shall be treated
as a typical infrastructural investment by the national government, as in the case of roads and schools.
The current maintenance and operation of these marketing facilities, however, must be carried by buyers, sellers, and the village, through fees or levies
of some sort.

Good rural market facilities are not only important for selling farm products, they are equally essential for bringing farmers more favorable prices of
the things he buys. For production, he needs fertilizers, seeds, and pesticides of a specific kind and
at specific times, and this, too, requires storage
facilities. For consumption, a wide range of goods
available at prices within the reach of farm families
has a strong stimulating effect on farm production
incentives as well as on demand for industrial products.

Good market facilities in rural villages, and
farm-to-market roads and motor transport to and from
the villages, are indispensable characteristics of
an environment which greatly speeds up progress.[14]

RURAL ELECTRIFICATION
AND COMMUNICATION WITH THE OUTSIDE WORLD

There are other fields of public investment
which also create an environment for progress: electricity and housing. Their effect is profound on
people's attitudes and living habits, on their demand for consumer goods, on their production incentives, and on their sense of dignity and citizenship.

Light in the homes after the sun has set stimulates intellectual activities: reading, writing,
learning, listening to the radio, and discussing
things in the family and with neighbors. It length-
ens the working day: The farmer can repair equipment, his wife and daughters can mend clothes and
weave carpets, the children can study their lessons.
Some say it reduces the birth rate: Less time is
spent in bed, and more of this for sleeping.

In the village, evening meetings can be held
with film projections, demonstrations, exhibitions,
group discussions. And, very important indeed, telephone connections can be established with provincial
and national markets for prices and other trade

information, with government offices elsewhere for
emergency services or advice and instructions, and
with hospitals for ambulances and doctors. With the
rapidly expanding developmental functions of government throughout the rural areas, telephone service to
the villages and local offices facilitates tremendously all administrative tasks.

Rural electrification stimulates the demand for
a whole series of industrial goods, from light bulbs
to radios, irons, cooking equipment, small tools,
water pumps, refrigerators (especially for storehouses). It can attract agricultural processing
plants and other small-scale industries into rural
villages.

The over-all effect is one of giving impetus to
whole sets of economic, social, and technical innovations. The village has moved a decisive step closer
to the city with respect to living essentials and
amenities of modern society. Yet, the great majority
of farmers and villages in the developing regions
live without electricity, and are deprived of the advantages and opportunities it offers.

The financial problems of rural electrification
have become less forbidding due to technological advance in the transmission of electric current, and in
the production of small generating plants. One die-
sel engine can supply a village with electricity at
moderate cost. The effective household demand for
electricity, even in rural areas, has been a surprise
to many planners and engineers in all the different
parts of the world. Wherever hydroelectric power is
generated, the demand from rural areas must be given
full weight in determining the capacity of the plant,
rather than counting only on city and industrial demands.

FINANCIAL AND ADMINISTRATIVE
DIFFICULTIES IN THE RURAL SECTOR

The four types of public investment we have
briefly examined are those most strategic in making

the rural sector capable of playing its role in the
development of the nation. In these fields of education, roads, marketing facilities, and electricity,
farmers are severely disadvantaged as compared to urban people. These public services are potent factors
in creating a rural environment in which farmers can
progress rapidly in modern production techniques, in
raising farm income, in becoming good customers of
industrial goods and active citizens in community affairs. They have in common that they are more expensive per person in rural than in urban areas. This
may be a partial explanation, but not a justification
for their neglect. National development planning
must give high priority to reducing the gap between
city and country in these vital conditions for progress.

The financial burden on the government can be
reduced by mobilizing local underemployed manpower.
Thousands of road miles and of schoolhouses have been
constructed with local voluntary labor in many countries. Rural people are keen on these investments
and are on the whole, responsive to opportunities for
helping to get them by contributing their spare labor
(see Chapter 13). Much more could be accomplished in
many countries if well-planned and administered programs were put into effect which would provide technical assistance, administrative guidance, and modest
financial support for such local community projects,
including some bulldozers, transportation of volunteers, and food for a midday meal. The timing must
be geared to the seasonal slack periods of agricultural labor requirements. In presenting such a program to rural people, it might often be useful to
emphasize the matching of government contributions
with voluntary local contributions, assigning an imputed monetary value to them, and to hire local supervisors and organizers who have experience in leadership and the respect of their community.

A danger exists of ambitious overplanning, of
getting too much bureaucratic procedure into such a
program, and of government supervisors expecting
farmers' labor contributions as a duty and treating
them as hired workers. A certain work discipline

must be maintained, but can often be done more effectively by building up a group spirit, by seeking the
advice of local people on many details of the work,
and by working with them in a pioneering way.

Where does the money come from that is needed to
close the gap between city and country? Let us examine several ways in which public rural investments in
these fields can be increased.

All governments in the developing countries are
facing the necessity of increasing their revenues for
the simple reason that their development functions
are expanding. In fact, many countries in recent
years have increased their government expenditures at
a higher rate than their national income.[15]

Administratively, the path of least resistance
is to give each branch of government or area the same
percentage increase over its present budget. This
keeps administrators happy, or at least acquiescent;
but it does not spur development. Increased funds
must be allocated differently to the various areas
according to their relative priorities, that is, more
to those urgently needed for accelerating economic
progress, and less to others. Such selective expansion is fairly easy if there are substantial increases in public funds most of which can be assigned to
high priority needs, giving the others a smaller increase or keeping them at the present level. This
does not require the painful surgery of reducing the
budgets of other departments or areas in the country.

For example, take the relative need for elementary education in urban and rural areas. If the percentage of children six to twelve years old in school
is 60 per cent in the urban and 20 per cent in the
rural areas of a country, a given increase of 50 per
cent in total primary school appropriations could be
allocated in such a way that this educational gap
will be narrowed. By increasing school facilities
11 per cent in the urban and 100 per cent in the rural areas, the proportions of enrolled children will
have risen to 67 and 40 per cent, respectively, as
shown in Table 18. A "proportional" increase of 50

TABLE 18

Examples of Planning Differential Targets for Primary School Enrollment in Urban and Rural Areas
(Country X)

	Actual 1965 %	Projection Assuming Proportional Increase in Enrollment 1970 %	Differential Plan Targets 1970 %
Per Cent of All Children 6-12 Years Old in School			
Nation	32	48	48
Urban	60	90	67
Rural	20	30	40
Increase in Enrollment, Per Cent over 1965			
Nation		50	50
Urban		50	11
Rural		50	100

Assumptions: 30% of all children in <u>urban</u> areas, of which 60% in schools in 1965.

70% of all children in <u>rural</u> areas, of which 20% in schools in 1965.

Projection: (1970)   Proportional increase of 50% in enrollment in both areas.

Plan Targets: (1970)   Increase of 11% in enrollment in <u>urban</u> areas.

Increase of 100% in enrollment in <u>rural</u> areas.

For simplicity of exposition of the principle, population increases and shifts from rural to urban areas have been disregarded.

per cent for both urban and rural schools would rapidly widen the gap rather than narrow it, resulting
in 90 per cent enrollment in urban and 30 per cent in
rural areas, as compared to 60 and 20 per cent before.

From the planning point of view, one of the
chief criteria for assigning priorities is the dis-
tance of the present position from an adequate minimum position expressed in the simplest measurable
terms. In our example, the guiding criterion is that
a six-year primary school education represents a minimum adequate standard for the nation's population.

This general line of reasoning applies, with
modifications, to other types of public investment
and services critically neglected in the rural sector.

There are, of course, many cases where a government department cannot receive sufficient increases
in funds to move ahead with major expansions in high-
priority fields without transferring present funds
from other uses with lower priorities. This is administratively more difficult to do since it requires actual reductions in the budget of some units
to increase that of others, and usually entails also
shifting people from their present positions. Yet,
it often must be and, in fact, sometimes is being
done.

What are some "lower-priority" fields from which
such transfers might be made? In principle, one
could take away some resources from activities which
can be routinized or better organized so that nearly
the same work can be done with less funds, and concentrate these "savings" upon a high-priority task.
For instance, perhaps 20 to 40 per cent of the personnel in the headquarters of the extension service
in some country might be transferred to field assignments in specific development programs. This could
spur agricultural progress greatly (see Chapter 12).
The dearth of trained manpower is often so much
greater in the field than at headquarters, that the
piling up of headquarter posts severely reduces the
effectiveness of development programs. A sudden

reduction of headquarter posts for assignment to rural areas is practically impossible for any department
to do. But a gradual move in this direction, e.g.,
on a selective basis as to personnel especially suited to specific field assignments and by transferring
headquarter posts to the field at the time they become
vacant, might well bring good results over a period
of years. Certain inducements in the form of field
allowances and other rewards are often necessary to
render such transfers to the field acceptable.

Another possibility is the transfer of personnel
and funds from one branch of the ministry to another,
or even from one ministry to another. A third possibility might be to pull out certain offices and units
from several ministries and reassemble them in a new
agency established for carrying out specific development programs, such as farm settlement, land reform
or irrigation projects, with powers of comprehensive
planning and implementation on the spot. All these
possibilities have been tried in various countries,
some with remarkable success, such as the INTA program in Argentina, the Water and Power Authority in
Pakistan, or the Regional Planning authorities in
Israel.

Financial and administrative decisions on the
differential allocation of additional funds, and on
transfers of present funds from one unit to another,
are complex and difficult to make. Rarely is agreement on priority rankings of a set of programs clear-
cut and unanimous among a council of ministers or a
committee of directors. Rarely will a minister or a
department director whose subject-matter field happens to fall into the lower end of the priority scale
accept this judgement and its consequences to his position without a fight.

Still, such decisions are being made all along.
Ministries and departments within a ministry do grow
by different rates; administrative reorganizations
are made from time to time, and new agencies are being set up here and there. The challenge to administrative leadership is to make these decisions in the
right directions, to face up to problems requiring

such painful decisions more courageously. Development planning and implementation does require strong leadership, especially for policies concerning the agricultural sector where the sheer physical distances, the complex human and intergroup relationships, and the heterogeneity of natural and cultural environments present much more difficult problems to the administration of development programs than in industry and commerce.

Governments have a great stake in overcoming these difficulties in rural action programs. If agricultural progress is too slow, economic development is retarded, frustrations and tensions build up, until a revolution sweeps away the old leadership which was overcautious, unappreciative of the rural people's needs and aspirations, and timid in adapting government administrative procedures to concrete demands of effective agrarian development policy. This course of events was demonstrated, for instance, during the 1950's and 1960's in Iraq, Syria, Bolivia, Cuba, and appears to loom ahead in other developing countries.

This course of events would not be so bad for the great majority of the people were it not for the fact that in the wake of a violent revolution, a severe setback in the rate of progress is almost inevitable. Many good technical and economic development programs are disrupted, many competent and well-motivated administrators and technicians are eliminated without officers of comparable competence available to replace them, and many of the new economic and social policies started with the best of intentions and ample enthusiasm are untried and prove unsuccessful. Recent experience suggests that after a violent revolution, progress in terms of production is retarded, and sometimes actually reversed, for a period of ten years or more.

Would it not be in the interest of the country and of all the people, rural and urban, if a cool consideration of these interacting forces would lead the present leadership to more enlightened and forceful action for accelerating progress, and would lead the present opposition to fight for more realistic reform programs by peaceful, nonviolent means?

NOTES TO CHAPTER 7

1. There are still several Latin American countries where illiterates are not entitled to vote.
Keeping the millions of small farmers and farm workers illiterate is an effective means for keeping them
from voting in political elections and for keeping
the traditional leadership in power. For a well-doc-
umented account of the extremely weak bargaining position of small farmers and workers, see Barraclough
and Domike, op. cit., p. 399; and Comite InterAmericano de Desarrollo Agricola, Land Tenure Conditions
in Brazil (Washington, D.C.: Pan American Union,
1966), pp. 13-21 and 194-297; also Land Tenure Conditions in Ecuador (in Spanish), pp. 83-103. Similar
conditions, in their essential aspects, are prevailing in some areas in Asia and Africa.

2. The general role of education in economic
development is well recognized and shall not be discussed here. For the specific role of education as
an accelerator of agricultural progress, see Arthur
T. Mosher, Getting Agriculture Moving: Essentials
for Development and Modernization (New York: Frederick A. Praeger, 1966), pp. 123-40. The special importance of primary education in developing countries
is convincingly demonstrated in a recent article by
Alexander L. Peaslee, "Elementary Education as a Pre-
requisite for Economic Growth," International Development Review, Vol. VII, No. 3 (September 1965), pp.
19-21. He warns against expanding secondary and
higher education too fast and at the expense of primary education which deserves high priority as a
means for accelerating progress. For an attempt to
estimate the economic value of education in terms of
returns to investment, see T. W. Schultz, The Economic
Value of Education, (New York: Columbia University
Press, 1963).

3. See United Nations Children's Fund, Children
and Youth in National Development in Latin America.
Report of conference, November 28-December 11, 1965,

Santiago, Chile (New York: United Nations Children's
Fund, 1966), p. 130.

4. During the early stages when school enrollment in rural areas is still far from universal, even
primary schooling may make young people, and perhaps
even their parents, feel that they are too good for
farm work and should seek clerical jobs in the city.
This happens especially if children enter primary
school very late, say at twelve or thirteen years of
age. At eighteen or nineteen years, with only a primary school education, they feel like secondary
school graduates. See W. Arthur Lewis, op. cit., Africa: Progress Through Cooperation, p. 117. Where
all farm children go to primary school starting at
the age of six years, this attitude is bound to subside.

5. For a clear exposition of education's role
in agricultural development, see Mosher, op. cit.,
pp. 123-28.

6. For an excellent summing up of this issue,
see Galbraith, op. cit., pp. 46-59.

7. See Daniel W. Sturt, Farm Operations and Ex-
penditure Patterns in Four Villages in West Pakistan,
Background Paper Series, Economic and Agricultural
Development Institute (East Lansing: Michigan State
University, June 1965).

8. See John Lossing Buck, Land Utilization in
China (Nanking, China: University of Nanking, 1937,
reproduced by the Agricultural Development Council,
Inc., New York, 1956), p. 351. For a recent report
on rural roads in Mainland China, see G. William
Skinner, "Marketing and Social Structure in Rural
China," The Journal of Asian Studies, Vol. XXIV, No.
3 (May 1965), p. 378. The national government has
greatly extended the highway network connecting the
major market centers. Thus "better (farm-to-market)
roads are being built by the provincial governments,
but most of them are being built on local initiative.
They are rarely fit for motor traffic; on the better
roads horses and ox carts may travel; on others hand-
carts can be pushed or pulled by man."

9.   See Wolfram U. Drewes, The Economic Development of the Western Montaña of Central Peru as Related to Transportation; A Comparison of Four Areas of Settlement (Lima, Peru: The Peruvian Times, 1958), p. 34. (27 soles = 1 U.S. dollar.)

10.   See Pan American Union, Farm-to-Market Roads in Latin America: Their Administration and Financing (Washington, D.C.: Pan American Union, 1964), pp. 1-8. (12.50 pesos = 1 U.S. dollar.)

11.   Robert B. Keating, "Research for Transportation Development," Development Research Digest, Vol. II, No. 1 (July 1963), p. 112.

12.   William and Paul Paddock, Hungry Nations (Boston, Mass.: Little, Brown and Co., 1964), p. 222.

13.   See J. C. Abbott, "The Role of Marketing in the Growth of Agricultural Production and Trade in Less Developed Countries," Monthly Bulletin of Agricultural Economics and Statistics, Vol. IX, No. 9 (September 1960), pp. 1-7.

14.   See Mosher, op. cit., pp. 89-98 and 111-22.

15.   See United Nations, Yearbook of National Accounts Statistics, 1965, op. cit., pp. 448-55.

CHAPTER **8** LAND REFORM: CREATING AN
INSTITUTIONAL ENVIRONMENT
FOR RURAL PROGRESS

Plans for bringing rural areas more nearly in
line with urban areas regarding such things as
schools, transportation, and marketing facilities often run into difficulties because the local conditions under which farmers live and work are inimical
to rural progress, to improvement in farm production
and the dignity of farm people. These land-tenure
conditions strongly influence agricultural development because they generate much of the social and
political climate, many of the human aspirations and
fears, economic incentives and obstacles for farmers
in their struggle for a better life.

Farmers must not remain poor and illiterate,
subservient to landlords, moneylenders, or the state,
deprived of economic opportunities, education, access to capital, and the support from farmers' cooperatives and associations. Farmers must participate
in community affairs. They must achieve effective
political representation and become respected partners in their relationship with trade, industry, and
government.

This calls for deep changes in the traditional
structure of rural life in many farming areas throughout the world.

WHY LAND REFORM?

Land tenure deals with the terms under which
farmers occupy and farm the land. These terms depend
largely upon who owns the land, and how much of what
kind of control owners exercise over cultivators.

If land is owned by many farmers who cultivate it themselves with the help of their families, and who have sufficient land and capital to earn an adequate income, the land-tenure conditions are not in conflict with progress toward higher levels of income, education, and citizenship. Hence, need for land reform does not arise under ownership by cultivators of adequate-sized farms. This situation is typical of some farming areas in Burma and Thailand, in some African countries, and in areas in which land reforms have in the past established such tenure conditions and farm-size patterns as in parts of Japan and Taiwan, for example. Even in these countries, however, there are farming areas where such conditions do not prevail.

If, on the contrary, landownership is highly concentrated in the hands of large landlords and plantation owners and the rest of the land is overcrowded with undersized farms on poor soils, the landowners exercise a very strong power over farmers, and the terms under which farmers occupy and farm the land are tilted strongly in favor of the owners, putting the cultivators de facto, if not de jure, in a relationship of subservient dependence. This holds particularly in areas where farmers have no alternative opportunities to settle as owners on new land or move into industry. Essentially, this situation still prevails in most regions in Latin America, and in some areas in the Near East and Asia.

Another typical land-tenure structure which impedes agricultural progress is characterized by many landlords, none of them owning very large areas, but each of them renting their land out to many more tenants than the land can support at decent living levels under the terms of tenancy imposed upon them. This holds particularly in areas of high-population pressure where too many tenants bid for a chance of farming too little land, which gives even a small landlord a strong economic power for collecting high rents and for evicting any tenant at will, and which places the tenant at the mercy of the landlord's good will. This situation still prevails in many areas in India and Pakistan, and other Asian countries, although much land-reform legislation has been passed to remedy the situation, but little of it has been implemented or has proven effective.

Not that landlords are villains; they are just human. Nor are they saints--only a saint can resist the temptation of exercising power over others to his own advantage. It is a natural desire of landlords to maintain the status quo and to resist changes that would weaken their power. For this reason, an appeal to landlords for giving tenants more entrepreneurial freedom, more security of occupancy, and a larger share of the crop, cannot be effective as long as landlords feel that the status quo can be maintained. For the same simple reason, landlords usually oppose attempts to strengthen the bargaining position of tenants and farm workers, to organize farmers' associations or cooperatives, since such organizations for the farmers' mutual protection challenge the status quo much more effectively than land-reform legislation that remains dormant on the statute books.[1]

However, once the political climate has changed sufficiently to make at least some landlords and traditional leaders doubtful of the possibility of maintaining the status quo, the enlightened among them will begin to support land reforms. They will sense the legitimacy of the farmers' aspirations and support their cause. Thus, they can win the confidence and the votes of farmers and maintain their leadership position. There are many examples of leaders from the traditional elite championing the cause of the cultivators and working for land reforms; some of them were landlords themselves. They recognize the mutual interest of the peasants and society, and sense the anachronism of a quasi-feudal social order which attempts to keep farmers and workers down. It is these progressive leaders who often have become the promoters of land reform and other changes in the economic and social structure of a nation. I need only mention John Stuart Mill and Disraeli in England; Gandhi, Nehru, and Bhave, leader of the Bhoodan movement, in India; Cardenas in Mexico; and more recently, Frei-Montalvo in Chile, for example.

What are the specific undesirable effects of
landownership concentration, landlordism and tenancy in developing countries?

Under tenancy conditions prevailing in many developing countries, five obstacles impede agricultural development:

(1) Farmers have little or no incentives to
increase production, especially under crop-share
renting; the returns from any extra effort the tenant makes he must share with the landlord;

(2) Farmers have no suitable access to production credit; usually they can get credit only at the
will of the landlord and at very high interest rates;

(3) Managerial responsibility is divided between tenant and landlord, and the landlord is rarely development oriented;

(4) The tenant's occupancy and livelihood is
insecure as the landlord can dismiss him more or
less at will and find another tenant instantly.
This discourages the tenant to improve the land,
housing, and other facilities for better production
and living conditions. If he does, the landlord increases the rent;

(5) The tenant's social status in the community is low as a result of this quasi-servile dependency upon his landlord, and impairs his participation in community affairs and his access to school,
marketing, and other facilities. Landlords tend to
oppose the development of cooperatives and tenants
access to them because they reduce the landlords'
and merchants' bargaining power in the market.

In principle, there are two major remedies:

(1) Land expropriation, with or without compensation, and redistribution of land to the tenants, at a purchase price payable over a period of
years or free of charge;

(2)   Restrictions on the landlord's exercise of his bargaining power by government control of rents, and protection of the tenant's occupancy rights, access to credit, and free participation in community affairs.

One or the other, or both, constitute the core of contemporary government land-reform programs in the developing countries. In fact, the majority of the countries have enacted some kind of land-reform legislation during the last ten to fifteen years, but few have succeeded in enforcing it and providing the necessary support of complementary measures whose importance is too often overlooked.[2]

If the government is too weak or not willing to enforce land reform, agricultural development will be too slow, tensions will increase, until either the government moves ahead with an effective land reform by peaceful means, or militant farmers strike against the owners and support a revolutionary movement to overthrow the government. The new revolutionary government starts with the liquidation of the landlords as a powerful landowning class, as in Mexico, Bolivia, Cuba, U.A.R., Algeria, and all the Communist countries.

Governments in countries where pressure for land reform is building up should ponder this pervasive trend in modern history. This might lead them to give the few progressive leaders they all have in their midst the necessary support for an effective land-reform program before it is too late-- too late, that is, for a nonviolent transition from a quasi-feudal to a democratic rural society, and along with it, from traditional to modern farming techniques.

Such a nonviolent land reform, if it is fast and effective enough, has the great advantage of avoiding the production-depressing effects which usually follow violent revolutions as a result of disruptions in the production processes and in the agricultural functioning of rural society. This advantage can be of direct benefit to farm and city

workers alike, inasmuch as they are usually the ones
who bear the brunt of setbacks in production and the
breakdown of technical and economic services. If
the government is genuinely determined to implement
a land reform, it will mobilize its administrative
and political power so that the skills of trades and
professional people, and public servants, can be put
to use in the interest of the cultivators and general economic development. (A successful land reform
will ultimately benefit these other groups as well
as the nation as a whole. (If, on the other hand, a
government passes land-reform legislation as a lip
service to a growing progressive opposition, it
merely borrows time for its own downfall.)

These considerations appear particularly ger-
mane to the present conditions prevailing in many of
the Latin American countries. President Eduardo
Frei-Montalvo of Chile, after six months of debate
on his agrarian-reform bill, appealed to Congress
for approval of this bill with these words: "Those
who now oppose reform in a democratic framework will
have to suffer it tomorrow with violence and disor-
der, as has happened to many other nations."[3] Even
a year later, in mid-1967, the bill was not yet
passed by the legislature.

THE INSTITUTIONAL SETTING:
FIVE GOALS OF LAND REFORM

Let us approach land-tenure problems from the
viewpoint of the institutional environment as it affects farmers, instead of the much narrower one of
legal property rights in land. For the purpose of
progress in farmers' production efficiency, living
levels, and active citizenship, it should make no
difference whether the farmer owns or rents the
land--and if he rents the land, whether the landlord
is an individual or the state--as long as the effect
of any particular form of land tenure upon the farmer's performance as producer and as member of the
community can be made to serve rural progress equally well.

What are, then, the basic characteristics of an institutional environment that can serve this purpose? Any land-tenure system conducive to human dignity[4] and vigorous agricultural development must create or permit the creation of five crucial conditions:

(1) Production incentives must be offered to farmers for adopting modern farming methods and increasing farm output;

(2) Farmers must have access to sufficient land and capital for technological innovations, for new inputs, for buildings and land improvements, and access to various types of services, such as production credit, technical advice, cooperative and other types of marketing and production facilities, necessary for efficient production and an adequate family income level;

(3) Farmers must have managerial freedom and responsibility for farming operations, limited only by the necessary protection of community and national interests concerning soil conservation, certain standards of husbandry and land-use practices, and the allocation of land among farmers;

(4) Farmers must have security of occupancy and use--rights in the land and protection of their investment in housing and other improvements they have made on the land;

(5) Farmers and agricultural workers must be free to participate in community and group affairs and avail themselves of all educational, health, and other communal services without intimidation and reprisals.

These five conditions can and must be greatly improved in most areas in order to accelerate progress. This can be done under ownership, tenancy, or other combinations of various tenure forms, and may require complementary institutional arrangements which are not usually considered part of the land-tenure system, such as credit programs and

extension services. According to the characteristics
of a particular area, it might be more feasible to
improve these conditions under the one than the other tenure type. For instance, in Japan, the land
reform converted tenants into owners; in Taiwan, the
land reform imposed upon the landlords control of
rental terms and occupancy rights of tenant farmers.
Both land reforms achieved similar results as to
production, income, and social status of the farmers.

Any land tenure system which is conducive to
establishing these five crucial conditions stimulates rural progress both in economic and human
terms. If it militates against one or more of these
conditions, the rate of progress will be retarded.
There are today many agricultural regions where land
tenure arrangements obstruct development and call
for reforms.

These guiding principles for land reform do not
postulate any preconceived structure of legal property rights; they should lead to various combinations of institutional arrangements which will bring
about, in practical ways adapted to the local situation, these five conditions, and so create for the
farmer an economic environment making him willing and
able to adopt modern farming techniques, develop his
entrepreneurial capacities, and exercise his citizenship.

ACCENT ON USE RIGHTS--PROMOTER
OF DEVELOPMENT INCENTIVES

The legal seat of landownership is much less
important than the concrete terms under which farmers occupy and farm the land. For instance, a tenant with secure occupancy, paying a low rent, and
entitled to compensation for improvements he made on
the land, may be better off than an owner-cultivator
with a heavy mortgage, high annual interest, and
amortization payments, who may lose his land and
livelihood through foreclosure in the wake of one
crop failure. A land reform, however, can prevent
the land from being used as a collateral for credit,

and if land taxes and other ownership obligations
are not higher than the tenant's rent, the two farmers under the different tenure systems are in an
equivalent position. A settler on state-owned land
with perpetual-use rights is, again, in a position
functionally equivalent to that of the other two,
although the legal seat of landownership is different in the three cases.

It is extremely important to regard property
rights in land not as ends in themselves, but as instruments for bringing about an institutional environment, which stimulates the farmer's production
incentives and opportunities for human development
on the one hand, and which safeguards the general
public interest in land use, conservation, and allocation of land among farmers on the other.

In no case is it advisable to grant absolute
and unrestricted property rights in agricultural
land[5] to anyone, be he an individual, a cooperative,
a corporate firm, or the state, because the public
interest is deeply affected by the control over agricultural landownership and use. The Western "fee-
simple" and almost absolute "freehold" title in agricultural land, which is also common throughout
Latin America and commercial farming areas in Asia
and North Africa, has brought severe hardships to
many farmers, and has retarded agricultural development in some areas as a result of concentration of
land into few hands through foreclosure or land purchases by large farmers or investors. This has often led to underutilization of land in large holdings on the one hand, and excessive land exploitation
and soil erosion on undersized farm units on the
other.

The power that unrestricted property rights in
agricultural land conveys to the owner is greater
and potentially more dangerous to the public interest
than that in urban land, houses, or almost any other
capital good. Land cannot be increased at will,
cannot be moved about and substituted or done without as most other marketable goods can. The mounting pressure of a growing world population upon

agricultural land resources, especially in the newly
developing regions, accentuates the crucial public
interest in the way agricultural land is allocated
among farmers, and occupied and used by them.

We shall see later that all the production incentives which landownership imparts to farmers'
motivation can be engendered by property rights more
restricted than those common in the Western tradition of private land property. Restrictions necessary to safeguard public interest need not conflict
with these private interests of the owner which motivate him to make the best use of the land.

What is important to a farmer is the secure occupancy of his land, regardless of who "owns" it, and
the assurance that whatever he invests in the land--
in the form of buildings, fences, irrigation facilities and other improvements raising the productive
capacity of the land and improving the living conditions of his family--belongs to him and cannot be
taken from him without adequate compensation. This
security of occupancy, and protection of his investment in buildings and land improvements, are the legal rights which provide incentives for long-range
planning of his production process, for soil conservation, land improvement, and good housing. If he
leaves his farm, for whatever reason, he is entitled
to receive a fair price for these improvements.
This principle is firmly established in the tenancy
legislation of the United Kingdom and several other
Western European countries, but hardly anywhere
else. There is every reason for promoting this
principle wherever farmers do not own the land, and
whoever the legal landowner may be--an individual,
a cooperative, or the state.

Security of occupancy and protection of his investment in land improvements are the two rights in
agricultural land which offer the farmer incentives
and opportunities to improve his living conditions.
Under tenancy, these two property rights must be
transferred from the landowner to the tenant. This
holds also where the state owns the land. The performance of state tenants in Denmark, for instance,

attests to the soundness of this principle.

RESTRICTIONS ON OWNERSHIP RIGHTS

Other landownership rights are of a much less fundamental nature regarding the farmer's interest in his production and living conditions. They, however, carry with them dangers for both the owner and the community. Let us briefly examine some of them.

The ownership right to offer the land as a collateral security for credit is a double-edged sword which can decapitate the owner (through foreclosure as a result of default in debt payments), and which can maim the community's tenure structure (through the proliferation of an insecure and poor tenantry in the wake of foreclosures). This has happened in many areas of Western Europe, the United States, and other countries, especially during periods of drought or economic depressions.[6]

It is true, land as a collateral for loans has opened up credit sources to farmers for improving the land and increasing production. Even today, the main source of credit in commercial agricultural areas in most countries is still based on mortgages on land. In high-income countries, for farmers with much good land, and in times of general prosperity, this works fairly well. It is, however, most unsuitable under conditions prevailing elsewhere, especially in newly developing countries, and for small farmers living on a narrow margin of subsistence.

Where farms are small and farmers poor and vulnerable in their bargaining position, the use of land as a collateral for credit is very dangerous indeed for the creation of a development-oriented and economically viable land-tenure structure. Such conditions invite concentration of landownership in the hands of moneylenders and other absentee owners, to the detriment of farmers, the community, and economic progress. Hence, an alternative access to credit must be provided, for instance, through

granting the creditor a lien on crops as security
for the loan, instead of a mortgage on the land.

Landownership rights could be restricted by a
provision that agricultural land cannot be mortgaged,
cannot be offered as a collateral security for credit. Concurrently, adequate sources of credit must
be provided, secured by the farmer's crops, and permitting deferment of debt payments in cases of delinquencies caused by conditions beyond the farmer's
control, such as crop failures due to floods or
drought. Such a farm-credit program will have to be,
at least in part, supported by a government agency,
as credit from private sources is not likely to be
forthcoming in adequate amounts and at terms required for a vigorous agricultural development.
Since by far the largest need for agricultural credit is for production purposes--for fertilizer, seed,
pesticides, farm machinery, etc.--these credit funds
are of a short- or medium-term nature. As each loan
is repayable in a one-to-five-year period, a revolving fund can be established and gradually increased
in accordance with the growing demand.

Closely related to the right to mortgage land
is the right to sell land to whomever wants to buy.
The agricultural land market is a most imperfect
one, and land prices often have little relationship
to its productive value. Land purchases by individuals for speculation in rising land values as a result of roads and irrigation schemes, of expanding
demand for residential or industrial sites, or for
hedging against inflation, serve no productive purposes and can readily be prevented by public policy
without ill effects on economic development. Absentee ownership and tenancy conditions arising from
such speculative land purchases usually have a negative effect on development.

Especially in view of the vulnerability of
small farmers, opening up the land market for unrestricted sale and purchase of land is highly inad-
visable. In the transition from self-sufficient to
market-oriented farming, a free land market invites
land sales by small farmers under various forms of

duress, under ill-founded hopes of moving to a city
for more remunerative employment, and under the
temptation of accepting a good price offered by investors who want to buy land for speculative purposes. At the same time, farmers on undersized
holdings, who should have the first priority for
buying additional land, are typically in the weakest
position and, in effect, excluded from access to the
land market.

Hence, it is in the interest of farmers and of
agricultural development that ownership rights be
restricted by a provision that agricultural land can
only be sold to a cultivator who wants to operate
the land himself. Such a provision is usually best
placed in the hands of a local body, with a strong
representation of farmers, for approval of the eligibility of the buyer.[7] Such regulatory functions
in connection with land-tenure policies are best en-
trusted to local committees under the supervisory
power of the government to whom appeals might be directed against a decision of the local committee.
The administration of those parts of agricultural
programs which require local judgement for their application is best delegated to local committees.
This approach to handling the local implementation
of government programs deserves much stronger emphasis than it is receiving in most countries.

Another desirable restriction on landownership
rights is a prohibition of subdividing the land into
economically undersized units through the inheritance
process. Undersized farms, often fragmented into
many dispersed and minute plots, make the application
of modern techniques almost impossible.

These three restrictions on ownership rights
against (1) mortgaging land, (2) selling land to
non-farmers, and (3) excessive subdivision of land
through inheritance, will **pro**tect and encourage the
progress-stimulating forces, and discourage or prohibit the progress-stifling forces. These ownership
restrictions have no production-depressing effects
on the motivations and incentives of farmers. Instead, they prevent conditions from arising which

would be inimical to technological innovations and
a development-oriented institutional environment. A
number of countries have adopted these ownership restrictions in their land-reform programs and farm-
settlement schemes with excellent results.[8]

One of the economic implications of these restrictions is that they take land out of a free commodity market. There is ample evidence that the advantages of doing this far outweigh the disadvantages,
both from the viewpoint of the typical farmer and of
rural progress. Since in vast agricultural areas
where small farms dominate no such commercial land
market exists at present, it would be folly to introduce it on the spurious ground that it would promote agricultural development.[9]

Two modern examples demonstrating how agricultural land can be used quite efficiently without
"guidance" by land market prices are offered by Russia and Israel: two countries where agricultural
land belongs to the state--but which differ widely
in many other aspects of their economic systems. In
Israel, the individual family-scale farm under
Moshav (cooperative) tenure is one of the outstanding examples of highly efficient family-type farming; yet the farmer does not own his land, cannot
mortgage or sell it, but has all the incentives to
use it efficiently, which in classical Western
thought had been ascribed to the individual ownership of the land by the farmer who cultivates it.
It is the security of its use, and of the reward for
the labor and capital the farmer puts into the land
which creates the incentives for raising its productivity.

The economic value of agricultural land can
still be appraised on the basis of its use value--
its productivity--in a similar way as the value of
labor is determined. Since the abolition of slavery, there has been no market of workers as persons.
But their services have a market price, a wage.
Similarly, land need not have a market price as a
plot of ground; its use value--its rental or taxation price--can serve for its efficient allocation

better than a price for land as such can under the
extremely imperfect conditions of agricultural land
markets prevailing almost everywhere. The very nature of land does not have the commodity characteristics essential for permitting supply and demand in
a free commercial market to function in the mutual
interest of individuals and the community.[10]

These are the basic principles concerning land
reforms in the developing world today.

NEGLECTED ISSUES IN LAND REFORM

We cannot go here into details of the many different problems of land reform. Let us examine some
aspects which are too often neglected or ignored.

The most common type of land reform expropriates
large landlords with compensation for the land, dis-
tributes the land to the tenants and makes them owners by letting them pay for their farms over a period
of twenty to forty years. This, indeed, is the simplest and most straightforward approach, and is
highly effective in meeting four of the five crucial
conditions for a good institutional environment. It
offers the farmer production incentives, gives him
managerial freedom and security of occupancy, and
expands his opportunities for participation in community affairs.

It does not, however, meet automatically the
condition of giving farmers access to capital and
various kinds of services. It is precisely because
of this neglect that merely redistributing land and
converting tenants into owners has often produced
disappointing results--both for the new owners and
for the community as a whole. This is particularly
so where the former landlords did furnish part of
the inputs to the farm, such as bullocks for draft
power, irrigation water, transportation of produce
to the market, etc. If these inputs suddenly stop
after the elimination of the landlord and no alternative source is provided to the new owner, his production might actually decrease. This production-

depressing effect was experienced in several land-reform areas (e.g., in Mexico and Bolivia) during the years following land expropriation, until the problem was recognized and other sources of these inputs were organized.

But it is by no means enough to provide alternative sources of these inputs which the landlord used to supply, because these inputs were insufficient and of a traditional nature. They were not geared for technical innovations and production increases. If nothing more were done than replacing the former landlord's contributions, agriculture would remain stagnant. Farmers would be somewhat better off, to the extent to which their annual payments for the land, plus taxes, would be less than their previous rents.[11] Farmers would be willing, but not able, to produce much more for lack of modern inputs and technical assistance. Hence, no significant rural progress would result; in fact, people in towns and cities might be worse off, because farmers with less of their output to pay for rent might retain more for their own consumption and reduce market deliveries of food for the non-farm population.

This is a most important issue for economic development. Any land reform program should be designed to assure that market deliveries of food and other farm products are not only maintained, but increased. This means, that along with land redistribution, effective programs for production credit, technical advice and extension services, and marketing facilities, must be organized to make farmers not only willing, but able, to expand production. It is imperative, of course, that poor farmers under a tenure system of high rents and dependency upon the landlord's favor be emancipated from their quasi-servile status and retain a larger share of their crop. Hunger is widespread among farm families in many areas, especially where farms are too small. But unless production is increased, the farmer's retention of a larger part of his crop for home use results in hardship for the non-farm population whose food supplies come in large part from the

rental shares collected and sold by the landlord.
Hence, it is the grave responsibility of government
to implement land reform in such a way that both
farmers and city people (most of them being poor,
too) are better off. And this requires increased
production.

The other main type of land reform is rent control and security of occupancy of tenants. This approach, by itself, improves only two of the five
crucial conditions for rural development: the farmer's production incentives, and his security of oc-
cupancy--and these only if the land reform measures
are well designed and effectively enforced.

Rent control will increase production incentives somewhat if the rental crop share is lowered,
say from one half to one third of the crop. The depressing effect of crop-share rent on tenants' production incentive is forcefully demonstrated in a
study of Indian farms and experimental data in the
State of West Bengal. Under cultivator-ownership
and under price conditions of 1958, the most profitable nitrogen fertilizer application was at the level of thirty-five pounds N per acre, yielding a net
profit of $4.28. If these farmers had to pay one-
half of the crop for rent, the most profitable application would have been two pounds N per acre with
a net profit of $0.01, that is, no profit at all,
hence no incentive to use fertilizer.[12] But even
under rent control, divided managerial responsibility remains an inevitable corollary of sharecropping, and will always have a depressing effect on
change in technology and production methods, unless
the landlord is personally interested in promoting
agricultural development, is competent and close to
the practical problems of farming, and respects the
tenant's viewpoint and interest. This, however, is
the exception rather than the rule.

The best type of rent control is conversion of
crop share to cash rents, and limitation of the level of cash rents. This increases production incentives as the total fruit of any extra effort put in
by the tenant belongs to him. It also raises the

farmer's managerial freedom. As long as the landlord
receives his cash rent, it does not concern him what
crops the tenant is growing. If the farmer finds it
profitable to raise fodder crops for cattle, the
landlord need not object; while under sharecropping
the landlord wants the land used for cash crops that
are readily marketable. Hence, it is only under cash
renting that a tenant can, in effect, operate the
farm as a full-fledged manager.

Administratively, it is much easier to control
share rents than convert them to cash rents and control their level. Hence, tenancy reforms are more
often controlling rental crop shares only. Moreover,
poor tenants on small holdings have a strong risk
aversion, and fear that if the crop is poor or its
price depressed they might be forced to sell most of
their crops to meet their fixed cash rent and not
have enough left to meet their subsistence needs.
This means that such tenants will oppose conversion
to cash rents, unless they are assured of ready access to credit at favorable terms and at the required time.[13] The source of such credit must be
the government or a cooperative with strong tenant
representation; otherwise, tenants cannot be expected
to have confidence in its availability. The whole
credit aspect in tenancy reforms is disconcerting
because much of the gains from rent control may be
vitiated by the tenant's dependence upon landlords
and local merchants for credit. Landlords may com-
ply with rent controls, but may be able to make up
for it by increased interest charges on tenants'
loans.[14]

It becomes clear that rent controls, to have
the desired effect on production incentives and
farmer's income, must be accompanied by a government
or cooperative credit program independent from landlords and geared to meet the tenants' needs.

The other main element in tenancy reform deals
with security of occupancy, with the usufructuary
rights of the tenant in land. In most developing
countries, a landlord can get rid of a tenant almost
at will. This holds usually even in cases where law

or custom may give the tenant some limited protection against eviction. The fact is that typically
the tenant's bargaining position is so pitifully
weak that he feels himself completely at the mercy
of the landlord and avoids any action which might
lose him the landlord's favor. Even if he has been
on his farm for many years and may have been born on
it, he knows that the landlord can terminate his occupancy in any year, and that it would be most difficult for him to find another farm to rent. This
feeling of utter dependency for the livelihood of
his family upon the good will of his landlord is the
most powerful institutional factor which keeps tenant farmers subservient, fearful of taking any initiative in farming or in community affairs which
might displease the landlord, and reluctant to organize themselves into unions or associations through
which they could deal as a group with the landlords.

The result: very little turnover of tenants,
i.e., almost perpetual occupancy without security,
and no incentive to modernize farming, to improve
the land, or to participate in group action that
might jeopardize their occupancy, and hence their
livelihood. For instance, farmers' cooperatives in
tenancy areas often experience opposition by landlords (who may be also merchants and moneylenders),
and if the cooperatives receive sufficiently strong
government support to get established, landlords
discourage their tenants to join them (see Chapter
14).

The legal instruments for providing security of
occupancy and of use rights in agricultural land are
usually restrictions on the landlord's right to
evict a tenant. As long as a tenant pays a reasonable rent and does his share in maintaining buildings and the soil's productive capacity, he cannot
be evicted, nor can his lease be canceled. If the
lease is only for a few years, he has the right of
renewal--except if the landowner or one of his children wants to operate the farm personally. Where
the tenants' bargaining position and status are weak,
such legal protection of their occupancy of the land
is very difficult to enforce because they can be

easily prevented from taking recourse to the law by
intimidation and other hurdles placed in their way.

The effect of establishing security of occupancy upon production incentives and rural progress can
be greatly increased by protecting the tenant's investments in buildings and land improvements. This
means that whenever a tenant moves, he would be entitled to a fair compensation for the remaining value of the buildings and land improvements he has
made. To make such compensation rights effective,
there must be some impartial appraisal of the improvements' value, and the landlord must be held responsible for the payment of compensation to the
outgoing tenant. He should be entitled, however, to
recoup the same amount from the incoming tenant if
rent control prohibits him from raising the rent by
an equivalent amount.

This compensation provision strongly reinforces
the tenant's security of occupancy, since the landlord knows that he will have to pay the tenant compensation upon termination of his occupancy and that
he may not readily find a tenant from whom he can
recoup the compensation payment. At the same time,
this provision encourages the tenant to invest in
land improvements and family housing. The provision,
therefore, strengthens the tenant's production incentive and stimulates rural progress in general.

Tenancy reforms, therefore, require three kinds
of measures: rent control, security of occupancy,
and compensation for land improvements. They must
be complemented by an agricultural credit program
freely accessible to tenants and independent of
landlords and local moneylenders. And if rent control takes the form of conversion of crop shares into cash rents, these tenancy conditions and the general institutional environment closely approximate
those under cultivator-ownership in meeting the five
crucial conditions for rural progress.

Administratively, it will usually be much more
difficult to implement such a tenancy-reform program
than a redistribution of landownership, because the

local operational demands on effective control are
much heavier, as we shall see presently. Unless a
government can really meet these demands and overcome the opposition to enforcement at the village
level, the tenancy-reform legislation is bound to
remain largely on paper--or at best will be only
partially implemented--with but little achievement
in accelerating farm production and improving the
lot of tenant farmers.

LAND REFORM IMPLEMENTATION:
STRENGTHENING THE FARMER'S POSITION

Land reform measures are commonly conceived as
massive nationwide legislative enactments. The de-
bates surrounding their political course to adoption
resound with dramatic phrases and political conflicts. This, indeed, is inevitable. When it comes
to the technical drafting of specific legislation,
the strong position of the landlord group often succeeds in whittling down the original scope of the
land reform. The administrative and technical difficulties arising in the implementation of the legislation on the village level further reduces, or actually blocks, the effectiveness of the reform legislation.

The execution of a land reform program requires
local government officials and technical experts who
can command the confidence of farmers and who do not
submit to the pressure of landlords to sabotage the
reform. A field staff of such quality for an immediate nationwide execution of the program is difficult to assemble in many of the developing countries.
Moreover, small farmers are typically in such a vulnerable position that they cannot organize themselves
for effective group action in support of the reform
program. The result is that much of the legislation
remains on the books and is not implemented. Frustration and tensions, however, continue to mount.

What has experience taught us that might be
useful in implementing land reforms?

Perhaps the most important condition for an effective land reform is a strong representation of
farmers in the local community through cooperatives
and farmers' associations. This is most difficult
for farmers to achieve by themselves, simply because
the prevailing tenure conditions prevent them from
doing so, as we have seen earlier. Farmers require
some sort of organizational support at the local
level.

One of the best examples of the need and the
comparative effectiveness of farmer representation
is offered by Venezuela where, during the 1940's and
1950's, the most popular political party (Accion
Democratica) helped organize peasant unions to gain
a mass electoral support. The other two major parties also started to organize peasant unions when
the 1958 election clearly proved the political power
of peasant support. Farmers--including landless laborers, crop-share tenants, and undersized farm
holders--voted for candidates committed to support
agrarian reforms, and hence were largely responsible
for the Agrarian Reform Act of 1960[15] (see Chapter
13).

It is not enough that land reform legislation
has been passed by the national government. True,
this indicates that there are some national organizations supporting the farmers' interest: various
political parties; occupational organizations such
as labor unions and cooperatives; and some influential progressive leaders within and outside the government who have become convinced of the need for
land reform. These national groups and leaders,
however, have usually very little influence upon the
power elite in the many local communities where land
reforms must be implemented.

A central government committed to a land reform
program has available at least three policy measures
with a high-potential effectiveness for strengthening the farmers' position in the local community,
and hence for implementing the land reform.

First, the assignment of carefully selected administrators to key posts of the land reform program at the national and local levels can be a decisive factor. The appointment of such officers must not be left to routine bureaucratic procedure, but requires a conscientious selection of persons, right down to the community level, according to their courage of conviction in the program, and their ability for being the spokesmen for the farmers and working in their interest. The special attention which top government leaders give to these appointments is a reliable test of their concern about the success of land reform. The local administrative staff must gain the confidence of the farmers that the program is fairly enforced and that the farmers are protected against reprisals on the part of landlords or other local groups opposed to the reform. And this requires that the local staff feels assured of the full support up to the top level of the national government.

Second, the government can encourage and support local organizations representing the interests of the farmers. Here, cooperatives can play a highly important role in land reform. Where these are well established and serve the great numbers of small farmers, the cooperative will readily take on various responsibilities for effective program implementation. For instance, cooperatives contributed much to the success of the land reforms in Japan and Taiwan. However, there are many areas where farmers' cooperatives are nonexistent, very weak, or dominated by large landowners, as in some Latin American countries. Here, the government needs to assume the responsibility of helping small farmers to organize and manage cooperatives so that they will meet their problems in marketing and credit, and will strengthen their position vis-à-vis landlords, merchants, and other powerful elements in the community.

Third, the organization of farmers' associations through the extension service or community development projects can become a potent factor in land reform. These farmers' associations usually focus upon certain production practices of local

importance. Much beyond that, however, they give
farmers an opportunity to learn from each other, to
deal jointly with some problems, and to discuss
among themselves the various economic and social
conditions which affect their farming methods, farm
income, and position in the community. Such associations can play a decisive role in the implementation of land reforms. As in the case of cooperatives, the small farmer is prevented by his vulnerable position and by his lack of organizational experience to create active farmers' associations by
himself; he needs his government's assistance in
getting him started on the road to self-help and organizational initiative. If his government lets him
down in this vital need of assistance, sooner or later some militant opposition group is bound to jump
in and fill this need.

The strategic importance of these three policy
measures in support of the small farmer's economic
and social position in the local community is all
too often overlooked. In the absence of these measures, the small farmers can easily be kept ignorant
of the land reform legislation. If they learned
something about it, they still could not avail themselves of its benefits; for even if they knew through
what channels to claim their rights, most of them
would not dare do so for fear of reprisals. These
are the facts of life in areas which are ripe for a
major land reform. A government committed to carry
out a land reform program must recognize its obligation to assist farmers in organizing cooperatives
and associations independent of landlords and plantations, and to do so requires an exceptionally
well-selected staff of administrative officers, from
the top down to the village. In many areas, these
officers must overcome a deep-seated distrust of the
government on the part of farmers who from past experience have found local officials serving the
landlords and wealthy owners rather than the small
farmers, tenants, and farm laborers.

To give just a few examples of these implementation measures: The Indian Government assigned
some of their outstanding administrative and

technical leaders to the land-reform program and
exerted its political and administrative influence
to get small farmers and low-caste rural workers
represented in the village panchayats. Egypt established new or reorganized existing cooperatives as
key instruments in carrying out the land reform, by
making membership compulsory and providing managers
for the first five years; during the initial period,
training programs were offered to farmers dealing
with the purposes and management of cooperatives so
that the cooperatives could be turned over to the
farmers for their direct control and management.
Japan, Taiwan, and Italy also used cooperatives as a
vehicle for implementing land reforms. In the Philippines and Malaysia, farmers' associations and local community development committees are receiving
support from the government, and might play a constructive role in various types of land-reform measures.

There are those who argue that these considerations of land reform measures are too academic and
assume that land reforms can be carried out in a
gradualistic, evolutionary manner. They point to
the frustrating experiences in many countries where
land reform legislation has been passed, but where
its implementation has been blocked by the intransi-
gent position of the power elite in the rural communities. They maintain that unless peaceful reforms
are carried out more quickly and effectively, only a
revolutionary government will be able to eliminate
the strangle hold of the landed gentry, and that
this applies to a considerable number of countries
where all attempts at gradual improvements in the
land tenure structure by legislative and administrative processes have, so far, been doomed to failure.
This view is often held particularly with respect to
the Latin American countries.[16]

This may be too categorical a position to take
for Southeast Asia and the Middle East, and hardly
applies to Africa south of the Sahara. Nor can it
be implied that the liquidation of the landlord
class is all that is needed for a successful land
reform. It may well be that this is a necessary

condition for progress in certain areas where the
present power elite is intransigently conservative;
but it will hardly prove a sufficient condition anywhere. The principles and deliberations presented
in this chapter remain crucially relevant regardless
of whether a land reform is initiated by a violent
revolution or by more gradual and peaceful processes.
Even after a radical liquidation of landlords, it
remains the responsibility of the new revolutionary
government to provide the social and economic conditions conducive to economic progress and human dignity of farm families (as outlined at the beginning
of this chapter).

As to the two main approaches to land reform:
Land expropriation and redistribution to tenants is
in many cases administratively easier to implement
than the control of rent, security of occupancy, and
compensation for land improvements, because the
elimination of the power of large landlords removes
a considerable element of resistance from the local
scene. This also makes the implementation of the
complementary parts of the program easier, such as
cooperative marketing and credit organizations, the
promotion of farmers' associations, the enforcement
of maximum and minimum farm sizes, the active participation of small farmers in public affairs. In
other words, converting tenants into owners strengthens their socio-economic position in the community.

The improvement of tenancy conditions through
government control of rents and other landlord-ten-
ant relationships may have a reasonable chance of
effective implementation where landlords do not own
large estates and do not exercise exclusive control
over the village economy, and where tenants are in-
terspersed with owner-cultivators, whose interests
and sympathies lean toward the tenant families--as
may be found in some areas in Southeast Asia. This
renders the administrative task of tenancy controls
more manageable and eases the tenants' access to cooperatives, credit and public services, and participation in community life.

THE SPECIAL CASE OF LATIN AMERICA

Severe obstacles to progress are built into the agrarian structure of many areas. Since land reform has in recent years come to the forefront in the discussion of development policy throughout Latin America, let us examine the conditions in this vast region a little more in detail.

The large plantation with a permanent hired labor force, drawing upon surrounding, very small and poor farms for seasonal labor, and producing mainly export crops--coffee, bananas, etc.--is a typical tenure system in much of Latin America. Another typical system is the large hacienda with many farm families to whom individual plots of land are allotted for supplying their own food, and whose members are obligated to work for the owner, cultivating food crops and raising livestock. This system is often referred to as "latifundia." The salient obstacles to progress are:

(1) The city-oriented outlook of the large landowner makes his savings go into urban real estate and commodity speculation, trade, foreign investments, and in recent years, also domestic industries; only a small part of his farm income is invested in agricultural improvements and production expansion;

(2) The agricultural laborer is very poor and, for lack of alternative employment opportunities, dependent upon the good will of the owner and his estate manager. To keep him subservient, his real wages are kept at bare subsistence level; education for his children is prevented or restricted by various, usually informal means; his participation in farmers' associations, cooperatives, or other economic and political organizations is effectively prohibited, if by no other means than tacit intimidation with an occasional exemplary elimination of a "trouble maker" as a reminder to others;

(3)   The very cheapness of farm labor gives the
owner no incentives to increase the efficiency of
its use.   In the owner's mind, his interest is to
maintain the status quo and invest his savings elsewhere at higher returns than he could get in agriculture under the traditional farming practices;
hence he wants to maintain the extremely weak bargaining position of his laborers as well as of his
neighboring farmers on undersized holdings--often
referred to as "minifundia";

(4)   The small farmers in the vicinity are con-
gested in undersized farm units on poor exhausted
land; they are chronically in debt to local merchants for food advances and other indispensable
things.   To repay at least part of their debts every
year they depend upon seasonal employment on the
plantation or latifundia; this establishes the community of interest between village merchant and
large landowner, who both feel rural education and
farmer cooperation as threats to their dominant position.

It is, indeed, hard to visualize a way for
overcoming these obstacles other than a land-reform
program of expropriation and redistribution of land
to agricultural workers and small farmers--unless,
of course, it were collectivization, as in Cuba.
The strong power position of the local elite might
not permit the implementation of national legislation of a milder nature, such as minimum adequate
wages; housing and working conditions for plantation
workers; cooperatives, credit, and schooling facilities for small farmers and plantation workers alike.
In fact, most of the Latin American countries have
such laws on the statute books--which, with all
their good intentions and economic reasonableness,
fail to become implemented at the local level.   The
few enlightened landowners who pay their workers
better, let their children go to school, and invest
in modern agricultural inputs represent the exceptions that disprove the rule.   The obstacles we are
examining here are of an institutional, not of a

personal, nature; they can be overcome only by institutional measures.

To get some sense of the order of magnitude of
the land reform problem in Latin America, let us
look at the farm size distribution shown in Table
19. The "large multi-family farms" represent the
latifundia and the plantations. In all the seven
countries for which comparable data are available,
concentration of landownership is extremely high.
In Guatemala, 0.1 per cent of the farms take over 40
per cent of the total farm area of the country; in
Peru, 1 per cent of the farms takes over 80 per cent
of the land. In sharp contrast, the undersized
"sub-family farms," or minifundia, make up nearly 90
per cent of all farms but take only 14 per cent of
the land in Guatemala, and in Peru even less, only 7
per cent of the land.

There is no major region in the world where
there is such an extreme polarization of farm land
distribution into few, very large estates and many,
very small farms of less than subsistence size.
This polarization is most pronounced in Peru, with
only 8.5 per cent of all farms being of reasonably
adequate family-farm size on only 4.5 per cent of
the farm land, and least pronounced in Argentina,
with 49 per cent family farms on 45 per cent of the
land.

This general size distribution typical for Latin America shows dramatically why land redistribution is by far the most important type of land reform needed in this region of the world.

The distribution of farm families by tenure
status further confirms this conclusion, as seen in
Table 20. In Guatemala and Ecuador, nearly 90 per
cent of all the farm families are on undersized
farms, or work as farm laborers on large estates in
extreme poverty and without any hope of working up
to a decent living level as long as no land reform
programs create new opportunities for them. Tenancy
reforms could make no dent in the situation as it
comprises less than 5 per cent of the families,

TABLE 19

Farm Size Distribution in Latin American Countries[1]

	Large[2] Multi-Family Farms %	Medium[3] Multi-Family Farms %	Family[4] Farms %	Sub-Family[5] Farms %
Guatemala				
Per Cent of Farms	0.1	2.0	9.5	88.4
Per Cent of Land	40.8	31.5	13.4	14.3
Ecuador				
Per Cent of Farms	0.4	1.7	8.0	89.9
Per Cent of Land	45.1	19.3	19.0	16.6
Peru				
Per Cent of Farms	1.1	2.4	8.5	88.0
Per Cent of Land	82.4	5.7	4.5	7.4
Colombia				
Per Cent of Farms	1.3	4.5	30.2	64.0
Per Cent of Land	49.5	23.3	22.3	4.9
Argentina				
Per Cent of Farms	0.8	7.3	48.7	43.4
Per Cent of Land	36.9	15.0	44.7	3.4
Chile				
Per Cent of Farms	6.9	16.2	40.0	36.9
Per Cent of Land	81.3	11.4	7.1	0.2
Brazil				
Per Cent of Farms	4.7	33.7	39.1	22.5
Per Cent of Land	59.5	34.0	6.0	0.5

1. Source: Solon L. Barraclough and Arthur L. Domike, "Agrarian Structure in Seven Latin American Countries," Land Economics, Vol. XLII,
   No. 4 (November 1966), p. 395.
2. Farms large enough to employ over 12 people.
3. Farms large enough to employ 4-12 people.
4. Farms large enough to employ 2-3.9 people.
5. Farms large enough to employ less than 2 people.

191

except for Argentina with 16 per cent.

From all the various types of land reforms enacted over the last twenty years by many developing
countries, it becomes clear that a determined central government is needed to implement these measures in the field, and that active support of the
reform measures is needed from enlightened local
leaders and organizations, such as farmers' cooperatives or associations, to overcome the resistance of
an ultra-conservative local elite. Only a few countries have succeeded in accomplishing this to a reasonably effective degree as, for instance, at least
in some of the areas in Italy, Egypt, India, Japan,
and Taiwan. In these areas where the land reform
measures became actually operative, they did overcome these institutional obstacles sufficiently to
produce a remarkable spurt of agricultural progress.
In most countries, the implementation of land reform
measures still awaits a breakthrough.

Note that in recent years the progressive forces pressing for rural education, cooperatives, and
land reforms have grown stronger and faster in central government circles than in rural villages (for
instance in Chile, Venezuela, Colombia, the Philippines). Our examination of the institutional obstacles goes a long way to explain why it is that so
many governments have passed well-intentioned progressive legislation but were not able to implement
it effectively on the local farm and village level.

WHAT TO DO ABOUT UNDERSIZED FARMS?

There are land tenure problems which cannot be
solved by either converting present tenants into
owners, or by improving tenancy conditions. The
most serious of these other tenure problems arises
where farms are too small in size to provide an adequate living for a farm family even under modern
production technology and efficient management.

A farm is undersized when its total, net farm
income under modern production techniques and

TABLE 20

Distribution of Farm Families by Tenure Status[1]

Per Cent of All Farm Families

	Operators of Large and Medium Farms	Owners[2] of Family Farms	Tenants of Family Farms	Owners of Sub-Family Farms	Landless Farm Workers
	%	%	%	%	%
Guatemala	2	9	1	63	25
Ecuador	2	8	1	54	35
Colombia	5	20	5	47	23
Argentina	5	18	16	26	35
Chile	10	17	3	23[3]	47
Brazil	15	14	3	8	60

1. Source: Solon L. Barraclough and Arthur L. Domike, "Agrarian Structure in Seven Latin American Countries," Land Economics, Vol. XLII, No. 4 (November 1966), p. 397.

2. Includes administrators of large and medium farms: about 2 per cent for Guatemala, Chile, and Brazil, and less than 2 per cent for Ecuador, Colombia, and Argentina.

3. Includes 16.6 per cent of "communal" owners (mainly Indians).

reasonably efficient management is not sufficient to
support a farm family at a decent living level.
This minimum adequate farm size will vary in terms
of acreage according to soil productivity, topography, and market location, even within the same area.
For purposes of farm enlargement through land reallocation among farmers, however, a minimum farm size
must be established in terms of a specific acreage
which would be applicable, to land of a specified
productivity range. For a farm producing under modern production techniques, 3,000 to 4,000 pounds of
rice per acre, for instance, a smaller acreage is
needed to support a family than for a farm producing
only 2,000 to 3,000 pounds per acre. Traditional
yields and farming methods should not be used in
long-range development planning for establishing
minimum farm sizes, as these should be replaced by
modern methods in any case.[17]

Many countries in Asia and Latin America are
facing this issue. The basic solution lies in enlarging undersized farms up to a minimum adequate
size by the reallocation of land among farmers. In
some localities, another solution can be found by
providing off-farm employment--either as laborers on
larger farms or in industry--for part of the family
labor force which would be sufficient to bring the
total family income up to a minimum adequate level.

This last possibility usually exists only in
the vicinity of large farming estates or of larger
towns and cities. For most agricultural areas with
many undersized farms, such supplemental sources of
income will not become available for some time to
come. Where small- and medium-scale rural industries fit into a development plan in such areas, non-
farm employment can contribute much to the solution
of the problem. For instance, a recent government
survey in Japan revealed that in 1965 slightly over
50 per cent of the total income of 5.7 million farm
families came from non-farm sources, and that only
20 per cent of all farmers lived on income solely
derived from agriculture.[18]

To provide small farmers with access to sufficient land and capital for efficient farm production
is rapidly becoming an urgent function of government
land-tenure policy. How can this be done?

One way is to establish a ceiling on farm sizes,
and reallocate land above such ceilings to undersized farms. A reasonable criterion for a maximum
farm size might be the amount of land one farm family can operate mainly with its own labor under modern methods. This might mean rather large farms of
several hundred acres, highly mechanized and well
equipped with buildings and transport facilities, as
in large areas in the U.S.A. and Canada. Where population pressure is heavy, the maximum farm size
might be placed considerably below that, but should
still be high enough to provide opportunities for incomes considerably larger than a minimum adequate
level of living.

The principle of establishing ceilings for farm
size is quite commonly used in farm settlement projects and in connection with land reform programs
where farms below the ceiling are not expropriated,
and where landlords can retain ownership of part of
their land up to the ceiling. Usually, however,
these ceilings are much higher than just suggested.

The lower the maximum farm size, the more families can have access to land. As in the case of the
minimum farm size, population pressure and the various types of farming best suited to the area and
to national needs should be considered as important
factors in determining a farm-size ceiling.

Systematic enlargement of undersized farms
should become a basic land reform measure in many
countries. Land expropriation and redistribution
programs usually leave the problem of undersized
farms unsolved by simply making all tenants, including those on undersized holdings, owners of the land
they operated as tenants, and leaving the owner-cultivators of undersized farms unaffected. What is

needed is a long-term program of enlarging undersized farms wherever they exist. Such a program
should also prevent undesirable subdivision into undersized farms which inheritance processes might
otherwise bring about.

The best long-term policy for enlarging undersized farms consists of a combination of three measures:

(1) Any buyer of agricultural land must get
government approval of his eligibility; if the sell-
er is not able to locate an eligible buyer, the government will buy the land and hold it until an eligible buyer is found. Operators of nearby undersized farms get first priority, and the government
extends long-time, low-interest credit to such buyers. For instance, if an undersized farmer moves
away or dies, a nearby undersized farmer must be
able to get a loan to buy the available land for the
enlargement of his farm--otherwise a wealthier farmer will buy it to add to his already adequate-sized
holding. This policy measure, although not as rigorously applied as proposed here, has brought some
good results in Germany, Sweden, and France, for instance, and is also applied in some of the Indian
states;[19]

(2) In new-settlement and irrigation schemes,
farmers of undersized farms in the vicinity are giv-
en priority in the selection of settlers, and provisions are made for their vacated holdings to be used
to enlarge other undersized farms;

(3) Large estates underutilizing the land's
productive capacity can be expropriated and subdivided into adequate-sized farm units for resettle-
ment of undersized farmers in the vicinity. Again,
this program must include reallocation of the vacated undersized holdings for farm enlargement.

All three measures deserve particular attention
in many Latin American countries where the contrast
between overcrowded minifundia areas and extensive
underutilized latifundia areas is so striking, and

creating ever-growing tensions.

The trouble is that undersized farms in over-populated farming areas rarely become available for farm enlargement. If the present owner moves, there are his sons or those of his relatives waiting to take over, at whatever familistic terms are agreed upon. The cruel fact is that farm enlargement reduces the number of farm families unless new farms are created by subdivision of large estates or by farm settlements on new land. As long as industrial expansion and the opening of new farming opportunities cannot absorb more than the annual increase in farm population, the process of enlarging undersized farms will be slow indeed. In these areas, training of young people and guiding their emigration to other less-crowded farming areas or into industrial employment is a most useful corollary to a land-reform program.

Many countries cannot count on reducing their farm population in the next ten or twenty years, because industrialization will not absorb more than the farm population growth and, in many cases, will absorb far less in the immediate future. Still, these measures for enlargement of undersized farms are urgent and highly beneficial, as they counteract the pernicious tendency of population pressure to proliferate undersized farms.

Apart from land reallocation for farm enlargement, there are three possibilities for undersized farms to become adequate-sized on the same acreage.

First, modern production techniques and better farm planning and management can double or treble farm production, even on a small acreage, by increasing crop yields and expanding livestock enterprises based on purchased feed (especially through poultry and hogs), and by shifting from lower- to higher-value crops, for instance to high-quality vegetables and fruits.

Second, improving market, road, and transport facilities can bring undersized farms economically

closer to market centers and render them adequate-
sized by intensified farming, or provide non-farm
employment opportunities for supplementing the insufficient farm income.

Third, many undersized farms can become adequate-sized by means of converting tenants into owners under a land reform program, through the combined effect of a larger share of the farmer's production being retained in the farmer's income, and
of the farmer's greater incentive and ability to
increase production.

In all these various land reform measures, vigorous programs for production credit, technical assistance, and marketing through government agencies
and cooperative organizations must play a key role.

THE CASE OF LARGE-SCALE FARMING

So far, we have talked about tenure conditions
of individual family-type farmers. It is true, they
form an overwhelming majority of farmers in most
countries of the world; but there are also millions
of agricultural laborers and their families working
and living on private plantations, or on land owned
and operated by large landowners, collectives, and
the state, that is, on large-scale farms.

By large-scale farm, I mean one which is worked
by farm laborers and their families under the direction and supervision of a central management. The
farm worker is, in effect, a wage earner and stands
in an employer-employee relationship to management.
The three most typical forms of large-scale farming
are the private plantation, the cooperative or collective farm, and the state farm. Problems in the
production process on large-scale farms have been
discussed earlier. Here, we want to deal only with
the land tenure and institutional aspects.

Many governments are facing the issue: What
shall we do with large-scale private farms and plantations? Some newly developing countries have

nationalized some or all of them (e.g., Indonesia, Tunisia, Algeria, Cuba, etc.);[20] some have established certain controls over private management, especially concerning wages, working, and living conditions of the laborers (e.g., Ceylon, India, Ghana, etc.); and some have left them alone so far (e.g., Liberia, the Philippines, several Latin American countries, etc.). When plantations are nationalized, the government faces the decision of whether to keep them operating as large-scale farms, or whether to break them up into family-farm units operated under state tenancy or cultivator-ownership. All these decisions affect the nature of the agrarian structure, the institutional environment under which farm families work and live, and their production incentives. On what grounds are such decisions best made, from the viewpoint of production, of the farmer's income, and of human dignity and citizenship?

Here again, the five crucial conditions for a favorable institutional enrivonment can serve as guide lines.

(1) The farmer's production incentives must be mobilized. On large-scale farms, this requires an appropriate wage structure which will bring forth the best effort of the worker. This is difficult to establish because farm work does not lend itself readily to labor specialization and work-quality control. Since large-scale farming is best suited for a monoculture type of crop production, such as sugar cane, sisal, rubber, and tree crops (cocoa, coffee, tea, etc.), there are seasonal troughs in labor requirements. Hence, to give scope to productive effort during slack periods, small plots of land can be allocated to each family for producing food and other farm products for home consumption and for sale by the farm worker, entirely for his benefit as a supplemental entrepreneurial income to his wage income. This holds whether the plantation is under state or private ownership and management. To assign small plots to farm workers for their own use is a recognized principle in collective farming in the U.S.S.R. and other Communist countries, and also

on many private plantations elsewhere; but in most
cases, this family-plot farming is treated by the
central management as a concession, a threat to the
supply and the discipline of the labor force, and
is, therefore, rather severely restricted to very
small plots and numbers of livestock. It might prove
very effective if the central management would increase these family-plot allotments as rewards for
superior work quality and effort of individual workers on the plantation.

Another aspect of importance is the production
incentive for management. The state or collective
farm may be so heavily burdened with mandatory deliveries to the state, that neither the farm as a
whole nor the managerial staff benefits from any extra effort and competence they put into the operations. Hence, production will suffer, and with it
the income and morale of workers and staff. This
has, indeed, been experienced in collectivized agriculture in several Communist countries, and is one
of the main reasons for the agrarian reform which
got under way in the U.S.S.R. during the 1960's. A
similar problem arises under private-plantation management, if the owners are not development oriented,
are content with the current income they receive,
and show no interest in rewarding superior effort on
the part of their administrative staff and of their
farm workers. This is a situation not uncommon on
many large-scale farms in Latin America, for example.
It might help if the government enforced adequate
wage and housing standards for the workers; this
would force management to increase production and
apply modern technology in order to meet the wage
demands and stay in business.

(2) The second condition for agricultural development calls for access to sufficient land and
capital for efficient production and adequate farm
income. In the case of large-scale farming, it
means not only that the plantation owner or the
state must provide sufficient capital for an efficient production process,[21] it means also that the
farm labor force must be trained in modern techniques and efficiently employed, and that the income

of the farm families must be sufficient to support
an adequate living standard, including housing and
working conditions.

Here, a natural conflict arises between the immediate interest of workers and management, as in
all large-scale production enterprises, be they pri-
vately or state owned. What for the worker is income, is expense for the management. This conflict
of interest does not arise in family-type enterprises which predominate in the agriculture of most
countries. In private industry, the most effective
safeguard for protecting the interest of workers is
collective bargaining through labor unions supported
by national legislation. Similar means for protecting the workers' interests in large-scale farming
will be necessary. Since farm workers are much more
difficult to organize into effective unions than industrial workers, the government must take a much
stronger responsibility for such protection in agriculture than in industry.

(3) For dynamic and imaginative management of
state farms, the directives by the central government are best given in the broadest terms only,
leaving a great deal of managerial discretion to the
local staff. In no major production line is decentralization of management as essential as in agriculture. In predominantly family-type agriculture,
a particularly useful role of large-scale state
farms is the multiplication of improved crop seeds
and animal breeding stock, the testing of modern
farm machinery in its performance under local field
conditions, and similar public services to farmers.
This is the case in Yugoslavia, for instance.

(4) Since farm workers on large-scale farms
have no occupancy rights in the land proper, there
should be a job security provision and some limited
compensation rights for the improvements on their
housing and family plots in case they leave the
farm. Such provisions can add a great deal to the
desirable motivation of farm workers, to their living conditions, attitudes, and general morale.
Again, these are important considerations in large-

scale farming under either private or state ownership which are usually neglected.

(5) The participation in community affairs and
access to schools and other public services on the
part of farm workers should be unhampered, in fact,
encouraged. Since workers on large-scale farms,
whether private or state owned, are vulnerable to
informal pressures and intimidation by management,
there is need for measures safeguarding farm workers' freedom for communal participation and citizenship activities. This holds particularly in many
private plantation and latifundia areas in Latin
American countries.

There is room for some large-scale farming in
the agrarian structure of most countries. Political
theorists and economic planners, however, must be
cautioned against considering large-scale farming
as a panacea for modernizing agriculture and raising
farm production (as we have seen in Chapter 6).

A SELECTIVE APPROACH TO LAND REFORM

In many countries, political and economic conditions are such that a sweeping national land reform is not feasible. But certain improvements in
tenure conditions in some areas might well be urgently needed.

There are few countries with a homogeneous tenure structure. In most countries, tenure conditions
vary widely between different farming areas. This
calls for a land reform policy consisting of several
sets of program measures directed specifically at
different tenure conditions. A comprehensive land-
reform plan contains measures for converting tenants
into owners, for controlling rents, for enlarging
undersized farms and creating additional farms on
subdivided land and on newly developed land; measures for marketing and credit cooperatives, for establishing collective or state farms, for controlling agricultural laborers' wages, working, and
housing conditions on plantations.

This means that each of these sets of measures
has a different geographic incidence, is more important in one area than in another, or applies to one
group of people and not to another.

This gives a development-oriented government
an opportunity for building up a land reform program
over time, by selecting tenure problems on the basis
of relative urgency, and political and administrative feasibility. Thus, it is possible to start
land-reform programs in selected areas, and concentrate good government personnel and sufficient financial resources upon these areas in a flexible and
effective way. For instance, the land reforms in
Italy and the U.A.R. were quite successful, perhaps
partly because they were initially implemented in a
few specific areas, with a trained local staff and
sufficient financial resources to carry out a limited, but effective, program. In the process, a
growing cadre of administrative and technical personnel can be trained for service in other areas.

With such limited programs in several places
throughout the country, much can be learned about
the feasibility of administrative procedures; about
ways of strengthening the tenants' and small holders' position in the community; and about how to encourage progressive local leaders. After such experiences, the government is in a much stronger position to implement the reforms on an expanding
scale and on a national basis.

Whatever the specific land tenure arrangement
may be, it should give every farm family an equal
opportunity to develop its productive capacities,
its knowledge and talents, no matter under which of
the various land tenure arrangements the farm family
lives.

The five conditions outlined at the beginning
must serve as guideposts in formulating the specific
measures of an agrarian reform program. Such a program can establish for the farmer and his family--
be he an owner-cultivator or tenant--a local economic and social environment which offers him:

(1)   Production incentives;

(2)   Sufficient land, capital, and public and cooperative services;

(3)   Managerial freedom and responsibility;

(4)   Security of use rights in the land (including compensation for land and building improvements); and

(5)   Full participation in community affairs and group organizations without intimidation.

Finally, it is most important to draw upon local committees of farmers and village leaders for specific consultative and administrative functions for which they are peculiarly suited. They must be recognized by the government and loyal to the basic purpose of the program, but must be given well-defined responsibilities and a free hand within their fields of assignment, such as advice and arbitration in administering various land reform measures. Such administrative decentralization is needed especially for those parts of agricultural development programs which require intimate knowledge and good judgement of local conditions for their implementation, which holds for many land reform measures. Beyond this specific purpose, the use of local advisory and administrative bodies has three other great advantages:

(1)   It reduces the demand on government personnel, finances, and red tape;

(2)   It keeps the detailed operations of the programs in the field more flexible; hence makes them more efficient and staves off the deadening grip of mindless bureaucratic procedure; and

(3)   It bolsters the spirit of local people, their feeling of self-respect and responsibility, and faith in their government!

NOTES TO CHAPTER 8

1.   For a discussion of agrarian reform in broad perspective, see Shri Asaka Mehta, "Toward an Agricultural Revolution," Indian Journal of Agricultural Economics, Vol. XX, No. 1 (January-March 1965), pp. 13-19; and Rainer Schickele, "Evolution

of Land Tenure in World Perspective," <u>AICC Economic
Review</u>, Vol. VI, Nos. 18-19 (January 21, 1955), pp.
59-64; see also <u>Problemas Agricolas e Industriales
de México</u>, Vol. VI, No. 1 (Mexico, 1954), pp. 45-
51.

2. U.N./FAO/International Labor Organization,
<u>Progress in Land Reform</u>, <u>op. cit</u>., <u>passim</u>.

3. See The New York Times, May 26, 1966. The
recognition of this trend is also found in some
Asian countries. See, for example, Vernon W. Ruttan, "Equity and Productivity Objectives in Agrarian
Reform Legislation: Perspectives on the New Philippine Land Reform Code," <u>Indian Journal of Agricultural Economics</u>, Vol. XIX, No. 3 (July-December
1964), pp. 114-30.

4. "Human dignity" here means that a person
has an opportunity to exercise full citizenship, to
participate in community affairs, to assume responsibility in various organizations of his choosing,
to benefit from educational, health, and other public services without discrimination on grounds of
race, religion, income, or social status, and is
protected by law against willful exploitation, coercion, and intimidation by others.

5. Private landownership is never "absolute"
in a strictly legal sense, even in Western society,
because the state always reserves the right to tax
and to expropriate land under its power of eminent
domain.

6. The undesirable effects of heavy mortgage
indebtedness of farmers exist even if the creditors
do not exercise their foreclosure rights in full.
As delinquencies pile up over the years, the farmers' debt burden may become so heavy that he has no
chance of ever paying off his debts. In fact, it
may often be in the interest of the creditor not to
foreclose and take title to the land in satisfaction
of the debt, e.g., if land prices are very depressed
and are expected to remain so for some time. In
such a case, it may be in the interest of the lender

to keep the farmer in perpetual debt servitude. For
the farmer, this may keep him in a position much
worse than he would be as a tenant. See Rainer
Schickele, Agricultural Policy (Lincoln, Nebraska:
Nebraska University Press, 1964), Chapter 14.

7. There are many ethnic groups who consider
the sale of agricultural land to outsiders socially
disruptive and undesirable, and who assign the function of allocating land among families to a council
of village elders. Such traditional arrangements of
assigning land to farm families with security of use
rights are not in conflict with production incentives and modernization of farming. In fact, they
might be readily adapted to modern development needs.

8. Good examples of these land reform measures
can be found in U.N./FAO/International Labor Organization, Progress in Land Reform, op. cit., pp. 127-
35, Tables I and II.

9. For a penetrating discussion of the dangers
involved in imposing Western land tenure and individual free-hold titles in land upon other cultures,
see Branislaw Malinovsky, The Dynamics of Culture
Change (New Haven, Conn.: Yale University Press,
1945), Chapter XI, especially pp. 128-37. He shows
how individual free holds in some African countries
(under colonial rule) have "created ownership without responsibility...titles to land without obligation of its effective use."

10. Such characteristics are, for instance,
homogeneity of the quality (or grade) of the commodity, mobility in space (for transport from places
with low to places with high demand), buyers and
sellers of comparable bargaining strength--to mention just a few. Agricultural land has few, if any,
of these characteristics.

11. For a discussion of this aspect, see M.
Riad El Ghonemy, Land Reform and Economic Develop-
ment in the Near East. Background paper for the
World Land Reform Conference, June 20-July 2, 1966,
Rome, Italy (New York: Food and Agriculture Organi-
zation of the United Nations, 1966).

12.   See Robert W. Herdt and John W. Mellor,
"The Contrasting Response of Rice to Nitrogen: India and the United States," Journal of Farm Economics, Vol. XLVI, No. 1 (February 1964), pp. 157-59.
The negative effect on incentives may be mitigated
if the landlord is required to pay the same share of
the cost of inputs (fertilizer, seed, etc.) as his
crop share.   This requirement, however, is nearly
impossible to enforce and is not likely to produce
vigorous increases in modern inputs because the
landlord's incentive and the tenant's ability to do
so are not great, and because they either have to
get together on this at every point or the landlord
imposes his will upon the tenant.

13.   The landlord also tends to oppose conversion to cash rent because he then bears the whole
risk of inflation--unless specific provisions are
made for adjusting the cash rents to changes of the
price level.   A simple way of doing this is by stip-
ulating a fixed rent in terms of a certain amount of
the main crop; for instance, so many quintals of
wheat or rice at the price prevailing at harvest
time.   This is sometimes called a "standing rent,"
or "fixed rent in kind."

14.   See U.N./FAO/International Labor Organization, Progress in Land Reform, op. cit., p. 125.

15.   See John D. Powell, "Venezuela: The Role
of Peasant Organizations in Agrarian Reform," Land
Tenure Center Newsletter, No. 24 (1966), pp. 10-19.
For a full report of this excellent study, see his
Ph.D. thesis on "The Politics of Agrarian Reform in
Venezuela: History, System and Process," Department
of Political Science, University of Wisconsin, 1966
(unpublished).   See also G. Ramachandran, "Temple
Land for the Landless," Avard Newsletter, Vol. 7,
No. 4 (July-August 1965), pp. 4, 22-23, which gives
a most interesting account of local farmers solving
a typical tenancy problem by cooperative non-violent
group action in India.

16.   Tenure conditions vary widely not only between Latin American countries, but also within

each of the larger countries. For instance, the
tenure problems in Costa Rica and Uruguay are much
less critical than in Guatemala, Colombia, and Peru.
See Edmundo Flores, Land Reform and the Alliance for
Progress, Woodrow Wilson School of Public and International affairs, Policy Memorandum No. 27 (Princeton, N.J.: Princeton University Center of International Studies, May 20, 1963); and Barraclough and
Domike, op. cit., for excellent discussions and observations on this issue.

17. In the short run, it may often be necessary
to accept as a standard a minimum farm size under
traditional farming methods for the immediate years
ahead, because a fairly wide adoption of modern
techniques might take five to ten years. In densely
populated areas, the future minimum adequate farm
size will tend to be smaller than under traditional
farming methods because of a much higher level of
purchased inputs; in sparsely populated areas, the
future minimum farm size may tend to be larger than
under traditional methods because of necessary mechanization of field work under extensive dry-land
farming systems. The issue of where to set the minimum farm size for allocating land among farmers is,
of course, very important where the population pressure is heavy, and where there are more farmers
wanting land than there are farms available. The
lower the minimum adequate farm size, the more farm
families can have access to land.

18. See Yoshihiro Takasuga, "The Efflux of Labour from Japanese Agriculture and the Rise in Prices," Rural Economic Problems, Vol. 3, No. 2 (Tokyo,
December 1966), p. 47; and The New York Times, February 20, 1966, p. 10.

19. For instance, France passed an Agricultural
Orientation Law in 1960 which includes measures like
those discussed here. By the end of 1965, the government had acquired 275,000 acres of farm land for
resale to undersized farms. This program is just
getting into its stride. See Paul E. Quintus,
"France Moves Ahead in Its Program of Farm Restruc-
turing," Foreign Agriculture, Vol. IV, No. 36

(September 5, 1966), pp. 3-4.

20. For example, see El Ghonemy, op. cit., p. 14.

21. Capital is usually more readily available to large-scale farms and hence, they have an advantage over family farms. But this need not be so, if credit supply and terms are really adjusted to meet the requirements of family farmers, including cooperative use of machinery.

CHAPTER **9** FARM SETTLEMENT ON
NEW LAND: PIONEERING
FOR RURAL PROGRESS

Public investment in the foundations of rural
progress, in roads, schools, marketing, transport,
and other communal facilities, and in land reform
for a dynamic institutional environment deals predominantly with the vast land areas now in agricultural use. It is on the present farm lands that the
bulk of the increase in production must be achieved
in many countries for the immediate years ahead.

Still, in the long run, developing countries
will need all the new land that can be put to agricultural use at reasonable cost in order to meet the
requirements of a much larger population at a much
higher nutrition and income level a few decades from
now. New land-development schemes often involve
heavy public investment. The technical and the human problems are complex and largely unknown in the
details needed for effectively developing and settling new lands. These problems tend to be underrated in their various aspects of time, finances,
organization, and the leadership and human energies
required. The manner in which these matters are
handled ultimately spells success or failure of land-
development and farm-settlement schemes.

WARNING OF UNWARRANTED HOPES

Everywhere, such schemes are in progress, and
more are being planned. They appeal to political
and administrative leaders, to irrigation and construction engineers, and to the general public, as
they symbolize dramatically visible efforts of expanding the land and water resources of the country;
of opening new farming opportunities for people from

overcrowded areas; and boosting the output of food
and industrial crops. To some groups, harassed by
popular pressure for land reform or by political unrest in the countryside, colonization schemes appeal
as an escape from facing reality in the old farming
areas, as safety valves through which discontented
elements in the population can be released and settled on the new lands.[1] Such high expectancy of
what land-settlement schemes can accomplish in the
near future has rarely materialized.

     Land reclamation and settlement are often under-
taken, in the first instance, for relieving population pressure on old farming areas or unemployment
in cities, or rewarding veteran soldiers and guerril-
la fighters. It is, of course, also expected that
the newly opened lands will boost the nation's agricultural production. Experience has been quite disappointing on both counts in many countries. New
settlement schemes often have not relieved the population pressure, and much of the increase in farm
production--especially in the densely populated re-
gions--has come from a more intensive use of land
in the old farming areas by reducing fallow or idle
land; by the application of modern techniques, such
as fertilizer and pesticides; and by improving the
socio-economic environment through land reforms,
credit and extension programs, cooperatives, and
marketing facilities in the existing rural areas.

     Still, there are also many countries where it
has been possible to increase the land area in crops
considerably during the last fifteen years, as shown
in Table 21. Of the twenty-two countries, eight
managed to increase their crop acreage by 50 per
cent or more. But ten countries expanded their
crop area by less than 15 per cent only. Moreover,
the increase in crop acreage is not a direct indicator of new-land settlement because in some countries
a good part of this increase comes from shifting
idle, fallow, and pasture land into crops within old
established farming areas. This increases production, but not necessarily new farming opportunities
for young families. Nor does the past increase in
crop area indicate the future potential. In Turkey,

TABLE 21

Increase in Crop Area and Its Effect upon Increase in Total
Crop Output, Selected Countries, 1948-63
(15-year period)[1]

Country	Increase in Crop Area[2] %	Crop Output Increase Due to Area Increase[3] %	Country	Increase in Crop Area[2] %	Crop Output Increase Due to Area Increase[3] %
Israel	68	26	Greece	22	30
Philippines	67	76	Chile	14	44
Turkey	62	70	Pakistan	14	51
Tanganyika	59	69	Taiwan	12	19
Brazil	55	84	Colombia	12	18
Venezuela	54	85	Yugoslavia	7	15
Sudan	50	31	Egypt	6	21
Mexico	50	53	Spain	3	8
Iran	39	60	Argentina	3	10
Thailand	30	42	Japan	1	3
India	26	59	Poland	- 1	- 2

1. United States Department of Agriculture, Changes in Agriculture in Twenty-Six Developing Nations, 1948-1963, Foreign Agricultural Economic Report No. 27 (Washington, November 1965), p. 19.
2. "Land area in crops," including multiple cropping.
3. The residual of this column indicates the change in output per unit of land and combines the effects of changes in crop yields and crop patterns, the latter shifting to more high-value crops and accounting for more than 20 per cent of the total change in crop output in four of the countries: Sudan 22 per cent, Poland 27 per cent, Chile 26 per cent, Japan 20 per cent.

212

TABLE 22

Potential Increase in Arable Land
in Selected Countries,
from the 1960 Base[1]
(based on physical soil characteristics only)

Per Cent Increase Physically Possible

Under 25%	25-74%	Over 75%[2]
Turkey	Mexico	Iran
Greece	Chile	Argentina
Yugoslavia	Thailand	Venezuela
Israel	Egypt	Colombia
India		Tanganyika
Poland		Sudan
Tunesia		Brazil
Taiwan		
Philippines		
Japan		

1. Source: United States Department of Agriculture, <u>Changes in Agriculture in Twenty-Six Developing Nations, 1948-1963</u>, Foreign Agricultural Economic Report No. 27 (Washington, November 1965), p. 27. Estimates based on soil maps and characteristics of soil types. Base year for the potential percentage increase is the year closest to 1960 for which the area of land now in arable use was reported. These estimates do not consider moisture limitations.
2. Iran's potential increase in arable land is estimated to fall within the range of 75-149 per cent; the other countries in this column have a potential of over 150 per cent increase (disregarding water availability).

213

for instance, there is evidence that the plow has pushed the dry-land wheat frontier too far into the pasture land, which invites serious erosion trouble and a deteriorating water supply for large areas. This might also hold for parts of Iran and the Sudan.

On the other hand, Colombia expanded its crop area only 12 per cent in recent years, but has a high, new arable-land potential, as seen in Table 22. In four of the most densely populated Asian countries, the upper limit for new arable land is well below 25 per cent; in contrast, six of the seven countries with a high arable-land potential are in Latin America and Africa.

In over half of the countries shown in Table 21, well over 50 per cent of the recent increase in crop production must be attributed to higher yields per hectare, and shifting from low-value to high-value crop rather than to more crop land. There are many countries where the best prospects for expanding production lie in raising output per hectare. This holds particularly true for countries with a low future potential of new arable land, because its further expansion runs into higher development costs, due to less favorable physical land characteristics and more distant or inaccessible location with respect to markets and population centers. For example, Taiwan and South Korea have recently undertaken pre-investment surveys for tidal-land reclamation. These surveys reveal a very high per hectare cost of development, and the reclaimable areas are very small compared with the country's total cultivated land. The popular hope that land reclamation will relieve population pressure is surely unfounded. It would appear wise to explore the feasibility of developing more intensive farming with higher output values per hectare in the uplands before heavy investments are made in tidal-land reclamation.

Even where there is ample new land suitable for cultivation, as in some regions in Latin America and Africa, the cost and organizational efforts required to develop and settle it with viable and well-equipped farms are much higher than is commonly recognized.

It is urgent, therefore, to carry on the whole
new-land development and settlement process from resources surveys to planning and implementing of
farming systems and roads, schools and other community facilities, marketing, credit, and government
services; and to settling farm families on adequate-
sized farms under favorable tenure conditions--to
carry on this whole process under a long-range comprehensive settlement program, at a rate not faster
than can be managed properly. If it is done with
haste, it will result in waste.

And it is haste and waste that have characterized much of land settlement. The prevailing idea
has been: Assign a farmer a piece of new land; from
there on it is his business to produce and make a
living. This is the old Western pioneering philosophy of the nineteenth century, with an imagery full
of individual heroism, self-reliance, and romance,
but with the actual experience of untold human suffering, of incalculable waste in physical and economic resources and in opportunities forfeited by
the lack of development planning and constructive
public policy and organization.[2]

It has meant that land unsuitable for cultivation was cleared and had to be abandoned, that settler families wasted time, energy, and health in
clearing heavily wooded land with their own hands,
while machinery and group action could have done it
much more quickly and cheaply. It has meant that
farmers used more primitive production methods than
in the old farming regions they came from, because
of lack of capital and supplies; that they produced
mainly for their own subsistence, as markets were
far away and their low productivity left little surplus for market delivery; that they suffered severe
hardship through lack of medical care, education,
cooperative, and public services, through isolation
from markets and population centers. It has meant
that many settlers, after years of frustration,
gave up and drifted back to their old farming areas
or to the cities. Such conditions still prevail in
many land settlement areas, such as in Brazil, Colombia, and other Latin American countries, in

parts of Indonesia, the Philippines and other Asian countries--especially in remote areas.

Under such conditions, the opening of new land will yield but a drop in the bucket of the nation's total production. This holds also for much of the spontaneous squatter-type settlement which is taking place along new highways being built through the interior of Latin America, Africa, and some of the islands of Indonesia and the Philippines.

In some countries, spontaneous settlement has taken place on the fringes of old agricultural areas and along roads not far from established market centers. These squatters could be protected in their occupancy rights, or if eviction is in the public interest, could be paid compensation for the improvements they have made, and could be settled elsewhere. Those who are on suitable land and within reach of a market and community center could be induced to adopt modern farming practices and become an invigorating part of the established community. Considerable opportunity for this type of "assisted spontaneous settlement" exists in various countries in Africa and Asia, but it, too, requires guidance and support to prevent misuse of land and settler families.[3]

One task of a development-oriented, farm settlement policy is to come to the rescue of these haphazard settlements that have sprung up spontaneously, or were poorly planned and insufficiently supported, and which are limping along under conditions of wasteful land use, inefficient farming practices, very low incomes of the cultivators, and utterly inadequate communal facilities. Chances are that the human qualities of these settler families are good, are responsive to opportunities offered and to technical guidance and assistance, since the very fact that they are there demonstrates their initiative and energy to break loose from their traditional surroundings and venture into new activities and environments.

This is merely a warning against haphazard or
no planning, against underestimating the time, finances, and organizational efforts involved in developing viable settlement schemes. Most countries
do have some land and water reserves that are worth
developing, and some countries have, indeed, large
amounts of such potentially productive land. Recent
estimates point to the possibility of doubling the
land area under cultivation for the world as a
whole, on the basis of climate, soil and water, and
topographic conditions, as shown in Table 23.

TABLE 23

World Land-Use Pattern and Potential
Increase in Cultivated Land[1]

	Present[3] Land Use (1954-55)	Potential[4] Additions	Potential Percentage Increase
	million ha.		%
Cultivated Land[2]	1,384	1,400	101
Grazing Land	2,407	400	17
Forest Land	3,839	600	16

1. Source: Food and Agriculture Organization
   of the United Nations, World Food Congress
   Paper No. 1, Washington, D.C., June 4-8,
   1963 (Rome: FAO, 1963), p. 2.
2. Includes Orchards.
3. Food and Agriculture Organization of the
   United Nations, Yearbook of Food and Agricultural Statistics (Rome: FAO, 1958).
4. Based on Fritz Baade, "Welternaehrungslage,"
   Rohwolt Deutsche Enzyklopaedie.

NEEDED: A LONG-RANGE
LAND DEVELOPMENT AND SETTLEMENT POLICY

The opening up of new land, the clearing of timber and brush, building irrigation and drainage systems, roads and many other communal facilities take much time before these investments come to full fruition.   This, of course, is no reason for not moving ahead with land development.

On the contrary, the longer a vital job takes, the sooner we should start it; yet the more circumspect and prudent we must be because the dangers of waste and misallocation of capital and trained manpower are great and often underrated.   This holds particularly for projects involving heavy investment in engineering works for irrigation and drainage.

It is of strategic importance to establish a long-range land development and settlement policy consisting of two types of activities:

(1)   A technical research and survey program for the appraisal of the potential land and water resources suitable for agricultural use, through soil and hydrological surveys, and agronomic studies of locally adapted crop varieties and their responses to various fertilizer treatments and cultural practices; and
(2)   A farm settlement and institutional support program for settling farm families on the newly developed land and providing them with technical advice, credit, organizational, and financial assistance for building houses and developing cooperative services, and for prompting the respective government departments to provide adequate roads, schools, health, and other communal facilities.

The first of these, the technical research and resources surveys, is, of course, extremely important.   Only lands with soil characteristics and water supplies worthy of the required investment should be developed for farming.   Fortunately, this is by now much better understood and more adequately

handled than before. The United Nations Development
Program (UNDP) and the Food and Agriculture Organization (FAO), through preinvestment surveys, and the
IBRD, through its missions on developmental loans,
have made many countries aware of the need for land-
resources appraisals before specific commitments of
funds and personnel are made for the opening of new
land areas for cultivation. The second type of action, the farm settlement guidance and support work,
requires a great deal more effort than it is usually
receiving.

Let us consider here only some crucial but neglected issues in land development and settlement
policy.

(1) There is the matter of size: Governments,
engineers, bankers, and economic planners tend to
favor large projects, big dams, big irrigation canals, in the belief that the bigger the project, the
bigger its impact on the economy, its benefit to the
people, its publicity effect which is so important
for marshaling financial funds. At the same time,
it is usually overlooked that the bigger the project,
the more difficult it is to bring it to full fruition, the more complex and demanding is the task of
organization and administration of all the various
facets, especially those dealing with farm settlement, production systems, and communal services.
The bigger the project, the longer it takes to complete it--to bring its production up to full capacity
--and the greater the waste resulting from low crop
yields, from benefits remaining well below costs.

There is often an alternative to a big irrigation scheme: a number of small- and medium-sized
schemes. These have the advantage of being more
manageable by the administrative and technical staff
available, or of requiring less foreign exchange and
of getting into full production in a shorter time.
Smaller schemes can be developed with more active
participation of local people--of farmers and vil-
lagers--and, therefore, can have a more widespread
demonstration effect upon modern farming practices.
Unfortunately, this alternative is less glamorous,

receives less publicity, and is more difficult to
get financed--although it could in many cases be
more effective, less costly, and even have a greater
long-time impact on the economy as a whole.

Indian experience illustrates this issue well.
In the Third Five-Year Plan, the irrigation target
for major projects was set at 12.8 million acres of
additional gross area; at the end of the plan period,
only 5.5 million acres were achieved, or 43 per cent
of the target. The minor-projects target was set
also at 12.8 million acres, and the performance was
13.1 million acres, actually somewhat above the target. In the Fourth Plan now in effect, the major-
projects target was reduced to 9 million acres, and
the minor projects raised to 17 million acres--a
lesson well learned.[4]

What appears as mutually exclusive alternatives
can often be turned into simultaneous lines of action. Once a country has embarked on a massive land-
development scheme, it may still be possible to
tackle a number of smaller ones if the critically
limiting resources are different in the two types of
projects and are not competitive with each other.
For instance, a good part of the resources required
for developing a number of the smaller irrigation
projects are available locally, such as construction
materials, manual labor, and technicians, while the
critical resources for a big project have to come
from abroad, such as large-scale construction equipment, machinery, and highly specialized engineers.
Hence, most of the resources needed for the smaller
projects could not be used in the large one, and
vice versa. This makes it possible to follow both
lines of action rather than only one or the other.
This is an important principle in development planning: Many things that appear theoretically as alternatives, as an "either/or" proposition, can be
turned into simultaneous compatible actions, into a
"both" proposition.

Much of the investment in a land settlement
project is required for land and water development
alone. In irrigation schemes, this part is usually

quite high--often between $300 and $600 per hectare
and sometimes even more--while on rain-fed land it
can be quite low, depending upon the difficulties
of clearing off bush and trees, of drainage, deep
plowing, terracing, stone removing, etc. The important thing to remember is that the greater the initial investment per hectare in land development, the
higher the per hectare returns must be to render a
project economically justified, to cover maintenance
and operation costs (and usually amortization) of
the irrigation works, and on top of this, to cover
the cost of farming operations and of an adequate
living level of the settler families. This cannot
be achieved with outmoded farming methods and poor
tenure conditions. Hence, the farm settlement phase
of the project holds the key to the viability of a
high-cost irrigation scheme. If the government
fails in this phase, the settler families suffer the
brunt of such failure. They pay for the mistakes
the government made in the planning and executing of
the project, in the form of poverty and frustration.

Let us take a closer look at the government's
responsibilities in the farm settlement phase which
follows the development of new land and water resources.

(2) There is the matter of following through
after land and water development: Usually, the public works or irrigation department constructs the
irrigation system for water delivery to large blocks
of land (i.e., to the secondary or tertiary canals).
There it stops, and no one has a clear responsibility
for laying out the field canals and drainage ditches
and for leveling the land, which often requires a
knowledge of what types of farming, crop rotations,
and farm sizes are to be established. Then, farmers
must be assisted in planting locally adapted crop
varieties, and using appropriate dosages of fertilizers and pesticides, which requires local adaptive
research for at least a few years, preferably before
the settlers come (see Chapter 10). Then, there
must be roads and marketing facilities, schools and
hospitals, and community centers with stores and
services. This follow-through in land development

and settlement projects--to the actual production processes, to the housing and living conditions of the settler families, to the communal services and the social and institutional environment--is usually very weak in the planning stage, and weaker still in the implementation, which accounts for the fact that so many settlement projects run at much less than full capacity, and thereby fall far short of their potential contribution to agricultural progress and to the raising of farmers' living standards.

(3) There is the matter of special purposes of settlement: If many countries cannot count on new-land settlement to increase total farm production rapidly or to relieve population pressure in over-crowded areas, they can often find specific strategic purposes for settlement schemes. For instance, opening up new land for certain key crops for export or industrial use, such as sugar cane, tobacco, cotton, rubber, coffee, etc., can play an important part in accelerating the economic development of a country. In some of the Middle Eastern countries, especially in Turkey and Syria, the breaking up of semi-arid grazing lands for mechanized dry-land grain farming has had a strong impact on agricultural production and on the foreign trade balance--although there are already signs that the cultivation frontier may have been pushed out too far into arid areas, with wind erosion, dust storms, and successive crop failures as punishment. In development plans for remote or backward regions and for new urban, industrial, or mining centers, new land settlement projects should play a strategic role, not only by producing food for the rapidly growing population of the region, but also by contributing to the balance of the region's economic and social structure.

(4) Potentially, the uniquely constructive purpose of land settlement projects is to serve as spearheads of modern farming methods, as laboratories, and demonstrations and training grounds for institutional and socio-economic innovations, such as effective tenure, cooperative marketing and credit arrangements, and various types of community organizations and services--all of which are more

difficult to achieve in old established farming
areas, as we shall see presently.

No matter what purpose and scope land settlement should have in any particular country, land development, farm settlement, farming systems, and
community services must be integrated into a comprehensive long-time, farm settlement program, and its
directorate must have the authority to draw upon the
various government agencies for carrying out their
respective responsibilities according to the time
schedule required. Only thus can much material
waste and human frustration be avoided.

STARTING FROM A CLEAN SLATE

Farm settlement schemes offer a rare opportunity
for pioneering with new farming practices, new production organization, new tenure and other institutional arrangements. Failing to seize this opportunity represents a real waste, and might even retard
progress in the old agricultural areas.

Here are the main opportunities which one dare
not miss:

First, the new land is free from an obstructive
agrarian structure. The many obstacles to farm development presented by undersized farms, absentee
landlords, a poor and subservient tenantry racked by
high rents and insecure occupancy--all these obstacles are absent on the new land. The settlement
agency is in the challenging position to start the
project from a clean slate, as far as these key environmental conditions are concerned, under which
the new settlers can develop their farms, their
houses, and their community. Such settlement
schemes should become pilots, laboratories, demonstrations for rural development approaches, for scientific, economic and administrative techniques, for
land tenure and credit arrangements, for organized
group action by farmers, from which the whole country will reap benefits. Is this not too precious an
opportunity to miss for a government eager to

demonstrate its capabilities and gain the confidence
of its people?

Second, farm settlement schemes are agricultural development projects in selected, limited areas
and require a resident staff of competent technicians and administrative officers. Ministers and
directors are under pressure for giving the project
high priority for qualified personnel and financial
support, by the publicity and the popular expectations which surround settlement schemes. This means
that the project manager and his team have more
ready access to top-level government officers for
securing current support and cooperation--an opportunity which is all too rarely enjoyed by field officers. This resident team should plan and carry
through the project from the very beginning, working
out the various farming techniques, farm sizes, tenure conditions, credit and marketing facilities,
etc., adapted to the area and needed to get farmers
off to a promising start.

Third, settlers can and should be informed of
the guidelines and terms of the project. They should
be told what is expected of them, and at the same
time should be assured that they shall have a voice
in the planning and be able to participate in the
working out of the details and day-to-day operations
as the project progresses. As the manager works
closely with farmers in developing new production
methods, crop and livestock enterprises, he must request from the settlers, as a quid pro quo, their
cooperation and genuine effort in making the project
a success. Settlers need to be held firmly to their
obligations concerning work performance and repayment of loans. I am inclined to argue that if settlers work poorly and expect government to hand them
an easy life on a platter and forgive their debts,
the cause of such attitudes can more often be traced
to faulty leadership than to innate character faults
of the settlers. Effective human leadership is required on the part of the resident officers.[5] Most
settlers will not resent being held firmly to their
obligations if it is done justly and with their own
welfare at heart, and if the obligations themselves

are reasonable and capable of being met by the settlers.

Fourth, if settlement projects are so conceived
and operated, they offer ideal conditions for practical on-the-job training of junior technicians and
administrative officers for subsequent field assignments outside the settlement projects, in old farming areas as well as in other new-settlement schemes.
The dearth of junior technicians is in many countries
a much more serious bottleneck than the lack of
highly trained academic people, because agricultural
progress demands a large widely dispersed corps of
field officers who can work with farmers and gain
their confidence. These field officers must be supervised by a senior officer of advanced training.
Many countries have some well-educated technicians.
But whom can they supervise in the tasks for which
they are trained if there are no junior field officers? The result: underutilization of the few senior technicians, and no effective links with farmers
who do the producing.

There is no better place for practical training
of junior officers than a new settlement project,
because here they experience the excitement of building a new farming system, a new set of institutions,
a new way of rural life. And it is the local farmer
who is doing the actual building. From this experience, the trainees get a realistic view of what can
be accomplished and how farmers can be motivated to
participate in working out the details of modernizing agriculture. With this experience and vision,
they will be much more effective in subsequent assignments in old farming areas than if they had never worked under the experimental "laboratory" conditions offered by new-land settlements. Thus, they
will accelerate the spreading of the benefits from
what was learned in the settlement areas to other
areas, and thereby boost the developmental process
there.

This spreading effect can be furthered by
bringing farmers from other parts of the country to
the settlement project for a visit during which the

settlers themselves do most of the demonstrating and explaining.

Clearly, this is the most constructive way for governments to conceive and carry out farm settlement programs. They can contribute most to development through pilot, demonstration, and training projects, leading the way to modern production methods, to institutional arrangements stimulating farmers' motivations, and to their emancipation as full-fledged citizens. Settlement projects can be made to function as catalysts and energize progressive forces far beyond the project areas. A farm settlement policy without this catalytic function is bound to yield disappointing results, often not more than a drop in the bucket, from the viewpoint of its effect upon total farm production and rural income levels.

There are but few countries where such a dynamic settlement policy is systematically applied, yet most countries would greatly benefit from it.[6]

SETTLER PARTICIPATION IN PROJECT AFFAIRS

For a farm settlement program to function as a pacesetter for agricultural development, experience has taught us some strategic lessons:

(1) Developing new farm settlements requires government support in the form of various technical, administrative, and financial services for five to ten years from the time the first farm families move onto the project. Too often, irrigation engineers have built a dam and a canal system, and when the irrigation water became available, the new farm settlers were not prepared to make efficient use of it, to intensify and change their crops and cultural methods, to buy fertilizer and new machinery and equipment needed under irrigation. Nor were government extension, credit, and research services available to help farmers plan and adopt a new farming system which made full use of the land, water, and labor resources. The result was a waste of opportunities for increasing production and farm income

over many years--an irreparable loss which retarded
progress much below what it could have been. The
production, in many cases, might have been two or
three times higher than it actually was.

(2) The size of a farm settlement program is
best determined by the number of competent personnel
and the amount of funds for supporting services that
can be mobilized. Since a settlement project offers
such unique opportunities for developing modern
farming systems under most favorable tenure conditions tailor-made to fit the local human and natural
resources, it is much better to start a project not
before the required staff and funds are actually
available. Farm settlements which merely duplicate
traditional methods and offer farmers no production
incentives and access to capital and technical advice are liabilities, both economically and politically: The output will not justify the cost, and
the settler will find his hopes for a better life
frustrated and will blame the government for it.

Hence, starting with a small number of farm-
settlement projects and expanding as additional
field officers trained on the job in these projects
become available for assignment to new areas is more
effective than a larger program ill-planned, ill-
staffed, and ill-serviced.

Experience indicates that the minimum unit size
of a settlement project at the beginning would usually be around 150 to 200 families. This would make
full use of a small resident staff of two or three
officers who would also supervise on-the-job trainees and would assist in the developing of the various
communal services essential to the success of a new
settlement. This small resident staff functions as
the contact point with the various national government departments for extension service, credit and
similar support action, and as the originator of
specific requests for such services on behalf of the
settlers. For large settlement projects of several
thousands of farmers, a breakdown into village communities of 200 to 300 families each is necessary to
develop close working relations with farmers and to

promote effective settler activities in advisory and administrative group functions.

(3) Active participation and organized responsibilities of settlers in project and community affairs is a basic requirement of a modern settlement scheme. Serving on settlers' committees is a new experience for most settlers. Initial guidance and encouragement must be provided by the project staff. At the same time, these committees must be given some real responsibilities, otherwise they will not function properly.

An important task that can be assigned to a settlers' committee is the disciplining of individuals and families for the maintenance of certain work performance and behavior standards. It is much better to delegate such problems as keeping settlers to their obligations and, in extreme cases, ousting an individual or family from a project, to a settlers' committee, than for the project manager to take this responsibility alone onto himself. It remains the project manager's function, at least in the initial years of the project, to assure that the committee is dealing with the various cases fairly, with both the individual and the community at heart. He will be wise to take a firm, yet a consultative attitude toward the committee and back it up whenever possible, although he should officially retain the administrative authority to implement or reject the committee's decision until the project stands on its own feet.

This is a basic principle of settlement project management which is often not genuinely accepted by government officials. If settlers are really given specific responsibilities and feel that they are trusted by the manager, their response is often surprisingly good, perhaps because human understanding and wisdom on matters of personal conduct and social behavior does not necessarily require formal training or even literacy. Perhaps it is a fundamental quality of the human race which can be brought to fruition under a certain environment of social responsibility within the context of democratic values

--which, after all, is the social philosophy in rapid ascendancy throughout the world today.

On the whole, the risk of permitting a settlers' committee to make a mistake now and then is much smaller than the risk of running the project down to the last detail by bureaucratic routine and the manager's administrative authority alone. If the manager in a specific case should feel that the committee's decision would be seriously harmful to the project, he should veto it but should take pains to explain to the committee why he cannot abide by their decision, in terms which will make sense to them.

The types of function which lend themselves well to settlers' committee guidance, apart from human relations, are in the field of cooperative marketing and product quality control, joint use of machinery, youth clubs, and various social entertainment. Initially, it is always the project manager's responsibility to provide the inspiration, organization, technical advice, and administrative support for these committees, simply because farmers are not used to thinking and behaving along these lines and can only learn by doing.

LEADERSHIP AND HUMAN GUIDANCE:
KEY TO SUCCESS

The success of a farm settlement project, apart from its general economic feasibility as to soil, climate, and location, hinges on the technical, organizational, and human guidance of the settlers. They are expected to do many things new to them, to adjust to environmental conditions very different from those they have known. Such guidance is too often inadequate and haphazard, and the reason given is lack of trained personnel--if, indeed, the sponsoring agency is conscious of the fundamental need for guidance.

The key to success is a few good technical and administrative men who live and work with the

settlers, understand them, gain their confidence,
serve and guide them at the same time. These few
settlement officers require support from their government department in the form of delegation of authority on administrative and financial matters, and
in the form of recognition of their crucial function
through adequate salary and promise of promotion after a number of years of good performances. If
these few things are provided, all the many other
necessary things will fall into proper place and can
be managed as the project develops.

Where can these few good settlement officers be
found? Developing countries are so short of trained
people that even the few needed for a major settlement project cannot be gotten through new recruit-
ment, or released from their present jobs. But is
this really so?

Perhaps it is primarily a matter of assigning
a high priority to these key officers. My impression is that their crucial function is often not
recognized by planners and ministry officials. Let
us assume that the director of settlement is convinced of their importance. He might send out talent scouts to locate one good agronomist, one good
farm-management economist, and one good agricultural
administrative officer, each with field experience
and known for his ability to communicate with farmers, to understand their problems and gain their
confidence.

The director might find a good administrative
officer in his own department, but he is a senior
man, has risen from the ranks, and is now a section
chief in the central office. How can he spare him
from his present job, and how can he get him to accept this much more arduous project assignment hundreds of miles away from the capital city? Perhaps
he can impress him with the importance of the new
job, offer him a "hardship allowance" or some other
form of financial inducement, promise him and his
wife two weeks stay in the city every six months on
duty and at government expense, and assure him of a
substantial promotion after five years of good work

in the project. Even if civil service regulations
do not provide for such arrangements, there usually
are ways for offering equivalent inducements if high
officials are determined to find them.[7]

Continuing our example: If the director finds
a good agronomist in another department, the problem
of getting this man on the settlement project is
more difficult. The director has to persuade another director to release him. He might succeed by offering his colleague a full share of credit for his
contribution to the project, by agreeing to have the
agronomist remain technically responsible to his colleague, and by offering to carry the cost of any inducements similar to those of the administrative officer on the project's budget. If the director
should fail to find a good farm-management economist, he might succeed in getting one through FAO or
bilateral technical assistance.

A word about the basic qualifications of such
project officers. One of a team of two or three officers must be designated as project manager and
team leader on his personality as key qualification:
a strong motivation to help and guide people to their
own interest in accomplishment and progress as human
beings; an ability to inspire people with new ideas,
purposeful effort, and confidence in his judgement
and unselfish intentions; a cooperative attitude
toward people, soliciting their voluntary participation, listening to them and willing to change his
own plans in favor of constructive suggestions put
forth by them, and giving them credit for it; an
ability to help them organize themselves for various
kinds of group activities, such as settler committees and cooperative work of various types.

The agronomist might best be chosen on his experience with the crops, soil, and climate similar
to those of the project area. He need not necessarily have an academic degree, if he has talent,
intellect, and sufficient scientific curiosity to
take important technical problems to competent scientists for advice. The agronomic problems facing
settlers in new farming areas are often puzzling,

since there has usually not been any local experience upon which to draw for guidance in working out
an efficient crop rotation and farming system.

The farm-management economist needs to be familiar with the costs of implements and machinery,
seed, fertilizer, and pesticides, the prices of various farm products, the marketing facilities required, the labor requirements during the seasons of
the year for the crops and livestock enterprises.
He works with the agronomist on what yields can be
expected from various crops under various fertilizer
applications, and works with the farmers on how much
of what crops he should grow and what livestock to
keep for making the best income from his land, labor, and capital resources. On any technical problem
beyond the competence of any of the team, the project manager arranges for consultation by a senior
technician from headquarters.

After project officers have delegated to settler committees more and more functions, have encouraged and trained leaders from among them, and
nurtured a democratic community spirit among the
settler families, special government support can be
gradually withdrawn as the settlers themselves take
on the management of the project.

This example merely serves to highlight the
key issues to which the settlement director needs to
devote great effort. These leadership problems are
much more difficult to manage than funds and routine
personnel assignments, but they can be managed, they
do play a dominant role and largely determine the
degree of success of farm settlement schemes. For
this reason, any effort along these lines will pay
high dividends in promoting agricultural development
and the government's reputation in the eyes of the
people.

EXPERIMENTATION IN SETTLEMENT POLICY

People are pressed, by force of the urgency for
rapid progress, into many technical, organizational,
and economic innovations, into changes from

traditional arrangements needed to open up many new
opportunities for increasing production and reducing
poverty.

There are dangers in literally transferring arrangements that have proven effective in the Western
industrialized or the Eastern Communist world to
newly developing countries, since cultural values
and the social behavior are, in many aspects, quite
different from those in the industrial West or East.
Hence, we cannot predict how people will respond to
this or that policy, whether their behavior will con-
form to that experienced elsewhere, to what extent
they will seize upon new opportunities offered.

Governments have many possibilities for experimenting with various policies on a small scale before promulgating them wholesale on a national basis, and for ironing out many weaknesses and improving development programs through experimental
processes. Settlement projects lend themselves most
readily to this approach.

First of all, every nation has already some
farm settlement projects in operation in various
parts of the country. The trouble is that usually
no reliable studies are being made as to how these
projects are working out, what has gone wrong and
what went right, and why. We know deplorably little
about why one project has been causing a lot of
trouble, frustration of settlers, poor economic performance, abandonment of farms, and other symptoms
of failure, while another project has progressed
fairly well. In the absence of such concurrent
studies, no one can really learn from these new and
most valuable experiences. Grave errors which could
readily be detected and remedied are often continued
with compounding dilatory effects.[8]

It would be a highly profitable investment for
every government to carry on studies of the current
functioning and detailed operational processes and
their results in various settlement schemes, with
the necessary support and freedom of inquiry granted
to the research workers.

In principle, these studies are best undertaken
by a university or a research group not operationally responsible for the project, because it is too
much to expect the administrators and project managers to be scientifically equipped and psychologically prepared to conduct such studies objectively.
To be realistic, however, the settlement director
and the project manager must be drawn into the confidence of the research worker who must discuss the
method of the studies and their findings frankly
with them and incorporate, as far as possible, their
experiences and judgements in the report. Before
the final report is submitted to the minister, the
director and project manager should be given the
right to attach their comments to the report. If
this kind of protection of the operating agency is
not assured, the researcher is not likely to get the
cooperation he needs to conduct the study.

The second approach to experimentation includes
the process just outlined, but provides further that
several projects in the nation's settlement program
are planned and organized differently by deliberately adopting various methods in order to find out
which of them proves to be the more effective. For
instance, one project might be organized so that
each settler is assigned a farm which he manages individually in all its production aspects, and the
government furnishes only technical advice through
extension workers and helps the farmer to set up a
marketing and credit cooperative for the purchase of
fertilizers and other supplies and for the sale of
his major products. Another settlement project
might be so organized that the government undertakes
the responsibility for the production and marketing
of a dominant cash crop, say cotton or ground nuts,
while the settler is free to use any of his land not
in that particular crop as he wants, for food crops,
forage for livestock, vegetables, etc., on his own
account (as is the case of the Gezira Scheme in the
Sudan). A third project might be organized along
the lines of a large-scale collective or state farm
with central management and with only an adequate
garden and orchard plot and facilities for some livestock and poultry for each settler family. Again,

for the farmers, the government, the nation to benefit from such organizational experimentation, concurrent studies are essential.

Unfortunately, there are very few countries
that have taken advantage of these opportunities for
experimenting and "learning while doing" in this
complex process of accelerating agricultural development.[9] The experience of ten years with such a policy of experimentation and concurrent field research
might well give the rate of economic growth a powerful boost.

A number of countries have, in fact, undertaken
various types of farm settlement. For instance,
Ghana and Algeria have set up collective farms and
state farms in some areas, family-type farms in others. Nigeria attempted to settle "school leavers"
on a semi-cooperative basis (in the Western and
Eastern Regions) and young farmers from a crowded
area as independent family-type farmers (in the
Northern Region). India and Pakistan encouraged
various types of cooperative farming. With the exception of India, however, there are no comparative
studies evaluating the experiences and performances
under these various types of tenure.[10]

Such studies would be all the more useful as
the different types of tenure might prove to be peculiarly suitable to certain conditions of farming
systems. For instance, state farms might work well
for the productions of sugar cane or rubber, family-
type farms for mixed crops and livestock farming,
various types of cooperative farming for the production of a cash crop like cotton or tobacco under
central management, with that of other crops and all
livestock under individual management--along the
general pattern of the Gezira Scheme in the Sudan.

The reason why governments have but rarely made
specific provisions for experimentation in settlement
projects is perhaps not a matter of ill-will or lack
of funds, but simply a matter of not being used to
thinking along these lines, not having become aware
of the tremendous advantages that can be gained

through such experimental procedures in evolving new
viable production, marketing, and institutional arrangements which promise to unleash pent-up production capacities and mobilize dormant motivations and
energies of farm people in a setting free from the
encumbrances of outmoded traditional farming systems
and local class and power relations.

NOTES TO CHAPTER 9

1. See, for instance, U.N./FAO/International
Labor Organization, Progress in Land Reform, op.
cit., p. 59; and Flores, op. cit., p. 8.

2. See, for instance, a penetrating account of
the settlement in the West of the U.S.A., by Walter
P. Webb, The Great Plains (Boston, Mass.: Ginn &
Co., 1931); and the review of Brazil's history of
colonization by T. Lynn Smith, Brazil: People and
Institutions (Baton Rouge: Louisiana State University Press, 1954), pp. 455-91.

3. See U.N./FAO/International Labor Organization, Progress in Land Reform, op. cit., p. 69.

4. See James H. Boulware, "India's Fourth
Five-Year Plan Focusses on Agriculture," Foreign
Agriculture, Vol. IV, No. 40 (Oct. 3, 1966), p. 4.

5. For a recent account of a comprehensive
farm-settlement program, see Alfred H. Siemans,
"New Agricultural Settlement Along Mexico's Cande-
larie River: Implications of Commitment to Planning
and the Ejido," Inter-American Economic Affairs,
Vol. 20, No. 1 (Summer 1966), pp. 23-39.

6. Israel offers an outstanding example of a
highly dynamic, comprehensive, and successful settle-
ment policy. See Raanan Weitz, The Next Stage in
Agricultural Settlement (Jerusalem: Jewish Agency
Settlement Department, December 1964); and his arti-
cle "Rural Development Through Regional Planning in
Israel," Journal of Farm Economics, Vol. 47, No. 3
(August 1965), pp. 634-51.

7. In many countries, the director could simply order the officer to assume the new project post, without offering any special inducements. But this may not be advisable as the officer could take this order as a punishment or injustice. He would not put his heart into the job and would start pulling strings to get transferred to another ministry.

8. For a revealing comparative study of farm settlement schemes, see Food and Agriculture Organization of the United Nations, Agricultural Development in Nigeria, 1965-1980 (Rome: FAO, 1966), pp. 339-47.

9. For instance, studies somewhat along these lines have been done in India where the Planning Commission established a "Programme Evaluation Organization" in 1952, and a "Research Programmes Committee" in 1953; for a discussion of these issues, see Government of India, Report on Methods for Evaluation of Effects of Agrarian Reform (New Delhi: Ministry of Food and Agriculture, Government of India, August 1958), pp. 12-13.

10. See U.N./FAO/International Labor Organization, Progress in Land Reform, op. cit., pp. 73-78; and Rainer Schickele, "Land Economics Research for World Agricultural Developments," Land Economics Research (Baltimore, Md.:   Johns Hopkins Press, 1962), pp. 100-24.

PART **III**

IMPLEMENTATION OF AGRICULTURAL
DEVELOPMENT: LOCAL PROJECTS AS
PACESETTERS FOR NATIONAL PROGRESS

CHAPTER **10** DEVELOPMENT

FROM BELOW

In Part I, we have explored the nature of the
critical issues people are facing all over the world
in accelerating their economic development. These
issues center around the moral belief that poverty
deprives the individual of his human rights and dignity and hence must be abolished, and around the new
knowledge that technology gives man the power to
abolish poverty. This moral belief and this technological knowledge, both new to the developing
world, combine into a powerful team of social forces
motivating people toward economic progress in Communist and non-Communist countries, in rich and poor
nations, in industry and agriculture, and in all
other walks of life.

In Part II, we have explored the peculiar nature of agriculture as compared to industry, and how
national development policies and plans must be
adapted to these peculiarities of the rural sector.

Now, in Part III, we shall explore the difficult problem of how to formulate agricultural policies and plans that can be implemented in practical,
local terms, and what specific types of programs and
projects are required to make farmers willing and
able to modernize their farming methods, to increase
agricultural production and income, and to participate as full-fledged citizens in community affairs
and group organizations.

This means that we have to descend from the
Olympian heights of national planning to the task of
developing agriculture from below, of preparing specific projects and applying practical means for
bringing about the desired results. This holds

241

particularly in agriculture where the implementation
of national policy is much more difficult and requires different administrative measures and more
field personnel than is true for comparable policies
in industry and trade.

CONCENTRATION ON DEVELOPMENT
PROJECTS AND LOCAL ACTION

Lord Chesterton said a hundred years ago:
"Nothing is vital until it becomes local." Until
economic plans are put into practice, are mobilizing
people working in specific localities, these plans
are not vital, remain on paper. This has been the
fate of many national agricultural development
plans. A well-known modern planner with wide experience puts this issue most provocatively: "Unless
preinvestment and investment studies of projects for
implementing a comprehensive plan are sufficiently
advanced, it does little good to prepare such a
plan. Yet, all too often this is exactly what happens." He concludes: "Planners have almost invari-
ably concentrated on aggregative planning rather
than on the proper preparation and execution of projects, but experience shows that countries with
well-prepared projects coordinated by sound budgetary procedures and controls can dispense with comprehensive plans, at least for a time, and still
maintain high rates of growth. It seems clear,
therefore, that improvements in project preparation
...are at least as urgent as the preparation of aggregative plans."[1] And, I might add, specific project preparation and execution are more urgent in
countries where data, trained personnel, and administrative services needed to implement such comprehensive plans are lacking.

The argument against a policy of piecemeal development, of implementing a large number of unrelated projects, is that this haphazard approach
leads to waste of scarce resources by producing too
much of some and too little of other things. Decisions on capital investment are made according to
the political power of certain groups rather than

economic returns and priority ranking of projects in
the national plan where all parts are fitted together to bring forth the maximum output.

There is, of course, a danger that some of this
might happen. But this danger can be met by introducing certain coordinating principles, certain restraints on the eligibility of projects, and certain
tests of the economic feasibility and general socio-
political justification of projects, which greatly
reduce the danger of waste and malallocation of resources under a piecemeal development strategy.[2]

Chances are very high, indeed, that as long as
specific development projects, say an irrigation
project, meet certain tests of economic, financial,
and administrative feasibility, it will fit into any
reasonable national development plan which might be
worked out later.

In fact, much of the planning that is actually
implemented is done just this way. The various government departments are currently preparing proposals in their respective fields for specific localities and submitting them to the finance ministry for
approval and financing. Whether or not an aggregative plan exists, the government must decide which
of these project proposals are accepted or rejected.
The question is: On what grounds are these decisions made? Should a well-prepared project be rejected because the aggregative plan would give it a
lower priority than an ill-prepared project with
little evidence of economic feasibility? If there
is no aggregative national plan, should no project
be implemented until the plan is available? These
rather rhetorical questions intend to show the mar-
ginal position that aggregative plans have in such
decisions on specific projects, and the dominant
position that the quality of project preparation
must occupy.

To put the issue in different terms: Developing countries need more of practically everything.
If the aggregate national plan should give a high
priority for sugar cane and a lower one for rice

production, and if in a given year a dubious sugar
cane project and a well-prepared rice project were
submitted, the rice project should be selected and
the sugar cane project rejected, because the country
needs more of both. The plan's priority for sugar
cane is probably based on foreign exchange needs--
which might be met by a good tobacco project not
contemplated at all in the plan, or by a good sugar
cane project next year. Moreover, even projects for
high-priority products must be economically feasible; if they are not, they lead to waste despite the
fact that the over-all plan assigns high priority to
these products. All this goes to show that the
quality of a project, its economic and administrative
feasibility, its social and institutional aspects
should be of primary importance for the implementation decision, and that its position on the priority
list of a national plan should be only of secondary
importance.[3]

CRITERIA OF SELECTING
LAND AND WATER DEVELOPMENT PROJECTS

Proposals for bringing new land under cultivation or raising the productive capacity of old agricultural land through clearing, draining, irrigation
dams, tube wells, canals, land leveling and terracing are major items in the rural development planning of most countries. Such projects expand the
land-resources base for new farm settlements and
more food and fiber production--which, of course,
arouses much political and economic support from influential quarters. What, then, are the criteria
which should govern the selection of land-development projects for implementation? What is needed
for a thorough preparation of a project?

Surveys of soils, hydrology, topography, and
other physical features determining the land's productive capacity are recognized as essential prere-
quisites for major irrigation and other land-development projects. Technical competence in the
engineering design and construction of irrigation
and other land improvements, and a reliable estimate

of construction cost and annual operation and maintenance costs are equally obvious requirements.
These engineering aspects can be checked fairly well,
as there is much past experience upon which to draw,
either in the country or outside. Here, the FAO and
U.N. Development Programs are rendering excellent
technical assistance under the Special Fund's preinvestment surveys and pilot projects.

Reliable estimates of future benefits and returns from the project, especially from agricultural
production, are much more difficult to make. Yet,
they are the dominant factor in determining the economic feasibility of the project. These economic-
returns estimates are usually the weakest part in
the project preparation because they are rarely made
by people with professional and practical experience
needed to make them, and because the assumptions upon which they must be based are of necessity con-
jectural. Agricultural-returns estimates should be
made by farm-management experts, in consultation
with agronomists (knowledgeable in crop varieties,
fertilizer use, etc.), economic-policy experts (familiar with national and international market prospects, farm product and input prices, agricultural
credit facilities and general budgetary controls),
and local farmers. Instead, they are often made by
engineers or general economists, perhaps in casual
consultation with agronomists, without reference to
farmers and their local institutional environment,
nor to concrete farming systems, farm sizes, enterprise combinations, etc.

The assumptions upon which the benefit estimates are based should stipulate modern production
techniques and their respective yields and input requirements, instead of outmoded techniques with low
inputs and low yields. They should further stipulate appropriate farming systems, farm-size patterns,
land tenure conditions, marketing facilities, and
cost-price relationships between inputs and farm
products which are required to make farmers willing
and able to adopt modern farming and produce increasing quantities of crop and livestock products.
For this, close consultation with farmers and a

systematic assessment of local production conditions
is required (see Chapter 12).

The justification for making these assumptions
for benefit estimates is that on new lands, no traditional farming methods, no repressive tenure
structures, no uneconomic farm sizes exist to obstruct the introduction of modern farming systems,
viable farm size and tenure patterns, and other desirable institutional conditions. The settlers, of
course, come with traditional notions on farming
techniques; but in the settlement project they are
placed in a new environment and under obligation to
adopt modern techniques, as a quid pro quo for getting land of their own and government services and
assistance. The project proposal must take advantage of this opportunity of starting from a clean
slate (see Chapter 9).

Also, where projects improve the land's productive capacity in old cultivated areas, provisions
must be made for the efficient use of the improved
land resources under modern production processes,
favorable land tenure, credit and extension service.
It will always be a matter of judgement as to how
far a government can achieve such conditions, but
realistic provision for creating them belong in any
well-prepared proposal.

Note that most of this information essential
for project preparation must be obtained locally,
must be built up from the ground, from local soil
surveys, from the experience of local field technicians and farmers, in order to be reliable and useful in the implementation of the project.

The set of information just outlined is needed
to get a "benefit-cost ratio" of the project. There
are many ways of computing benefit-cost ratios, and
many ways of interpreting them. In any case, no
benefit-cost ratio, not even the most comprehensive
one, should be considered as the sole, or even the
dominant, criterion for the priority to be given a
project. My experience suggests that a simple
benefit-cost ratio, showing the proportion of the

net returns to farmers (before water charges but after adequate family living allowance) to the project's operation and maintenance costs is most useful for determining the minimum requirement for economic feasibility. If this simple ratio is less
than one, the project is bound to become an economic
liability to the country, and the farmers will bear
the brunt of it in one way or another.[4]

Beyond this use for setting a minimum requirement of economic feasibility, the benefit-cost ratio has little more to contribute to the decision on
development project selection.

Nor does the conventional criterion of "financial feasibility," which measures the project cost
to the government and the reimbursements and charges
it expects to collect from the beneficiaries, deserve to be given much weight, because it depends so
heavily upon specific financial arrangements between
the government and the various private parties involved. These arrangements are flexible and can be
geared so that the distribution of the financial obligations among the various parties is equitable and
conducive to development. For instance, the government may decide to cover the interest and amortization cost of the project's fixed investment from its
general tax revenue, as it does in the case of roads
and other infrastructural investments, instead of
collecting it from the farmers as the direct--but by
no means only!--beneficiaries.

Other criteria become much more important for
choosing among project proposals, once they meet a
minimum economic feasibility test. Since we cannot
go into detail here on project-appraisal methods, I
shall only mention some criteria which are rarely or
only informally used but deserve much greater attention.

The criteria for assigning priorities among a
number of competing project proposals should be
those which indicate how effective the project
promises to be in:

(1)   Reducing poverty;

(2)   Increasing output of farm products most
urgently needed for improving nutrition levels (e.g.,
vegetables and livestock products) or for earning or
saving foreign exchange (e.g., sugar cane, cotton,
etc.);

(3)   Benefiting the greatest number of rural
people;

(4)   Promoting participation of farmers in community affairs and in organizations serving their
interest, such as cooperatives and farmers' associations or unions;

(5)   Creating complementary assets such as
electric power, or supporting other projects, such
as transportation links with other areas or market
centers, rural agricultural processing industries,
etc.; and

(6)   Providing adequate administrative support
for its implementation--including on-the-job training of field technicians for later assignment inside
and outside the project area.

These criteria should be explicitly dealt with
in the preparation of the project, including provisions for an effective follow-up after the engineering and construction phases have been completed.
On the effectiveness of this follow-up in terms of
extension service, production credit, cooperative
marketing, farmers' associations, etc., will depend
the success of the project. Too often, this follow-
up is neglected or not carried out at all, with the
result of production levels much lower than could be
achieved, and hence, incomes insufficient to cover
the cost of the projects and yield an adequate living for the farm families.

It stands to reason that any agricultural development project that meets these criteria is bound
to fit into any realistic national development plan.
But what is equally important to realize: Any national development plan must be broken down into a
set of such concrete and localized projects before
it can be implemented.

Resources can be developed, and people and production processes can be organized only in the context of specific localized action programs. Planning boards or councils of ministers are in a strong position to request government departments and agencies to improve their project preparation. They can make clear that project proposals will be screened according to certain explicit sets of criteria along the lines we have just discussed. This, in itself, would bring about a good deal of coordination of the different projects prepared by various ministries and departments, especially if the planning board would offer the assistance of its experts in the preparation of project proposals. This would also be of great benefit to the planners, as it would get them in closer contact with the practical problems of implementation. It certainly would speed up the process of screening project proposals for final decision on selection and implementation.

The national planning board has also the function of aggregating the inputs required for implementing the proposed development projects, that is, the fertilizer, machinery, equipment, and specialized trained manpower which must be provided to bring the projects to a successful completion. Whether these required inputs originate in the private or public sectors, the national planning agency must program for making available the needed inputs according to sources of supply and the time schedule. This programming of the implementation of development projects requires much more attention than it receives in many countries.

LOCALIZING AGRICULTURAL PROGRAMS--GIVING EXTENSION SERVICE ROOTS AND A FOCUS

So far, we have considered projects of a type which involves fixed capital investment in land and water development and, hence, is of necessity bound to specific selected areas. Other types of agricultural development programs are conceived on a

nation-wide scale and do not necessarily call for
implementation in selected limited areas. These
types of programs are mainly of an educational, advisory, and demonstrational nature and do not involve permanent investments in agricultural land improvements. Let us explore their problems of effective implementation.

Planners and high government officials may well
know what kind of agricultural programs the country
needs to get off the ground and accelerate its development. For instance, they know that agriculture
needs a strong extension service for adult education
and technical assistance to farmers. They may agree
that a land reform and a credit program are necessary to offer farmers incentives and opportunities
for increasing production. These policies are conceived in terms of national programs, of nation-wide
implementation, and their administrative and financial provisions are based on national operational
requirements.

This conception of agricultural policies is
theoretically sound, but practically, often unrealistic and misleading, and is resulting in much waste
of scarce trained manpower and financial resources.
The reason: Agriculture is so dispersed, production
is in the hands of so many small farmers, and farming methods vary so much with local conditions that
a nation-wide agricultural program requires a staff
of technical officers much larger than most countries have at their disposal at the present time.
Since it is often physically impossible to implement
a national agricultural program effectively everywhere at the same time, it is much wiser to select
certain strategically located areas, concentrate the
trained personnel in these areas, and implement the
program there efficiently, rather than dissipate the
scarce personnel over so large an area that their
efforts leave no impact.

There are many ways in which this can be done.
In principle, formulate a realistic project whose
subject and approach fits the area selected, assign
one or more good officers to it, complement them

with junior or apprentice staff to assist the officers and, at the same time, receive on-the-job training from them. After several years, when the project
has gotten well started, move the team to another
area and set up additional teams with newly trained
officers to cover more and more areas. An example
of this approach is given in Chapter 11. To clarify
this important issue, let us think through some administrative and logistic problems that must be
solved.

For instance: A country may have 200 trained
agricultural field officers and one million farmers.
This makes one field officer per 5,000 farmers.
What does this one agricultural officer do in his
district? He advises a few local landlords and
large farmers on some improved crop variety or pesticide; he arranges film shows in his town and in
some of the accessible villages nearby on how farmers work in Italy or the United States or Russia; he
writes many reports to headquarters and answers much
correspondence from headquarters asking him to do
this and that for a number of agencies in the ministry of agriculture. Agricultural extension officers
in the field seem to spend only about one-third of
their time on farm visits and group activities--
that is, on their primary task--in many countries
(see Table 25, p. 259). Our agricultural officer is
busy all day. But what is his impact on the modernization of farming, on the increase in agricultural
production in his district?

Now, let us consider an alternative way of de-
ploying the 200 agricultural officers: Assign a
team of two officers and two junior assistants to
each of 100 selected areas with around 2,000 farmers
each. They work out, in consultation with farmers,
a farm development project fitted to each area. Of
the two officers, one should preferably be an agronomist, and one a farm economist. The project is
worked out in detail and operated by this team of
two agricultural officers. Each officer establishes
direct personal working relations with 100 new farmers each year. In this way, 200 farmers, or 10 per
cent of all farmers in the area each year, become

cooperators in the project.

Each officer has assigned to him a junior assis-
tant, a secondary or vocational school graduate, for
on-the-job training in the project. After three
years, the two extension officers move to a new project area, and their two assistants carry on in the
old area, under the general supervision of an officer newly assigned to it, to bring new cooperators
into the program and get modern farming methods
adopted by the rest of the farmers. Another group
of 200 agricultural officers has been trained during the first three years and is now being assigned
to 100 more project areas.

The principle of this approach is illustrated
in Table 24. Note that at the end of the ninth
year, the whole agriculture of the country is covered by local custom-built projects, and that over
half of the farmers are formally cooperating. Many
of the other farmers will have improved their practices due to the demonstration effect of the program. If the projects are well managed, if farmers
participate and have confidence in the officers, we
can expect cooperating farmers to double their production within three or four years. This would
bring about a 55 per cent increase in the country's
agricultural production in nine years, representing
an annual growth rate of 5 per cent. Such growth
rates are well within the range of technical possibility, and have, in fact, been achieved by a few
countries in recent years. If each cooperating
farmer had one neighbor who followed him only half-
way in modernizing farming methods, production would
be increased 75 per cent, at an annual rate of 6.5
per cent.

The rate of farmers' response and technical
change will vary greatly by areas; some will move
much faster than shown in our example, others will
move more slowly. For instance, a recent study of
four villages in northern West Pakistan shows a high
degree of eagerness for innovations on the part of
farmers. In one year (1962), 34 per cent actually
made some changes in production methods, and 93 per

TABLE 24

Area Project Approach to Extension Service
(Hypothetical Example)

	1st Period (1-3 years)	2nd Period (4-6 years)	3rd Period (7-9 years)	4th Period (10-12 years)
First 100 Areas				
Number of Officers	200	100	100	200
Percentage of Farmers Cooperating	30	60	90	95
Second 200 Areas				
Number of Officers		400	200	400
Percentage of Farmers Cooperating		30	60	90
Last 200 Areas				
Number of Officers			400	400
Percentage of Farmers Cooperating			30	60
Total Number of Officers in Field	200	500	700	1,000
Number of Farmers per Officer in Project Areas	1,000	1,200	1,400	1,000
Number of New Officers Trained	300	200	300	150[1]
Number of Junior Assistants	200	600	800	2,000
Percentage of Farmers Cooperating	30	40	55	80
Expected Percentage Production Increase in Project Areas at End of Period[2]	30	40	55	80

Assumptions:

1. Country's total number of farms: 1 million.
2. Project area (unit): number of farms: 2,000; total project areas: 500.
3. Project area: team of two officers and two junior assistants for three years.
4. Follow-up: one officer and two assistants until new officers become available to place two officers in each area again.
5. Total number of extension officers available for field work at start: 200 assigned to 100 project areas in first three years.

1. During this fourth three-year period, the rate of training of extension field officers might be reduced to the normal replacement requirement plus need for strengthening the staff of intermediate and headquarter officers for supervisory and more highly specialized tasks.

2. Each cooperating farmer can be expected to double his production by the end of the three-year period (in terms of value at constant prices).

cent aspired to make some changes. By far the most
important reason why the desired changes were not
made was lack of credit (blocking 78 per cent of all
desired but not-made changes), followed by lack of
local availability of materials such as improved
seed, fertilizers, farm implements (blocking 20 per
cent of desired changes).[5]

We must realize, of course, that our extension
workers and cooperating farmers must be supported by
modern inputs such as fertilizer, pesticides, machinery, improved crop varieties and seeds, and by
credit arrangements to make them accessible to farmers, in order to achieve such output increases. In
recognition of this principle, several Latin American countries, for example, are supplying extension
officers in certain areas with a small stock of such
new inputs for sale to the innovators among farmers
until the demand has increased sufficiently for the
local merchants to make it worth their while to meet
it.[6] At the same time, without the encouraging and
technical assistance of the extension workers, the
farmers would not be willing or able to adopt so
many innovations in an efficient manner in so short
a time.

There is no doubt in my mind that a decisive
task of the extension officers in these projects is
to arouse aspirations and hopes for a better future
in the farmers, not only for themselves but for
their country as well. There are many different
kinds of motivations which make people strive for
progress--of which sheer individual profit is only
one, and not a very strong one if the farmer feels
there is a lot of risk involved. Doing things together, contributing to building a better community,
can become an exhilarating experience and a strong
motivating force. If farmers realize that so much
will depend on their success in raising production,
this realization itself can become a strong additional motivation.

A Western observer recently visited a Chinese
commune and reported how its chairman explained the
impressive production achievements since 1961:

"These striking increases were achieved first and foremost by the study of the thoughts of Mao Tse-Tung and by the organization of the people. Secondarily, this year industry had supplied more chemical fertilizers and pesticides, and more irrigation work had been carried out."[7] Stripped of its political setting, this statement conveys the proposition that inspiration (wherever it comes from) guides the motivation and the organization of the people; only then can they take full advantage of the technological innovations which bring higher production and income. There is much truth in this. Might it not be that a better understanding of these motivational forces would be most helpful in accelerating agricultural progress also in non-Communist countries?[8]

Through the cooperation of agricultural officers, farmers, and villagers in a farm production development project, a community spirit can be fostered which leads to the organization of cooperative marketing and credit, of farmers' associations, and of various social and educational community activities. This further increases the demonstration effect and the impact of the project on agricultural production.

KEY POSITION OF THE
FIELD AGRICULTURAL OFFICER

This example illustrates the principle of effective deployment of scarce manpower resources which is so much more difficult to do in agriculture than in industry and trade. Experience suggests that assigning to one agricultural field officer an area containing more than 1,000 farmers is likely to result in dissipated effort and loss of impact of his advisory work on the agricultural performance of the area. In Japan, for instance, it has been found that one extension field officer should not be assigned to more than 600 farms lest his effort become dispersed and lose its effectiveness.[9] In highly developed countries, we find often one extension worker for every 400 to 500 farmers.

An argument against this selected-area approach
is often made on the ground that it discriminates
against all the farmers outside these areas. This
is not a valid argument, since the effectiveness of
an agricultural field officer is physically limited
by the contacts with farmers he can make. If he is
assigned a district with 10,000 farmers, he still
will not be able to effectively advise and gain the
confidence of more than around 100 farmers per year.
All the other 9,900 farmers don't get the benefit of
his advice either. Farmers are widely dispersed
throughout the district, travel absorbs a large part
of his time, and the contacts are superficial and
casual. The demonstration effect of leading farmers
is much stronger if they cooperate within the framework of a vigorous area project and with the support
of community activities and their impact on neighbors, than if the leading farmers are widely dispersed and improve their practices in isolation.
Similarly, the efforts of the agricultural officer
are bound to be more productive if they are guided
by a well-defined area project worked out with the
help of local people, including typical small farmers, and if they are supported by government programs for credit, cooperatives, and supplies of inputs, than if the officers have no focus and depend
largely upon a wide variety of requests from national headquarters or from some influential local individuals, which is the rule rather than the exception in many countries. Finally, using a small number of technical advisers working together as a team
in such area projects has great advantages, technically as well as psychologically (see Chapter 13).

Here lies a great opportunity for national extension-service directors to increase the impact of
the field staff and of the whole extension program.
The obvious advantages of this project-area approach
can be made clearly visible to political leaders as
well. Their support is often useful to administrators on matters of this kind.

Our example in Table 24 shows a considerable
strain on the training facilities for extension

officers over a nine-year period. Here are a few comments on how to meet the task.

First, let us remember that headquarter officers are useful only to the extent to which they really serve the functions of the field officers who deal directly with the farmers. Headquarter officers and those at intermediate levels are most effective if they spend most of their time backstopping the work of the field officers, maintaining contact with experiment stations and other government agencies to help the field officers solve the many technical problems they encounter in the operation of their area projects. However, there are countries where 20 per cent or more of the extension staff is at headquarters and intermediate levels, as shown in Table 25. The majority of these officers would be more effective if they were assigned to field work--except for the few highly skilled specialists who are best stationed at regional or state centers to be on call for the field workers. To make best use of extension-service personnel as effectively as possible means that most of them work directly with farmers in the field. This is of utmost importance for progress in agriculture. The weakest link is typically the field officer, the most critical man linking theory with practice, conveying knowledge to the primary producer in a form which the farmer can practically apply, and conveying needs of farmers up the line to the government agencies. For instance, Japan, with its highly effective extension service, keeps only 0.4 per cent of its large staff at the national or provincial level and 8.2 per cent at the intermediate level, leaving over 90 per cent of all extension workers assigned to field work at the village level (see Table 25).

Secondly, reverting to our example, a good number of promising junior assistants with secondary or vocational schooling can be trained on the job by the field officers and given short-course training during slack seasons over a period of three to six years, and then can be promoted to field-officer assignments. In Nigeria, for instance, the government

started an oil palm improvement scheme for small
farmers in 1962 for which extension agents were recruited from people with six years of primary schooling and were given one to two years of general extension training and a thirty-day course in oil palm
technology--especially planting seedlings, fertilization, and weed control. These junior agents func-
tioned well and helped to render this scheme successful. After the fourth year, 30,000 acres on nearly
4,000 small holdings had been planted with improved
seedlings and techniques of fertilization and weed
control.[10]

No developing countries can afford to wait until it can assign an officer with four years or more
of academic training to serve 600 farmers each. Another promising method of overcoming the initial
dearth of trained field staff is exemplified by Indonesia's "Mass Agricultural Extension Programme"
which started in 1964/65. For the 1965/66 rice-
growing season of seven months, 6,000 students from
the universities were sent in pairs into 3,000 villages. The students were given a one-week special
training course focused upon three types of activities they were to perform: (1) help farmers to increase the rice yields, (2) improve the management
of cooperatives, and (3) teach and work with farmers
in groups of eight to twelve. Reports from 1964/65
indicated that in the first 250 villages, where 500
students worked with the farmers along these lines,
farmers achieved an average increase of 40 per cent
in production during the first year.[11]

Another approach to forging a link between
farmers and trained field personnel has proven successful in some of the African countries. Villagers
are asked to elect one of their typical farmers as
an animateur, who serves as a liaison between the
local farmers and the extension officer (called con-
seilleur d'animation). This animateur or representative farmer carries out some selected modern techniques on his farm as demonstrations and attends
once a month a two- or three-day training course at
the nearest regional center in which the conseil-
leurs or extension advisers also participate. The

TABLE 25

Distribution of Extension Officers Between
Field and Headquarters
in Asian Countries[1]
(around 1959)

| | Total Number of Extension Workers # | Percentage of Total Extension Workers Assigned to: | | | Per Cent of Field Worker's Time Spent on Farm Visits and Group Activities % |
		Village Level %	Intermediate Level %	National or Provincial Level %	
Japan	13,566	91.4	8.2	0.4	52
Burma	1,262	89.8	10.0	0.2	
Taiwan	884	88.1	8.0	3.9	30
Malaya	317	88.0	11.4	0.6	54
Philippines	1,623	81.0	17.0	2.0	20
E. Pakistan	4,847	79.8	20.0	0.2	50
Korea	937	76.1	19.1	4.8	34
India	48,579	61.0	38.0	1.0	n.a.
Thailand	328	51.0	20.0	29.0	55

1. Source: C. W. Chang, Extension Education for Agricultural and Rural
    Development (Bangkok: FAO Regional Office for Asia and the Far East,
    March 1963), pp. 103 and 170.

representative farmer is expected to enjoy the confidence of most villagers, to report to them on what
he learned in the training course, and to organize a
group of local farmers interested in adopting modern
production methods. This removes the stigma of a
deviant from the innovator and makes him function as
a part of the community rather than a nonconformist
individualist who sets himself apart and is resented
by the group. The extension adviser meets with these
groups during his visits to the villages in his area
and discusses the demonstrations and results of new
techniques adapted to the local situation. This approach has worked well in Senegal and the Ivory
Coast.[12]

The key importance of extension field workers
is not sufficiently appreciated. National extension
services print educational pamphlets for farmers.
Often they are well done, and the minister (who allocated funds for this purpose) and the extension
director-general are well pleased with these pamphlets. But if there are no field officers to help
farmers read and understand them and apply them to
their farming work, these pamphlets are of no use to
agriculture and the nation.

It is gratifying to assume that whatever information the extension service puts out does reach the
farmer and does influence his farming methods. That
assumption, however, may not hold because the links
between the field staff and the masses of farmers
are so tenuous--and in many areas and villages, non-
existent--that most farmers never hear or see anything of the work of the extension service. Radio
programs and films, these much-heralded, audio-
visual mass media, can, of course, be useful, but
mainly for arousing interest. Unless they are followed up by local field officers, through visits to
individual farmers, demonstrations on farmers'
fields, small group meetings, and various other personal contacts, no action will result from these
mass media--except in areas where farmers are already well advanced in farming techniques, are literate, and know how to go about getting the additional information and assistance needed on their
own initiative. This, however, is not the case in

most developing countries.

We have used here as an example for a localized-project approach the introduction of modern techniques adapted to the peculiar conditions of each project area. The same reasoning holds for other agricultural programs, such as land reform, marketing, production credit, livestock production, mechanization, farm management, and various forms of co-operative organization. All these programs must be localized and put into concrete terms before they can be practically put into effect; and the localizing and interpreting agents are field-level workers, the various technical and administrative officers who come in personal contact with individual and small groups of farmers in the field and in villages.[13]

Some types of agricultural policies which do not require localization at the farm level, do not involve local participation and administration. For instance, import and export duties and excise taxes affecting agriculture are of this nature. But even here, the incidence of these policies on the farm producers in the different areas may vary widely, and may bring forth quite different production responses and other impacts in the various areas. These types of policies affect farmers' incentives and the agricultural production process in different ways and degrees depending on farming systems and local environmental conditions. To learn about these problems and find ways for solving them, we must come back again to the key position of the field agricultural officer in the process of rural development (see Chapter 12).

ADAPTIVE RESEARCH:
TRIALS ON CULTIVATORS' FIELDS

Let us take another example where local adaptation of a development program is of fundamental importance to agricultural progress.

Production methods in agriculture are intimately affected by microecological conditions of plant
growth, by soil, moisture, and climate conditions of
specific localities, which vary widely often within
short distances. A highly productive crop variety
developed in an experiment station may be found much
less productive under somewhat different soil conditions. For instance, certain wheat varieties lodge
easily where nitrogen is ample, or are susceptible
to yellow rust or some other disease which was absent in the experiment station locality. A fertilizer dosage proven highly effective in one place may
show disappointing results in another if moisture in
the soil is lacking. This dependence of plant
growth upon the specific local conditions makes it
very difficult to standardize and routinize recommendations for many farming practices which can be
relied upon to produce satisfactory results over a
large area. This is all the more disconcerting as
a wrong recommendation to farmers may deal a severe
blow to their confidence in extension advice and to
the rate of progress in farming techniques.

Some countries are approaching this problem by
setting up branch experiment stations in various major farming regions. This helps to some extent, as
it does bring the experimental work closer to the
ecological conditions of a particular region. But
even within such a region, the variations of soil
and moisture conditions are wide indeed and can produce very different results from a certain crop variety or fertilizer application. Moreover, the research techniques employed at branch stations tend
to be much the same as those used at central stations. Hence, the results obtained are again
strictly applicable only to the very specific microecological conditions of the branch station's location.

There is a different and, for purposes of truly
adaptive research, much more efficient approach that
can be used to take account of variations in microecological conditions: systematic simple trials on
cultivators' fields. Without going into detail on
research methodology and experimental design, I

shall only touch upon some of the key issues involved.

From the viewpoint of the conventional scientific method of controlled variation of one or more
independent variables and constancy of all other
factors, trials on cultivators' fields have obvious
and severe limitations.

First, the control of the independent variables,
such as the quantities of plant nutrients and water
applied, the time of planting, tillage methods, preceding crop, etc., is inaccurate and incomplete.
With thousands of small plots dispersed over wide
areas, and with the field work--from planting, fer-
tilizing, and weeding to harvesting--resting in the
hands of scientifically untrained field assistants
and farmers, one cannot expect degrees of accuracy
commonly required under experiment station conditions. However, the results of experiment station
work are not supposed to be applied by other experiment stations, but are intended to be applied by
farmers. And farmers never can control these variables very closely anyway. Hence, a crop variety
that has proven superior at an experiment station,
but does not maintain its superior performance under
widely varying and less ideal conditions of practical farming, is of little value to agriculture.

Second, the constancy of all other factors cannot be maintained, for the obvious reason of the
ecological heterogeneity of a farming area. But it
is precisely because of this heterogeneity that we
need trials on cultivators' fields. If a specific
fertilizer application to a certain crop shows excellent results at an experiment station, but fails
to do so under practical farming conditions, this
must not be recommended to farmers as a good practice. It becomes clear, therefore, that what are
strictly scientific liabilities are very important
practical assets of trials on cultivators' fields
for testing the applicability of experiment station
results to actual farming conditions over wide
areas.14

In principle, we might state the issue in terms
of a complementary division of labor between experiment station work and trials on cultivators' fields.
Experiment stations are most suitable for improving
the internal genetic capacity of crops to transform
plant nutrients into the useful parts of the crop,
to develop resistance to certain pests and diseases,
and to breed for certain crop characteristics, such
as stiff straw to reduce lodging of grain, long staple of cotton fiber, etc. For this, standard scientific methods of control of variables and <u>ceteris
paribus</u> conditions are essential.

Trials on cultivators' fields, on the other
hand, are most suitable for testing the range of variations in ecological conditions which a promising
crop variety can tolerate and still maintain a superior performance under farming conditions. For this,
the conventional scientific constraints in research
techniques must be greatly relaxed, and the conventional experimental designs greatly altered.[15]

It is unfortunate that the scientific frater-
nity, on the whole, has shown but little interest in
a systematic use of trials on cultivators' fields as
an essential corollary of experiment station research. As a result, much of the research work has
remained of little use to agriculture, and the lack
of performance tests under local farming conditions
has sometimes led to wrong advice and unfavorable
effects.

Developing countries have a high stake in promoting an early and successful marriage of experiment station work and trials on cultivators' fields.
In practical administrative terms, this requires cooperation between experimentation scientists and extension workers who serve as a professional link
with farmers in general. Without farmers' participation, trials on cultivators' fields cannot be conducted, and without knowledge of how to approach and
deal with farmers their cooperation will not be
forthcoming. The professional and administrative
isolation of experiment station scientists and extension workers, which is typical in many developing

countries, is a serious retarding factor in agricultural progress.

This localizing of adaptive agricultural research has another most significant aspect. The heterogeneity of microecological conditions in a certain farming area does not mean that these conditions are unique to the area. Many of the ecological variations can be found in other countries also. Hence, if adaptive research through trials on cultivators' fields has proven a certain crop variety with a certain fertilizer treatment superior in an area with a certain pattern of ecological variations, it can be expected that this crop with this treatment will also bring good results in other areas with a similar pattern of ecological variations. A systematic development of trials on cultivators' fields in many developing countries would greatly increase the transferability of experiences with different crop varieties and treatments from one area to another, within as well as between countries. Thus, many errors in introducing new crops and techniques could be avoided, and the rate at which farmers accept innovations could be much enhanced.

Finally, we must not underrate the effect which adaptive research of this nature is bound to have on the farmers who cooperate in these trials, on their neighbors, and even the village community where the purposes and results of the trials should be presented and discussed in group meetings and demonstration visits to the fields.

We are tempted to believe that we know much more than we do about what farming practices can be successfully introduced in a certain area.[16] There is still a lot we must find out about the transferability of practices from one area to another, and from experiment stations to local farming conditions. Trials on cultivators' fields, on many typical farms representing various soils, farm sizes, and other environmental conditions offer the most promising approach for finding out what technical innovations, farming practices, and production patterns fit into an area, and what an extension service can confidently extend.

Now let us turn to the problem of organizing the extension work in adaptive research.

I have been at many farmer meetings where scientific principles were taught in a classroom atmosphere at grade-school level, instead of in a committee atmosphere where practical problems are solved and plans for action are worked out. Adult farmers with little or no formal schooling learn best by doing, and only after they have seen the results of new practices and have adopted some of them, will explanations of the scientific principles begin to make sense and interest them.

An extension service approach of assisting farmers to do specific things on their farms accelerates progress much more than an approach of educating farmers through lectures in technology, for instance on why fertilizers produce higher yields. This means that the extension service must get directly involved in action projects on the farms, in helping individual farmers to adopt specific new farming practices, that is, in technical assistance.

The operational strength of such extension projects as demonstrations of how new practices work on typical small farms lies in the fact that farmers receive specific help in adopting certain practices, and in return, they commit their own land, labor, and capital, they obligate themselves to follow instructions concerning these practices and to help their neighbors to do the same. Conventional educational meetings, exhibits and demonstrations at fairs, and even advice given to farmers involve no such commitment of their resources, nor any obligation to follow the advice and help neighbors to modernize their farming techniques.

Hence, a progressive extension strategy for introducing technical innovations concentrates on technical assistance to selected farmers in adopting selected practices and promotes the demonstration effect of spreading these practices to other farmers.

This strategy requires action projects in selected
areas where the cooperating farmers receive technical assistance and usually some material and financial aid (e.g., free fertilizer for demonstrations
and trials, or production credit at favorable terms),
and where they, in return, follow the technical instructions, use the material aid as planned, and
share their experiences with neighbors. This action
approach, if well organized, works much faster than
the broadside educational approach despite the fact
that initially only a small proportion of the farmers are involved in active participation. For instance, the FAO Fertilizer Program under the Freedom
from Hunger Campaign has shown a very impressive
effect of this extension strategy, as we shall see
presently.

This approach bears a realistic promise of accelerating agricultural progress by harnessing adaptive research on cultivators' fields and technical-
assistance extension to farmers in a powerful team
for introducing technical innovations. The complementary purposes of researching what to extend, and
extending the results of adaptive research, are
joined on the cultivator's field where the production process takes place. The cultivators' fields
become widely dispersed little laboratories for the
scientist, demonstrations for the extension worker,
and a direct involvement in progress for the farmer.

To implement this approach, it will take a good
deal of adjustment in the currently prevailing attitudes of experiment station scientists and extension
workers--but not necessarily major surgery in the
administrative structure of experiment stations and
extension services. The major obstacle here is the
mentality of scientists to whom the concept of farmers' fields as laboratories is heretic, and the mentality of administrators and civil servants whose
loyalty to a strict hierarchical line of command in
the bureaucratic structure makes interdepartmental
cooperation difficult. Government officers can be
as tradition-bound and against change as the prover-
bial peasant. Imaginative leadership of a few top
people and the pressure of necessity to improve

agriculture's performance are probably the most effective forces to overcome this obstacle.

In many countries, the prospects for a faster
rate of introducing technical innovations are becoming better every year, and the experiment stations,
extension services, farmers' cooperatives, and farmers' associations must play a decisive role in accelerating this process. For this challenging task,
on-the-farm action projects through trials and demonstrations on cultivators' fields, reinforced by
pilot schemes for increasing the number of cooperating farmers and for making modern inputs available,
offer the best hope for success in modernizing farming techniques.

We shall see in the next chapter that the manpower and finances required for an adaptive research
program, coupled with pilot schemes for rapid introduction of modern production methods, are within the
reach of most developing countries. To get this
type of program started, foreign technical assistance in the form of a few highly qualified experts,
critical materials and equipment through FAO or bilateral agencies can be extremely useful and yield
quite dramatic results.

NOTES TO CHAPTER 10

1. Albert Waterston, "A Hard Look at Development Planning," The Fund and Bank Review, Vol. III,
No. 2 (June 1966), p. 90; and Waterston, Development Planning: Lessons of Experience, op. cit., pas-
sim.

2. See also Chapter 4 above. For an excellent
analysis of the two contrasting positions on comprehensive versus piecemeal planning, see Albert O.
Hirschman, The Strategy of Economic Development (New
Haven, Conn.: Yale University Press, 1958), Chapters 3 and 4.

3. For a succinct summary of the problems of
implementation of national plans and of the strategic

role of project preparation and evaluation in this process, see Waterston, _Development Planning: Lessons of Experience_, _op. cit._, pp. 365-68.

4. The reason for this benefit-cost ratio is simple and straightforward. In estimating the benefit side, the costs "associated" with the farming operations, such as fertilizers, machines, labor, must be deducted from the gross farm income to arrive at "net farm income" representing the "benefit" to be compared with the "cost"; hence, "associated costs" must not include any water rates charged to pay for the cost of the project. Since the term "net farm income" usually allows in the "associated costs" for wages paid for hired labor, but no living allowance for family labor, and since most of the labor on the new farms will be contributed by the family, the "benefit" to the farmer to be compared with the "project operation and maintenance cost" must be the "net farm income minus allowance for a minimum adequate living level of the farm family" which we call here "net returns to farmers." From the excess of "net returns" over "project operations and maintenance cost," additional charges for repayment on interest and amortization can be collected from the farmers. This may be desirable for fiscal or other reasons, but is not necessarily required for rendering the project economically justified. Note that this benefit-cost ratio is not one of the conventional ratios which include, on the cost side, the annual interest and amortization rates on the fixed investment, and on the benefit side, do not deduct an adequate family living allowance (or wage equivalent for family labor) from the farm income; in fact, the benefit side consists usually of gross returns from major crops, or of gross returns minus associated costs of certain major inputs, such as fertilizers, livestock feed, etc., calculated from estimates of area aggregates. Examining benefit-cost ratios of many projects prepared by different agencies reveals that they are not comparable in most cases because of the many different methods used and assumptions made in calculating the ratio. Before they are used in the selection of project proposals, their comparability must be assured to

avoid errors in judgement. There are, of course, projects which create direct non-farm benefits as well, such as electric power, fishing, navigation, etc. These are not discussed here, but must, of course, also be taken into account. For a useful discussion of this issue, see Federal Inter-Agency River Basin Committee, Proposed Practices for Economic Analysis of River Basin Projects (Washington, D.C., May 1950, revised June 1958).

5. Sturt, op. cit.

6. See David Hapgood, ed., Policies for Promoting Agricultural Development (Cambridge, Mass.: Massachusetts Institute of Technology, 1965), p. 188.

7. Colina MacDougall, "A Peking Commune," Far Eastern Economic Review, Vol. LI, No. 2 (January 13, 1966), p. 51.

8. See Jack Gray, "Agrarian Policies in China Today," Bulletin for Atomic Scientists, Vol. 22, No. 6 (June 1966), pp. 32-39. This issue also contains very informative articles on present-day China by Joan Robinson, Han Suyin, and Audrey Donnithorne.

9. See C. W. Chang, Extension Education for Agricultural and Rural Development (Bangkok: FAO Regional Office for Asia and the Far East, March 1963), p. 170.

10. Carl K. Eicher, Transforming Traditional Agriculture in Southern Nigeria: The Contemporary Experience. Paper presented at Annual Meeting of the African Studies Association, Bloomington, Indiana, October 26-29, 1966, p. 21 (mimeo.).

11. See Bulletin of Indonesian Economic Studies, No. 3 (Department of Economics, Research School of Pacific Studies, Australian National University, (Canberra, February 1966), p. 18. No data are available to me which would permit checking the accuracy of this estimate of output increase. The order of magnitude is possible of achievement in small selected areas provided the necessary modern inputs

are, in fact, supplied to the farmers at favorable
terms of credit and prices, and farmers are advised
on how to apply them efficiently.

12. See David Hapgood, "Rural Animation in
Senegal," International Development Review, Vol. VI,
No. 3 (September 1964), pp. 15-18; and John C. de
Wilde, Experiences with Agricultural Development in
Tropical Africa (Washington, D.C.: International
Bank for Reconstruction and Development, June 1966),
pp. 230-32.

13. For a penetrating discussion of the difficulties faced by field-level workers, see D. C.
Duboy and Willis Sutton, "A Rural Man in the Middle:
The Indian Village Level Worker in Community Development," Human Organization, Vol. 24, No. 2 (Summer
1965), pp. 148-51.

14. A strong plea for trials on cultivators'
fields as a regular research and extension service
function is made in Hapgood, Policies for Promoting
Agricultural Development, op. cit., pp. 192-94.

15. H. L. Richardson, formerly Project Manager
of the FAO Fertilizer Use Project under the Freedom
from Hunger Campaign, formulated this distinction
between trials in experiment stations and cultivators' fields most succinctly in a letter to me as
follows: "With fertilizers, experiment stations are
most suitable for studying effects that are likely
to be small--for example, differences between different forms of nitrogen fertilizers--or cumulative
and residual effects over a period of years. On the
other hand, results obtained at experiment stations
for direct responses to primary nutrients (N, P, and
K) may be quite misleading if applied to farmers'
fields, because the fertility of soils at experiment
stations has usually been improved by past manuring,
so that they show little or no response to certain
nutrients that are still widely needed on farmers'
fields. This is particularly marked in developing
countries where the farmers may never have used
fertilizers or manures, and where the soils are
starved by continuous cropping. Thus trials on

cultivators' fields are essential for ascertaining the direct responses to fertilizers in an area, for studying the economics of fertilizer use, and for determining the fertilizer treatments that will give the farmers the best results. Results obtained at experiment stations may actually be misleading and lead to erroneous advice in these respects."

16. For a frank exposure of our ignorance about these matters, see W. David Hopper, "Mainsprings of Agricultural Growth in India," Indian Journal of Agricultural Science, Vol. 35, No. 2 (June 1965), pp. vi-x.

CHAPTER **11** INTRODUCING TECHNICAL
INNOVATIONS: THE FAO FERTI-
LIZER PROGRAM AS A PROTOTYPE

We have examined major lines of action for localizing agricultural programs, for giving roots and
focus to extension work in the field, and for adapting research to the production conditions on typical
farms. Let us now explore in some detail the practical problems of actually putting such programs into operation.

For this purpose, the FAO Fertilizer Program
which started in 1961 as one of its Freedom from
Hunger Campaign Projects with the financial support
of the World Fertilizer Industry is extremely well
suited. It combines the extension service and the
research aspects discussed in the foregoing chapter
in a most promising way, and deserves to become a
prototype project for many developing countries. In
its sixth year of operation, twenty countries in the
Near East, Africa, and Latin America are participating.[1] Similar programs are underway in several
Asian countries under somewhat different sponsor-
ships and administrative arrangements--such as in
India, Ceylon, the Philippines, South Korea, Pakistan and Iran--but they all have the basic approach
in common.

FERTILIZER USE: LEAD PRACTICE
AND CATALYST FOR INNOVATIONS

If you want a horse to produce more, you must
give it more feed. So it is with crops: If you
want them to produce more, you must give them more
plant food, above what the soil makes available.
Quantitatively, the most important source of such
additional plant nutrients is chemical fertilizers.

273

Within a certain range of application, one kilogram of plant nutrients per hectare (usually N and P_2O_5, and K_2O where needed) can increase grain yields by about ten kilograms. The problem is to apply the right dosage to the right crop on the right soil for the best profit.

In developing countries, fertilizers are used mainly on export crops in plantations and on larger farms. Only a very small part of the acreage in food crops on the millions of small farms receives fertilizers. Yet, many cultivator field trials have given crop-yield increases of around 50 per cent with moderate rates of fertilization and under the traditional farming practices. The reasons why farmers don't use fertilizers is that they don't know about them, that they can't get them in the villages or don't have the money to buy them, that they feel dubious about the financial risk involved, and that rental terms or fertilizer and crop prices offer little incentive. If farmers could be induced to use fertilizers efficiently, food production could increase readily by 30 to 50 per cent, and much more if complementary techniques such as improved crop varieties and pesticides were used along with fertilizers.

Here is a single input, which can be easily applied in any quantity, in any combination of nutrients, on small fields; a single input which shows to the naked eye its strong effect on plant growth within a few months. This makes fertilizer use a "lead practice," something to introduce first, in a simple way, and then follow up by supporting its effect with better crop varieties, weed and pest control, and other modern techniques.

There are dangers in this approach. Fertilizer applied to some local unimproved crop varieties may bring no yield response or might even depress yields, for instance through heavy lodging of weak-strawed grain varieties. For research purposes, this is useful to know so that a better crop variety can be quickly introduced in the area; for demonstration purposes, it is very damaging, as farmers may become distrustful of fertilizers in general.

Another danger is waste resulting from incomplete measures. For instance, if a small farmer buys fertilizer on credit, but he permits his crop to be damaged by weeds, insects and disease, he loses his investment and is worse off than before. Or he got a response of 30 per cent yield increase from his fertilizer, but had he used a better crop variety yielding 60 per cent more, he would have doubled the return on his investment. There is no doubt that a "package" approach of combining a set of mutually supporting practices, of fertilizer, improved crop varieties, weed and pest control, and better water use on irrigated land can increase production and profit much more than a single fertilizer input can.

Why then does the FAO Fertilizer Program not follow such a package approach from the beginning? Because in many areas we would bite off more than we could chew. Adaptive research has not yet told us how responsive local varieties are to fertilizer. The FAO program has shown that some local varieties respond well, and some don't. Nor do we know which improved crop varieties are best adapted to a particular location. Some that do very well in one area may do rather poorly in another. Often, improved varieties are not yet commercially available in sufficient quantities. Pesticides and their application further involve farmers in new cash expenses and technical skills. Moreover--and this is very important, as we shall see presently--the efficient use of fertilizer by itself is a rather complicated matter about which much has yet to be learned in each area, by means of adaptive research as well as by training farmers in efficient application. Finally, the commercial production and distribution of fertilizers of all kinds and compositions is administratively and financially easier to expand rapidly than is true for improved crop varieties and some of the other practices in the "package."

This renders the use of fertilizer a good "spearhead" for introducing modern farming techniques into traditional areas.[2] This very concept, however, requires that we do not stop there. We might begin with fertilizer use, but as soon as possible we must introduce other complementary practices which, together with fertilizer, raise output and net income levels much above what fertilizers alone can achieve. The decision of whether a fertilizer or a package program should be implemented in an area should rest on the practical feasibility of carrying out a complex program during the initial stage; in any case, a fertilizer program should always be followed up with complementary practices in the second or third year of the initial stage, whenever experience shows that the efficacy of fertilizer is hampered by the lack of responsive crop varieties, of pest and moisture control, etc. Once farmers have experienced the benefit of fertilizer, they are more prone to adopt other new practices than if they are urged to adopt three or four new things all at once, with which they have had no previous experience, and each of which involves much risk and uncertainty in their minds as to outcome, and cash expenses to boot.

Therefore, a fertilizer program is most appropriate for a start in areas where a majority of farmers have not used fertilizers before and where few adaptive research findings are available on other complementary practices. Within a year or two, however, it should be expanded to a package program. Conversely, a "package" program of complementary practices is most appropriate in areas where many farmers are already using fertilizers and where some experiences have been gained with improved crop varieties and other practices adapted to the area.

In the following pages, let us concentrate on the practical problems involved in launching a fertilizer program in its initial phase.

ORGANIZATION OF FIELD WORK

Under the FAO program, a fertilizer expert is placed in the Near East, West Africa, and northern Latin America as a regional leader who discusses with the various governments the concepts, purpose, and operational requirements of the fertilizer program. The minimum requirement is that the government undertake not less than 500 demonstrations and trials on cultivated fields annually, assign an adequate number of field extension workers to the project, and place them under the FAO expert's technical supervision; and that the senior officers in extension and research give active support to the project, including local transportation of men and materials. FAO furnishes one fertilizer-use expert with a vehicle for each country and all or part of the fertilizer required for the trials and demonstrations on cultivators' fields.

Essentially, that is all there is to formal agreements, and red tape is kept to a minimum. Everything else is played by ear, as the project develops, and is planned in cooperation with extension and research officers in the government and universities of the participating country, and with field extension workers and local farmers in the various areas. Thus, the selection of crops for demonstrations and trials, the various fertilizer treatments, and the major farming areas are determined.

Operations of the FAO program started in the spring of 1961, and by the summer of 1962, within one year, nearly 5,000 demonstrations and trials had been laid out in twelve countries. By mid-1966, after six years, 100,000 demonstrations and trials had been conducted in twenty-one countries. The program could have expanded even faster, but lack of FAO funds prevented additional countries entering the program.

The staffing of the program is shown in Table 26. In 1965/66, about 4,700 government workers in twenty countries were assigned to the various country projects, mostly on a part-time basis, under the guidance of twenty-three FAO experts. With 30,000 demonstrations and trials per year, this means that one full-time (senior) extension worker was responsible for looking after about 100 of them on the average. The cost to the government was, in most cases, not an additional expense for hiring new personnel, but a transfer of existing officers and vehicles from whatever they were doing before to the fertilizer project. This, again, is a good example of using scarce personnel more effectively. Top level officials obviously recognized that the deployment of their staff to such a practical action project is much more productive than what they used to do before--otherwise they would not have made available to the FAO project leader an average of fifteen full-time officers (mainly of senior grade) and about 240 field-level workers on a part-time basis. FAO project leaders reported that for many of the extension workers this was the first time they visited individual farmers repeatedly, developed mutual respect, and entered into dialogues with them--which is all too rare in most developing countries. The average estimated cost to the government was $39 per demonstration or trial.

All participating countries conducted training courses for field officers and field days for farmers to visit the demonstration plots. In 1964, eleven countries with 1,300 field officers assigned to the project held training courses of one or two days each for 3,500 staff members, and arranged 920 field days with an attendance of over 17,700 farmers, averaging nineteen farmers per field day. This means that what happened on the demonstration plots of one farmer was witnessed by eighteen other farmers in the neighborhood--for them to learn and think about.

In addition to training courses, much on-the-job training is done, particularly in laying out plots, weighing and controlling the application of

TABLE 26

Sources of Personnel and Contributions to the FAO Fertilizer Field Program,[1] 1961/62-1964/65 (4 years)

		Total FAO Field Program	Near East	Regions: West Africa	Latin America
Countries Participating:[2]		20	4	8	8
			Turkey	Nigeria	Honduras
			Syria	Ghana	Guatemala
			Lebanon	Cameroun	El Salvador
			Morocco	Togo	Costa Rica
				Senegal	Ecuador
				Gambia	Colombia
				Ivory Coast	Nicaragua
				Sierra Leone	Panama
Personnel: FAO	nos.	23	9	10	4
Governments:[2] Total (as of 1965/66)	nos.	4,781	1,455	2,725	601
Full-time (senior)	nos.	294	51	185	58
Part-time (field level)	nos.	4,487	1,404	2,540	543
Value of Contributions:[3] (First 4 years)					
FAO	in $1,000	804	313	311	180
Governments	in $1,000	1,754	611	785	358
Total	in $1,000	2,558	924	1,096	538
Average Cost per Demonstration or Trial:[4] (First 4 years)					
Total Cost	$	57	51	63	59
Cost to Government	$	39	33	44	39

1. Source: Food and Agriculture Organization of the United Nations, "Appraisal of the FAO Fertilizer Program: Progress During the First Four Years," Rome, May 1965 (mimeo.).
2. Food and Agriculture Organization of the United Nations, Summary Report of the 11th Session of the FAO Fertilizer Industry Advisory Panel Held in Rome, 12-13 July 1966 (Rome: FAO, 1966), p. 19. Dahomey left the Program in 1964; Panama entered in 1964, and Cameroun in 1965.
3. Most of the cost of the program is for personnel and transport, very little for fertilizer. The government contribution consists of the estimated cost of personnel and transport assigned to the project most of which did not involve additional expenditures, but transfer of present personnel to the project. The FAO contribution includes the fertilizer made available to the trials and demonstrations and to the pilot distribution and credit schemes.
4. Based on 45,000 trials and demonstrations conducted during the four-year period.

fertilizer dosages, harvesting and weighing the crops from the different plots, and recording results and observations for each demonstration and trial. All this field work, of course, is done with the farmer, who experiences for the first time the nature of a wholly different approach to farming, a scientific rather than traditional approach. Each year, the demonstrations are conducted on new farms, to spread this experience as widely as possible, and to cover ever wider areas with the results of trials and demonstrations. At the same time, the former participants are encouraged--and, if necessary, helped--to continue to use fertilizer and help their neighbors to adopt this practice.

The involvement of the local people, of farmers and villagers, is pursued not only through farmers' days visits to the plots, but also through many individual contacts with farmers, through evening meetings in the villages, and reports on the project at various business, educational, and social functions.

Some governments did quite an elaborate job in making signs for each plot (thousands of them), labeling each treatment. Usually the extension officers had to do this; in Turkey, they solicited the help of the farmers, of neighbors, and their children who enjoyed making these signs and became all the more involved in the project.

CROP YIELD RESPONSES
AND THEIR PROFITABILITY

A difficult task right at the start is to determine what crops should be included, what fertilizer treatments should be selected, and in what proportions trials and demonstrations should be conducted. Trials on cultivators' fields must of necessity be kept simple, because under practical farming conditions only few independent variables can be handled with sufficient accuracy. Hence, the practical limit lies usually within a nine- to sixteen-plot trial with eight to fifteen different treatments.[3]

Demonstrations are simpler yet, usually comprising only two to four plots for demonstrating the
result of one to three treatments. As the name
says, demonstrations are intended to demonstrate
something that is already known and tested, and
should ideally be based upon considerable trial data
from which the most favorable treatments have been
selected for wide demonstration. In developing
countries, it is important to save time by conduct-
ing trials and demonstrations simultaneously within
the project. Even if the demonstrations do not at
first use the best treatments, they still show profitable yield responses in most cases. Demonstrations are cheaper, can be spread over more farms and
wider areas, and when they include two or three
treatments, they can serve the same purposes as
trials and reveal useful knowledge. Due to their
larger numbers, a proper statistical handling of
demonstration results can impart to their findings
a degree of reliability comparable to that of trials.

In the FAO Fertilizer Program, about 85 per
cent of the fields were used for demonstrations, and
15 per cent for trials (see Table 27). Often, the
FAO experts had to fight hard for trials, as the
governments were anxious to have the greatest number
of demonstrations. This reflects a widespread over-
rating of the general applicability of experiment
station results to practical farming conditions.
These results are often misleading as we have point-
ed out before, and need testing on farmers' fields
before fertilizer recommendations can be made with
confidence.

Since trials on cultivators' fields offer a
wider choice of treatments than demonstrations, they
are more apt to reveal the most efficient ones. For
instance, the best treatments in the trials produced
an average value-cost ratio of 8.4 (i.e., the value
of the yield increase was 74 per cent higher than
the cost of the fertilizer applied), while the best
treatments in the demonstrations produced a value-
cost ratio of only 3.7 (i.e., a profit of 270 per

cent).

Most of the national averages of the best treatments in demonstrations centered around a 50 per cent increase in yields of the various crops, ranging from 33 per cent in Nigeria to 97 per cent in Costa Rica and Guatemala.

These responses are quite impressive, indeed, particularly if we keep in mind that in the great majority of cases the fertilizer was applied to local unimproved crop varieties, that the crops were grown under ordinary, largely still-traditional farming practices, and that the "best treatments" in the demonstrations were, in many cases, still not the most appropriate ones, as the results with trials indicate.

Not less impressive is the broad coverage obtained within a five-year period: 3-4 demonstrations and trials per 1,000 farmers, or about one demonstration or trial for every 300 farms, which corresponds roughly to one for every one or two villages. In reality, the demonstrations are, of course, more clustered in the major farming areas and in more accessible locations, but their demonstration effect is not seriously reduced by that fact since it is from these very areas that the bulk of production increases must be expected to come.

One aspect of key importance is the proportion of unsuccessful demonstrations. With only a few treatments per demonstration, and with often few research findings and no practical experience for guidance, the chances could be pretty high that a demonstration would not show a profitable yield increase. Yet, only 8 per cent of the demonstrations from which results were available did not include a treatment with a positive value-cost ratio for the three regions combined. These unsuccessful demonstrations reached 15 per cent in the West African region. In successive years, however, there has been a decline in the proportion of unsuccessful demonstrations in a number of countries, as a result of locally better-adapted treatments revealed by

TABLE 27

Results of Demonstrations and Trials,
FAO Fertilizer Program, First Five Years

		All Regions	Near East	Regions: West Africa	Latin America
Demonstrations and Trials[1]	nos.	65,701	26,125	24,715	14,861
Demonstrations	nos.	56,479	24,859	19,557	12,063
Trials		9,222	1,266	5,158	2,798
Demonstrations and Trials Per 1,000 Farmers[1]	nos.	3.4	4.7	2.5	3.6
Estimated Number of Farmers	mil-lions	19.4	5.5	9.8	4.1
Average of Best Yield Response[2]					
Demonstrations	%	56	59	46	76
Trials	%	71	70	68	82
Percentage of Positive Yield Response[3]					
Demonstrations	%	100	100	100	99
Trials	%	100	100	100	100
Average of Best Value Response[4]					
	Value-Cost ratio				
Demonstrations		3.7	3.1	4.2	5.4
Trials		8.4	5.7	7.8	11.9
Percentage of Positive Value Response[5]					
Demonstrations	%	92	96	85	99
Trials	%	96	86	99	90

1. See H. L. Richardson, "The Freedom from Hunger Campaign in Five Years of the FAO Fertilizer Programme," Outlook on Agriculture (London), Vol. V, No. 1 (1966), p. 15. Includes the first five years, from winter 1961/62 to winter 1965/66. Number of farmers refers to estimates for the participating countries in recent years.
2. Source: "Physical and Economic Summary of Trial and Demonstration Results, 1961/62-1964/65"(Preliminary), FFHC Fertilizer Program, FAO, Rome (mimeo., LA:FFHC/67/3). Average yield response of the best positive treatment of each demonstration or trial set.
3. At least one treatment showed a positive yield response. For instance, 1 per cent of all the demonstrations in Latin America did not show a positive yield response.
4. Average ratio of value of yield increase over fertilizer cost of each demonstration or trial set. For instance, the value-cost ratio of 3.7 means that $1 of fertilizer produced $3.70 of crops, or a profit of 270 per cent. This ratio is based upon local crop prices and fertilizer cost.
5. At least one treatment showed a positive value-over-cost response. The response data are based upon 23,781 demonstrations and 3,258 trials for which yield and value-cost ratios were available.

trials and demonstrations in previous years. These
reports, however, may be painting too rosy a picture. In every project, many more demonstrations
have been laid out than reports on their results
have been received. We dare not neglect this important aspect. During the first four years of the
program about 38,000 demonstrations were laid out,
but only 23,800 usable reports on yield responses
were obtained, amounting to 62 per cent of the total.[4] Unfortunately, field reports on reasons for
abandoning demonstrations are very incomplete. If
locusts or Quella birds or drought severely damage
the demonstration crops, farmers can understand
that; but if no such external causes are visible,
they rightly wonder whether the extension workers
know what they are talking about, and may come to
distrust fertilizers. Such distrust might be more
difficult to overcome than the original wariness
that farmers might have had at the start. It is indeed a serious matter if the government comes along
and preaches fertilizer use and persuades farmers to
demonstrate its glorious benefits, and then the demonstration fails.

The over-all results of the program are nevertheless most encouraging. One cannot expect a high
degree of accuracy and completeness in the reporting
process of a large staff of part-time field-level
workers with no more than a one- or two-day short
course and some on-the-job training. These imper-
fections are no reason for holding back on projects
of field trials and demonstrations. At the same
time, any extra effort of reducing the number of unsuccessful demonstrations, of getting at least a
minimum of data from every demonstration laid out,
of evaluating the results obtained as quickly as
possible, and of incorporating these results in the
determination of treatments for subsequent demonstrations, is highly worthwhile. There is no more
efficient way of arriving at fertilizer recommendations to farmers than trials and demonstrations on
cultivators' fields.

There are two ways for keeping the number of
unsuccessful demonstrations down. One is to use

more trials that offer a wider choice of treatments
from which to select the best for use in demonstrations. The other is to introduce key complementary
practices--which means to make a step in the direction of a "package" approach.

For instance, in Nigeria many disappointing
demonstrations were traced to the unresponsiveness
of local maize varieties to fertilizer treatment.
The answer is: Introduce improved varieties in
subsequent demonstrations. Another frequent reason
for poor results was weeds, since they benefit from
fertilizer, too, and take the plant nutrients away
from the crop. The answer is: Introduce better
weed control. If these two complementary practices,
improved crop varieties and weed control, were introduced in subsequent fertilizer demonstrations,
unsuccessful results would drop substantially.

One warning must be sounded, however: Only
those complementary practices should be introduced
that have a reasonable prospect of being carried out
by farmers under practical farming conditions. This
means that the improved maize variety must be made
available to farmers in sufficient quantity to meet
the increasing demand, and the weed control measures
must be within the capacity of farmers to apply,
technically as well as economically, for instance,
through better seed bed preparation and better tillage implements, rather than through expensive weed
killers. Under the pilot scheme for fertilizer distribution in Western Nigeria, for example, fertilizer was sold only for use on improved maize varieties;
but so little improved seed was available that only
25 per cent of the planned acreage was actually
planted with improved varieties, and fertilizer
sales dropped correspondingly. The restriction was
justified, but the government should have provided
an adequate supply of improved seed in the pilot
area.

PILOT SCHEMES FOR
FERTILIZER DISTRIBUTION AND CREDIT

After the first year or two of fertilizer demonstrations, many farmers wanted to use fertilizers
but did not find them available at the right time in
their localities, nor find the cash with which to
buy them. Since the whole purpose of the program is
to persuade farmers to use fertilizers as a regular
farming practice, fertilizer demonstrations must be
followed up by making the required kinds and quantities of fertilizers available to farmers in their
localities at prices that will make their use profitable. Since most small farmers are poor and lack
the ready cash for buying fertilizer, effective
credit at terms attractive to farmers must also be
provided. These two arrangements, a well-functioning
market distribution of fertilizer and a well-adapted
credit system, will greatly speed up the use of fertilizer.

For this, government action is needed to open
the area to fertilizer distribution. Where little
or no fertilizer was used before, commercial firms
have no agents in the villages, local merchants are
not equipped to handle and store fertilizers, and in
many countries, government must allocate foreign exchange for fertilizer imports. One thing is certain: Unless fertilizer is available to farmers at
the village level, of the kind and at the time they
need it, and at prices they can afford to pay, they
will not use it, the demonstration effect will be
lost on them, and fertilizer consumption in the
area will not reach a level which will make it worthwhile for commercial firms and local merchants or
cooperatives to provide a reliable fertilizer supply and distribution system. The government, therefore, must help to get consumption started and over
the hump so that cooperatives and private trade can
carry on.

For this reason, the FAO Fertilizer Program is
organizing pilot schemes for fertilizer distribution and credit in selected areas where

demonstrations on cultivators' fields have been conducted and where farmers are willing to use fertilizers on their own. This part of the program also
introduces, along with demonstration of fertilizer
use, complementary factors and practices, all contributing to increasing farm production through efficient use of fertilizer. The pilot schemes build
upon the experiences gained by the fertilizer demonstrations and trials and add to the program certain key components that multiply the effectiveness
of fertilizer use. In short: The "single-input"
program becomes a "package" program.

The typical pilot scheme consists of the following arrangements:

(1) A pilot area is selected, comprising
around 5,000 to 10,000 farmers, in which fertilizer
demonstrations have been conducted and where many
farmers appear willing to use fertilizer, but where
supplies and credit facilities are lacking;
(2) The government receives a donation of a
certain amount of fertilizer, which it agrees to
sell to farmers in the pilot area, for cash or on
credit; the money collected is placed in a revolving
fund for purchasing a similar amount of fertilizer
in subsequent years, over a period of at least three
years. The minimum donation required to start a pilot scheme should be around 300 tons of fertilizer
per year, representing $20,000 and serving about 800
to 1,000 farmers in the first year. The donations
are coming now mainly from the fertilizer industry
or bilateral sources (i.e., from donor governments)
under the FAO Freedom from Hunger Campaign;
(3) The government designates an agency with
adequate field personnel to be responsible for the
transport and sale of the fertilizer to farmers.
This agency is usually the Extension Service or an
association of cooperatives. It guarantees that the
fertilizer is distributed and used by farmers according to the advice and under the supervision of
the FAO Fertilizer Program;
(4) Information, instructions on fertilizer
use, and general wide publicity are given through
farmers' meetings, leaflets, radio, etc., with full

explanations of the purposes and procedures of the pilot scheme and of the fertilizer program as a whole. Training courses and demonstrations are organized for field personnel and farmers;

(5) After a three-year period, cooperatives, private firms, and merchants are expected to carry on the fertilizer distribution in the area and outside, and new areas are selected for further pilot schemes where necessary.

Ghana started the first pilot scheme in 1963 covering a rather large area comprising 30,000 farmers (see Table 28). In the second year, 20 per cent of all the farmers in the pilot area bought fertilizer. An estimate at the end of 1964 by the field personnel indicated that ten times as much fertilizer could have been sold if an adequate supply and distribution system had been in existence. In 1965, an additional pilot scheme started in the northern part of the country, and in 1966, the number of farmers buying fertilizers under the pilot schemes nearly doubled. The government purchased, with its own scarce foreign exchange, increasing amounts of fertilizers, and after three years, the fertilizer donations had phased out.

The catalytic effect of the fertilizer program and pilot scheme is clearly revealed in Table 28. In Nigeria, El Salvador, and Turkey, the fertilizer distribution and credit schemes gained momentum rapidly and opened up local distribution channels and access to fertilizer supplies for more and more farmers.

In all pilot schemes, farmers must promise to use the prescribed kinds and amounts of fertilizer on specific crops, according to the recommendations based upon the trials and demonstration results obtained in the area. This is adaptive research in practice, and there is nothing that can replace it. The project leaders usually don't approve a treatment that does not show a value-cost ratio of at least two--as a safety factor to guard against the many mishaps that may occur.

TABLE 28

Pilot Schemes for Fertilizer Distribution and Credit[1]
Freedom from Hunger Campaign, FAO Program

		1963	1964	1965	1966
Ghana					
Farmers in Pilot Areas	nos.	30,000	30,000	30,000	60,000
Farmers Buying Fertilizer	nos.	3,800	6,100	7,000	13,000
Per Cent of All Farmers	%	12	20	23	22
Fertilizer Sold Under Scheme	tons	380	730	880	1,627
Per Farmer	kg.	100	120	125	125
Cost per 100 kg.	$	6.80	7.00	7.40	7.40
Crop Acreages Fertilized	ha.	1,800	3,200	3,500	6,300
Sources of Fertilizer					
FAO and Donors	tons	230	280	370	---
Government	tons	150	2,220	510	3,000
Commercial Firms	tons	3,620	5,270	n.a.	n.a.
Total Supply, Ghana	tons	4,000	7,770	n.a.	n.a.
Nigeria: West and Midwest Region					
Farmers Buying Fertilizer	nos.	---	2,500	4,200	5,600
Fertilizer Sold Under Scheme	tons	---	125	207	315
Per Farmer	kg.		50	50	56
Cost per 100 kg.	$		4.00	9.00	9.00
Nigeria: Eastern Region					
Farmers Buying Fertilizer	nos.	---	---	4,000	16,800
Fertilizer Sold Under Scheme	tons	---	---	80	420
Per Farmer	kg.	---	---	20	25
Cost per 100 kg.	$	---	---	7.50	7.50
El Salvador					
Farmers Buying Fertilizer	nos.	---	35	888	1,034
Fertilizer Sold Under Scheme	tons		17	331	396
Per Farmer	kg.		49	37	38
Cost per 100 kg.[2]	$		6.90	8.90	13.90
Turkey (Wheat Scheme)					
Farmers Buying Fertilizer	nos.	---	---	253	496
Fertilizer Sold Under Scheme	tons	---	---	206	395
Per Farmer	kg.	---	---	814	798
Cost per 100 kg.[2]	$	---	---	5.70	5.20

1. Based on reports by Regional Project Leaders, FAO-FFHC Fertilizer
   Program.
2. Includes improved seed and pesticides, computed by dividing total
   credit to farmers under the scheme by amount of fertilizer sold.

Some countries place a minimum quantity on fertilizer sold per farmer, e.g., 50 kg., and a maximum
of perhaps 500 kg., in order to make sure that the
program serves mainly the average small farmer.

The credit aspect of the pilot scheme in Ghana
requires liberalization. Credit was available only
to members of cooperatives. Only 20 per cent of the
purchasers in the first two years bought the fertilizer on credit. This indicates that mainly the
financially better-situated farmers were able to
benefit from the scheme. In Nigeria (Western Region), the first pilot scheme started in 1964, with
2,500 farmers buying 175 tons of fertilizer (50 kg.
average per farmer) at a subsidized price, and 70
per cent of them bought it on credit. In subsequent
years, the initial cost subsidy was reduced or eliminated in some areas, but the availability of credit
remained of critical importance. This has been the
general experience in other countries where pilot
schemes are in operation, in Turkey, Syria, Morocco,
El Salvador, and Honduras. More countries are expected to start such schemes in 1967. The schemes
follow the general pattern described for Ghana, except that much more emphasis is placed on credit
facilities--without which one could hardly expect
more than 10 or 20 per cent of the farmers to be able to buy adequate amounts of fertilizer.

Several countries include in their pilot
schemes specific provisions encouraging complementary practices. In El Salvador, the government con-
tributes to the pilot scheme improved seeds and
plant protection in the form of insecticides and
fungicides and their application. In Turkey, farmers in a cotton area are required to use a specific
cotton variety, to insure a uniform and high-quality
lint from the cotton crop of the area.

A dramatic demonstration effect of the combined
use of fertilizer, improved seed, and a combined
seed-fertilizer drill on yield was obtained in the
Eskisehir Pilot Scheme in Turkey (in 1965-66), where
fertilizer on local seed increased wheat yields almost 3-fold (280 per cent), and on improved seed

almost 4-fold (380 per cent). For that first crop
year, it was difficult to find 253 farmers willing
to cooperate; in the next year, so many more farmers
were anxious to cooperate that a large number had to
be left out due to lack of credit funds. The repayment of the first year's fertilizer credit was 97
per cent, one month after the due date.[5]

Let us conclude the discussion of fertilizer
distribution and credit schemes with a portentous
remark by F. W. Hauck, the Regional FAO Soil Fertility Expert in West Africa during these pioneering
years: "It is advisable to combine in one organization the supply of fertilizers and other materials
to the farmer, with orderly marketing of the farm
products. This facilitates the provision of credit.
Such a development normally leads to an intensive
'agricultural supply, marketing and co-op organization' in many countries throughout the world, especially in areas with many small farmers. Thus, the
establishment of fertilizer distribution to the
farmers could result in solving one of the basic
problems of agriculture: to bring small farmers in
contact with the economic development of their country."[6] Again: the spearhead approach, this time
applied to introducing innovations in the local marketing system.

THE PRINCIPLE: A FOCUS IN A PATTERN

The human mind has no universal focus. It can
function only in one direction at a time. A person's
action requires a central purpose around which he
groups a selected number of supplementary activities
in a functional pattern. Nothing is more frustrating than being asked to do many new things all at
the same time--particularly if they seem unrelated
to each other. Herein lies the danger of trying to
introduce many innovations all at once: It leads to
confusion, to dissipation of effort, or simply to
resistance. The other danger is to concentrate on
one thing alone, in isolation, without reference to
even closely related things: It leads to waste of
energy and lack of balance. In shaping a development

project on the field level, the clue to success is
to establish a limited focus, a narrow but vitally
important purpose, and to group around it a small
number of closely related activities selected for
their functional importance to the main purpose.
Economic planners are prone to the errors of dissipation, to do too many things at once; technical
specialists are prone to the errors of lopsided concentration on one isolated thing, to lack of balance, to disregard for other closely related aspects.

Many professionals concerned with development
planning, of course, are well aware of these tenden-
cies; but when it comes to localizing national agri-
cultural-development programs into operational area
projects, this awareness tends to fade away. Community development projects, which are predominantly
in the hands of generalists, often attempt to do too
many things at once and don't have even one agricultural expert on their staff to give the project some
professional focus upon the community's source of
livelihood. Soils, irrigation, and livestock projects of the respective government departments, on
the other hand, are usually concentrated on one isolated aspect, and rarely include experts from other
disciplines on the project staff. The problem is to
find a good balance between these two extreme approaches.

One way of solving this problem is illustrated
by the FAO Fertilizer Program: starting a project
with a single purpose, the introduction of a single
innovation and subsequently broadening it by adding
supplementary practices serving the main purpose.
Even a "package" program does well to have the various items in the package grouped according to their
functional importance around one major purpose. It
might be one of the weaknesses of the Indian package
program that the structuring of the items in the
package has been too stereotyped, has not been adjusted well enough to the local conditions of the
various areas. Even in one district, there may be
three blocks where fertilizer use should be the main
focus, while in two other blocks, irrigation water

management or double-cropping should be the major purpose, still keeping the other items of the package in the picture. In the Philippines, this "package-program" type of extension work combined with technical assistance has recently been launched in major rice-producing areas and appears to be promising.[7]

Another way of finding a good balance for introducing innovations in farming methods is to run two or three different projects side by side, which may deal with different groups of people, but which, from the area viewpoint, also complement each other. For instance, a fertilizer-use project for first users and a crop-improvement project for farmers familiar with fertilizers, each conceived as a package program but with the items in the package structured quite differently, would strengthen each other. After three to five years, both projects might be replaced by some livestock or farm-management projects, and the fertilizer and crop-improvement projects shifted to a new area where these practices have not yet been adopted.

These considerations apply to action projects involving farmers adopting new practices. The psychological and economic conditions of general educational programs are quite different since they involve farmers only in attending meetings of one form or another, but not in committing part of their land, capital, and labor resources to the program. These educational programs are most effective if they can draw upon the results of the practices in demonstration and pilot projects, and if their main purpose is to strengthen the demonstration effect of these intensive-action projects. These meetings encourage the nonparticipating farmers to inquire about these practices, visit the demonstrations, and adopt these practices themselves. This approach imparts to educational meetings a vital local focus which stimulates farmers and motivates them to follow up with action on their own. Involving small neighborhood groups in the adoption of modern practices by innovating farmers is greatly bolstering the demonstration effect, and prevents the

innovators' isolation from the community as they
work individualistically on their own and in de-
fiance of local custom.

This action approach, if well organized, brings
results rather quickly despite the fact that initially only a small proportion of the farmers are
actively participating. The example of the FAO Fertilizer Program has shown an impressive spreading
effect.

Similar action projects on the farm level can
be worked out for other practices as well. Improved
crop rotation and tillage methods, farm implements
and machinery, irrigation water use, livestock breeding and feeding methods, farm management planning
and budgeting--all these modern farming techniques
lend themselves readily to this action-project approach on the farm level for introducing their adoption.

An outstanding success of such a field-action
program for testing the yield responses of improved
wheat and maize varieties under farming conditions
in various areas over a period of years and promoting the adoption of varieties best suited to the
areas was achieved by the Rockefeller Foundation Program and the government of Mexico. Over a twenty-
year period, national average wheat yields increased
more than 3-fold from 11 bushels to 39 bushels per
acre--with practically the total wheat acreage in
improved dwarf and semi-dwarf varieties and proper
fertilization by 1965. This represents an annual
compound rate of 6.5 per cent increase. The Rockefeller Foundation started a similar program in West
Pakistan together with the government in 1961. By
1965, Mexican dwarf wheat varieties were tested and
grown for seed multiplication on fields of 2,500
farmers throughout the wheat-growing areas, and on
thirty government research or seed farms. Since the
Mexican varieties are not fully acceptable in Pakistan, due to grain color and perhaps lack of resistance to certain diseases, new crosses are being
selected and tested in the West Pakistan program.[8]

It must be understood that the approach of focusing upon the introduction of a few key practices is peculiarly suited to areas where farming methods are still largely traditional, where most farmers are small and have had little or no schooling. In fact, after a period of about five or ten years, it may be advisable to shift such projects to new areas and replace them by projects better suited to a more advanced stage of agricultural development.

In more advanced areas where a good proportion of even the small farmers are using several modern techniques, where their educational level is higher, where a good many of them belong to cooperatives and farmers' associations, the key problem is no longer one of breaking with traditional farming habits, but one of using modern techniques more efficiently, of finding the most profitable level of inputs and combination of crops and livestock enterprises. In such areas, working on an advisory basis through farmers' meetings and group projects, and drawing upon highly skilled specialists for difficult technical problems become appropriate. Cooperatives are often in an excellent position to improve certain practices and introduce new ones as well. This need not be done by persuasion only, but in some cases as a condition of membership, for instance by requiring members to grow only one superior cotton variety as is the case in some areas.

There is still great need for action projects on the farm level even in more advanced areas; only their main purposes must be different. Instead of simply introducing certain new techniques, farm-action projects must be concerned with raising the managerial efficiency of the farmer. Farm planning and budgeting ranks perhaps highest as a useful focus for such action projects in many areas. In others, it may be cooperative grazing of livestock as a complement to individual arable farming that should be the focus of a package program--a much-neglected issue in many developing countries in view of the urgent need of increased livestock production --or terracing, crop rotation, and tillage methods on hilly land, for instance in Taiwan and South Korea. These key projects deal with changes in the farming system, in the over-all production process, rather than with the introduction of a few selected practices.[9] But here as there, the principle holds that agricultural development programs must be localized at the farm level, that extension projects must be structured around a focus, a central theme, and involve farmers in action.

HOW TRADITION-BOUND IS THE PEASANT?

I avoid the term "peasant" because it tends to prejudice the reader's mind against the farmer. But farmers in developing countries are often referred to as peasants, with the implication that they are tradition-bound, unresponsive to new economic and social opportunities, inept at modern skills and techniques, backward-looking, and acquiescent in their subservient station in life. If this were truly so, there would be no peasant revolts, no land reforms, no rural schools; indeed, no progress throughout the developing rural world.

The myth of the peasant's imprisoned mind is rapidly being demolished by his own deeds—rapidly in terms of decades rather than years. The adoption by farm people of bicycles and radios, their acquisition of mechanical skills in driving trucks and tractors, the ease with which young farm people migrate to cities and learn the skills of all sorts of industrial and service jobs attest to their versatility and resourcefulness. There is no evidence of innate conservatism, of inborn physical and mental lack of capacity to learn new skills and to adapt to new ways of life.[10]

What binds the peasant to the traditions of farming is lack of opportunities to acquire knowledge of modern techniques, is poverty preventing him from buying modern inputs and risking losses from untried methods, is the social power structure, which puts him under pressure to remain docile and "keep him where he belongs" (see Chapter 8).

In many areas of deep and widespread poverty, these
forces obstructing change are underlain by a pervasive general apathy of people, by an indolent fatal-
ism which is so often a corollary of hunger and abject poverty from which they see no hope of escape.
These attitudes of indolence, of clinging to the old
customs as their only way of survival, of tolerating
the subservience imposed upon them by the old social
and economic institutions--these attitudes evaporate
quickly if hopes are kindled and opportunities offered for a better life.

These conditions making for rigid traditional-
ism and pervasive apathy of small farmers in the developing world are changing. Contact with stores in
the villages, trips to cities, and members of farm
families finding non-farm jobs are arousing new aspirations. The emancipation of the poor from servitude and their ascendancy to political power awaken
hope and create new energies for changing farming
methods as well as ways of life in the direction of
economic progress and human dignity. These forces
are at work everywhere and manifest themselves in
the gradual but relentless innovations in farming
techniques, changes in economic arrangements and social relationships within and outside the family.
Education and communication lead farmers to ever-
expanding areas of contact with urban people, with
different occupations and institutions and social
outlook. There is no turning back to the static
quasi-feudal structure of rural society which prevailed unchallenged for centuries in most of the
newly developing countries until recently. Where
this structure still prevails, it is not likely to
outlast the present generation.

Of course, this emancipation process is not
smooth. There will be setbacks in some areas, violent upheavals in others. The peasant's progress
toward a modern farmer and citizen creates many
frictions within families and between groups, especially where a recalcitrant rural elite tries to
maintain the status quo by intimidation and sometimes even violent means. Viewed in historical perspective, in terms of decades rather than years,

these conservative quasi-feudal forces are waning--
although in some countries perhaps not rapidly
enough to forestall violent revolutions.

The point I want to make here is that the prospects for a rather fast rate of progress in agriculture are, on the whole, becoming better every year
(and in some countries more than in others), and
that the extension service, farmers' cooperatives,
and farmers' associations must play a decisive role
in accelerating this process. For this challenging
task, on-the-farm action projects through trials
and demonstrations on cultivators' fields, through
"package" programs reinforced by pilot schemes for
distribution of modern inputs and credit facilities,
offer the best hope for success in modernizing farming techniques. And this success is necessary for
winning the race between food and population.

NOTES TO CHAPTER 11

1. See H. L. Richardson, "The Freedom from
Hunger Campaign in Five Years of the FAO Fertilizer
Programme," Outlook on Agriculture, Vol. V, No. 1
(1966), pp. 3-16. I am most grateful to Dr. H. L.
Richardson, Project Manager for the first six years
of the FAO Fertilizer Program, and to J. W. Couston,
Economist of the Program, for the generous assistance they have given me in the preparation of this
chapter.

2. See the Food and Agriculture Organization of
the United Nations, The State of Food and Agriculture, 1963 (Rome: FAO, 1963), Chapter IV.

3. Usually a trial plot includes factorial combinations of the three primary nutrients N, P, and K
at two or more levels of application. Individual
trials are not replicated, but the large numbers
laid out provide an element of replication and make
the results reasonably reliable for practical farming conditions.

4.   For the total number laid out from winter 1961/62 to winter 1964/65 inclusive, see Richardson, op. cit., pp. 14-15; for the total number reporting results, see "Physical and Economic Summary of Trial and Demonstration Results, 1961/62-1964/65" (Preliminary), FFHC Fertilizer Program, FAO, Rome (mimeo., LA:FFHC/67/3).

5.   See M. Mathieu, "Field Progress Report No. 29," Near East and North Africa Region, FFHC-FAO Fertilizer Program, October 27, 1966 (mimeo.).

6.   F. W. Hauck, "Pilot Schemes for Fertilizer Distribution in West Africa." Paper presented at the Second Meeting on Soil Fertility and Fertilizer Use, Dakar, Senegal, January 11-16, 1965 (mimeo.), p. 10.

7.   See Isagani C. Belarmino, "The Rice Problem: An Appraisal," Economic Research Journal, Vol. XII, No. 1 (June 1965), pp. 4-27.

8.   See A. H. Moseman, "Food and People--The World." Paper presented at the Annual Convention of California Fertilizer Association, Los Angeles, November 1, 1966 (mimeo.).

9.   See Arthur T. Mosher, "A Note on the Evolutionary Role of Extension Workers," Land Economics, Vol. 42, No. 3 (August 1966), pp. 387-89; the author traces the changing role of the extension worker through various stages of development until in highly developed areas, it shifts from farming techniques to problems of national and international policy as it affects agriculture.

10.   See Milton L. Barnett, "Subsistence and Transition in Agricultural Development among the Ibaloi," (the Philippines). To be published in Beyer's Festschriften in 1967.

CHAPTER **12** MODERNIZATION OF FARMING:
FARM PLANNING FOR
AGRICULTURAL DEVELOPMENT[1]

The great variety of physical land and water
resources, of economic conditions of prices and
costs, of institutional structures of tenure, credit, and market facilities we find in the various local farming areas prevents us from setting up a few
model types of modern farming units for application
on a nationwide basis. Such model-farm plans simply would not fit the many different technical, economic, and human conditions prevailing on most
farms. Hence, the process of modernizing agriculture must be worked out on the spot, must be adapted
to the soil, climate, market location, size of farm,
and various social characteristics of each area and
its farm people.

In the two preceding chapters, we discussed the
problems of localizing action programs, of giving
roots and focus to extension work, and of introducing specific, relatively simple technical innovations in farming practices. This approach is necessary, but not sufficient because each farm is an integrated unit in which several different production
processes are carried on, with various crops in the
different seasons, with various livestock enterprises; and they all must fit together to keep the
family labor force profitably employed during the
year, to make the best use of the land and water
available, and to yield an adequate family income.
This is the task of farm management or farm production economics.[2]

THE TASK OF FARM DEVELOPMENT PLANNING

Essentially, what is needed is an experimental approach, at the farm and village level, to find out what changes in land use and crop rotations are needed, what crop varieties respond well to what kind and how much fertilizer, how much credit farmers will need and at what terms of interest rates and repayment, and what cost-price relations will make it profitable to farmers to adopt various sets of these modern techniques, which--applied to crop rotations and livestock enterprises--make good use of land and labor resources. This information can be obtained from systematic trials and demonstrations on selected typical farms and in well-located pilot project areas representative of major farming regions; by judicious use of analogy and transfer of experience obtained from experiment station research work and in practical farming cases under similar conditions elsewhere; by a much wider and more sophisticated use of typical case- and farm-group studies; and by organized teamwork with specialists in agronomy, marketing, land tenure, and agricultural policy who contribute their up-to-date knowledge of technology and institutional innovations.

This calls for farm planning and budgeting. Our inquiries center around the key questions:

(1) What types of farming, crop and livestock combinations, crop varieties, and levels of capital and labor input are needed to use land and labor resources fully and efficiently?

(2) What changes from the present position are needed to get there?

(3) What farming practices, fixed and operating capital, and what incentives and facilities through credit, cooperative and government services, tenure and marketing conditions, and cost-price relations are necessary to make farmers willing and able to bring about the desired changes?

There are some beginnings of work along these
lines going on in developing countries. For instance, the Food and Agriculture Organization of the
United Nations started, in 1954, a series of farm-
management seminars throughout the Far Eastern Region, which were centered around the key problems of
forward-looking farm development planning and the
adaptation of farm planning and budgeting methods to
local conditions in the various countries.[3]

In a number of universities in the developing
regions, some research has been conducted and some
training courses have been offered in farm planning
and budgeting. This type of farm management work
represents a promising start. Its dominant focus,
however, has usually been the internal production
organization within the farm boundary, with the external environment of tenure, credit, marketing, and
price conditions treated as given. These external
factors, however, are also amenable to improvement
and must be treated accordingly in farm development
planning.

In 1960-61, India started the first large-scale
government action program somewhat along farm development planning lines anywhere in the world: the
"Intensive Agricultural District Programme."[4] In
principle, the approach of the Programme rests upon
farm management planning and budgeting and institutional improvements for raising agricultural productivity.[5] In practice, the implementation of the
Programme concentrates on using very simple partial
farm plans and budgets, limited to a "package" of
modern practices including fertilizers, improved
seeds, pesticides, etc., and applies them to groups
of farms in selected districts by promoting a joint
effort of farmers to adopt the "package" of practices. "The choice offered is a simple one, between
the old way and the new one which includes not only
improved practices but also the assurance of supplies, credit, and guidance. The farm plan is then
used to inform the local cooperative of the farmer's
expected needs--of great importance where the distribution system is poorly developed--and is further
used to develop the farmer's loan application for

production credit."[6] There is no doubt that this
general approach is sound and promising.

Two types of inquiries are required: One deals
with the internal farm production organization, the
other with the external environmental conditions of
tenure, credit, marketing, prices, and costs.

IMPROVING INTERNAL FARM ORGANIZATION

Concerning the organization of the internal
production process in each farm unit, the emphasis
needs to be placed on problem-solving.

This means, first, the identification of problems. The dominant problem is how to increase productivity per acre and per man, within the physical
limitations of soil and climate. What are the various alternatives a farmer has for raising the productivity of his land and labor resources, and what
are the capital requirements for the various inputs?
We know that additional capital is needed to modernize agricultural production; the question is how
much and in what forms?--and that will vary according to the alternative farm plans. The input requirements and the expected output of farm products
under the various feasible alternatives of crop rotations and livestock enterprises (such as cattle,
sheep, poultry, etc.), of fertilizer use and feed
rations, of kind and degrees of mechanization, must
be estimated. Cooperation with agronomists is needed for information on improved crop varieties and
their yield response to fertilizer, with agricultural engineers on the technical feasibilities of tractor and machinery use for various field operations
and transport tasks.

Local progressive farmers are to be consulted
on tillage and crop practices (such as weed control
and harvesting, etc.) and other methods they have
found to increase production. On the basis of these
technical data and discussions, the farm management
worker tentatively selects a few alternative farm
plans for a set of "typical farms" representing the

main types of farming, according to soils and farm
sizes of the area, that would utilize the land and
the family labor force as fully as possible the
year-round, and which would expand or introduce
high-value crops and livestock products where this
seems feasible. It may often be sufficient to work
out only partial farm plans involving only a few key
enterprises and related new practices.

    Secondly, for these high-priority alternative
farm plans we can budget the costs and returns of
the production plans under prevailing local prices
of factors and products. In close consultation with
local farmers, we determine the credit requirements,
the interest, loan repayment, rent charges, and taxes they would have to meet under now-prevailing conditions. These cost-return calculations of the production plans need to be carried out only for the
more important crop and livestock enterprises and
only in approximate terms, by simple arithmetic.
The physical output of each alternative plan is
bound to be substantially larger than the present
output. But their net financial returns to the
farmer may in some cases be little higher than at
present, due to unfavorable cost-price relations (of
fertilizer and crop, for instance), or due to high
rents and interest rates eating up too large a share
of the increase in returns, or due to high-risk losses in case of a crop failure.

    Thirdly--and this is a crucial step--we identi-
fy the obstacles in the present external environmental conditions which render the technically much
superior production plans economically unattractive
to the farmer. In consultation with local farmers,
village leaders, and managers of cooperatives, we
explore in some detail the nature of these obstacles, such as lack of credit at interest rates and
repayment terms acceptable to farmers; lack of supplies of the inputs required or available only at
costs too high to make their use profitable; farmers' fear that prices will drop too low if they produce more, that rents or taxes might take away too
large a share of the increase in returns. In these
discussions, we must try our best to obtain a

realistic sense of the nature and the extent by
which these obstacles would have to be reduced in
order to motivate farmers to adopt the superior farm
plans.

Since this is a step much needed in farm management work, but has been sorely neglected by planners and experts, let us discuss it in a little more
detail.

A simple example can be used to illustrate the
various ways in which innovations on typical farms
can be planned and budgeted, and how the results can
be of decisive use in formulating national policies
for production increases.

Table 29, Part A, shows the present farming system on a typical five-acre rice farm in Southeast
India or East Pakistan, and the problems which the
introduction of fertilizer use on rice raise in the
mind of the farmer and of the national planner and
policy-maker. Part B indicates how crucial the relationship between rice price and fertilizer cost is
to the farmer's incentive to use fertilizer. At a
farm price of 6 Rs. per maund of rice, and at a fertilizer cost of 3.60 Rs. per pound of N to the farmer, he has no incentive whatever to use fertilizer.
There have undoubtedly been many areas in Asia where
the actual prices received by farmers for rice, and
paid by farmers for fertilizer, were so unfavorable
as to prohibit the introduction of fertilizer use.

A critical test of the profitability of fertilizer use is the returns from the crop-yield increase per rupee invested in fertilizer use. Since
the small farmer is very vulnerable and fears the
risk he sees in departing from traditional farming
practices--an attitude which is perfectly rational--
he will not adopt modern practices until he is persuaded that the returns are sufficiently high and
certain to compensate for the risks of crop failure
and increased indebtedness. The experience in recent demonstration projects for fertilizer use indicates fairly clearly that unless farmers can expect
at least a return of 2 Rs. for every rupee invested

TABLE 29

Planning and Budgeting Fertilizer Use
on Rice in a Typical Five-Acre
Asian Farm (India or East Pakistan)

A. Present Farming System
(Area in Crops: 5 Acres)[1]

Crops	Acres	Yield Per Acre	Production	Price Per Maund	Gross Income (Crop Value)
		maunds	maunds	Rs.	Rs.
Rice	4.0	17	68	6.0	408
Gram	1.3	7	9	6.0	54
Sugar Cane	0.8	700	560	1.6	896
Jute	0.1	15	1	18.0	18
Mustard	0.1	6	1	18.0	18

Acreage of Crops per Year	6.3	Total Gross Income 1,394
		Total Farm Cash
Per Cent of Crop Land		Expenses 102
Double-Cropped	26.0	Net Farm Income 1,292

B. New Farm Plan
(Farm Size and Crop Acreages Remain the Same)[2]

Effect of Fertilizer Use on Income from Rice, 40 Lbs. N per Acre
(rice production increase 6.6 maunds per acre, or 26 maunds total)

306

ADDITIONAL

	Gross Income Rs.	Expenses Rs.	Net Income Rs.	Return per Rupee Invested Rs.
At Rice Price of 6 Rs./Maund[3]				
At Fertilizer Price of:				
0.84 Rs. per lb. N	156	34	122	4.6
0.80 " " " "	156	72	84	2.2
2.70 " " " "	156	108	48	1.4
3.60 " " " "	156	144	12	1.1
At Rice Price of 12 Rs./Maund[3]				
At Fertilizer Price of:				
0.84 Rs. per lb. N	312	34	278	9.2
1.80 " " " "	312	72	240	4.3
2.70 " " " "	312	108	204	2.9
3.60 " " " "	312	144	168	2.2

1. The "present" farming system corresponds to a typical five-acre rice farm in India or East Pakistan as reported in W. Y. Yang, Methods of Farm Management Investigations for Improving Farm Productivity, FAO Agricultural Development Paper No. 80 (Rome: FAO, 1965), pp. 149-52 (revised edition).

2. The "new farm plan" involves only one major change from the "present" one: the introduction of fertilizer use on rice, based on yield response as reported in P. C. Raheja, "Economics of Fertilizer Use," Farm Planning and Management. Papers presented at the FAO Development Centre, October 14-November 9, 1957 (New Delhi: Government of India Press, 1959), pp. 155-56.

3. The rice and fertilizer prices pertain to the years around 1956-57. The rice price of 6 Rs./maund is taken from Yang, op. cit., p. 145, representing a typical price received by farmers; the rice price of 12 Rs. is taken (as is the wholesale fertilizer price of 0.84 Rs. per pound of N) from Raheja, op. cit., p. 156, and represents a wholesale price. The fertilizer price of 3.60 Rs. per pound of N is taken from Food and Agriculture Organization of the United Nations, Fertilizers—An Annual Review of World Production, Consumption and Trade, 1962 (Rome: FAO, 1963), p. 163, where "prices paid by farmers" for bagged Ammonium Sulphate in India in 1956/57 is shown as 167 Rs. per 100 kilograms, which corresponds with a 21 per cent concentration of N to 3.60 Rs. per pound. The prices of 2.70 and 1.80 represent government cost subsidies of 25 per cent and 50 per cent of the farm price, respectively.

in fertilizer, they may be well advised not to use
it. In our example, where 6 Rs./maund of rice represents a fairly typical price received by many
farmers, especially in remote areas, and where the
fertilizer cost is 3.6 Rs., or even 2.7 Rs. under
a 25 per cent cost subsidy, there is no effective
incentive for farmers to use fertilizers, especially
if they must buy the fertilizer on credit at high
interest rates. No one can blame them for laziness
or stupidity if they don't respond to extension service and general government exhortations to use fertilizer.

If, therefore, the government is serious with
its planning for output increase, it will have to
either increase the rice price actually received by
farmers, reduce the fertilizer cost actually paid by
farmers, or do both in combination up to a point
where average return per rupee invested by the farmer is safely above 2 Rs.[7]

This relationship between returns from the additional input (in this case, fertilizer) and the
cost of the input is a simple example of a benefit-
cost ratio often used to judge the economic feasibility of a new technique or investment. Its interpretation for passing such a judgement is, however,
not so simple. From the individual farmer's point
of view, a 1:1 ratio is not sufficient for his adopting a new technique involving substantial cash out-
lays; it yields no profit, and it does not cover
various risk losses from drought or floods or pests,
nor interest paid for credit needed to buy fertilizer (not to mention the red tape and embarrassing in-
quisitions about the farmer's credit worthiness),
nor compensation for the extra labor needed for applying the fertilizer. Just how much higher than
1:1 this ratio has to be varies between areas, between crops and different techniques, and can best
be determined through farm planning and budgeting
studies carried on in the field in close consultation with farmers. For some crops, the ratio required might be only 1.5, for another it might be 3,
depending on the factors just mentioned. Once the
critical level of the benefit-cost ratio is

determined, the planners and policy-makers can gear
their price policy measures to this critical level
of producer incentive and response. There are many
other examples of this very strategic role of farm
planning and budgeting in gauging the amount and
kind of production incentives which development policy will have to provide to farmers.

This benefit-cost ratio is also dependent upon
the physical yield response to fertilizer application. If, for instance, a 40-pound nitrogen dosage
yields an increase of 10 maunds of rice per acre
instead of 6.6 maunds--which might well be the case
if an improved rice variety is introduced--the benefit-cost ratio is raised from 1.4 to 2.2 in the case
of a rice price of 6 Rs. and a fertilizer cost of
2.70 Rs. This means that a fertilizer subsidy of
only 25 per cent would be a sufficient incentive to
farmers to use fertilizer, instead of the 50 per
cent subsidy needed for a yield response of only 6.6
maunds.

Our example can also serve to illustrate the
effect of crop-share rent on farmer's incentives.
If the tenant pays half of the crop to the landlord
for rent but must bear the cost of fertilizer, he
will not use fertilizer unless his benefit-cost ratio is at least 4, instead of only 2 in the case of
an owner-cultivator. From Table 29, we see that an
owner-cultivator will find it profitable to use fertilizer at a 6 Rs. rice price and a 1.80 Rs. fertilizer cost, giving him a return of 2.20 Rs. per rupee invested. A share tenant, however, will receive
only 1.1 Rs. per rupee invested, and hence has no
incentive for using it. Here, again, farm planning
and budgeting can indicate, in a practical way, the
level of income incentives required to motivate
farmers to use fertilizer under various tenancy conditions.

One other issue can be illustrated by our simple example. Prices of crops actually received by
farmers, and prices for inputs actually paid by
farmers are difficult to ascertain, and are usually
not known and statistically reported. Hence,

studies of the economics of fertilizer use often employ wholesale prices, the only price data currently
available. This makes for a strong favorable bias
in the benefit-cost ratios. The table shows that
this ratio based on a wholesale price of 12 Rs. per
maund of rice and a wholesale fertilizer price of
0.84 Rs. per pound of nitrogen is 9.2, while farm
prices obtained presumably from a few sample surveys
indicate a rice price of 6 Rs. per maund (or half
the wholesale price), and a nitrogen price of 3.60
Rs. per pound (or four times the wholesale price),
resulting in a benefit-cost ratio of 1.1. This
points to the great need for much better data on
prices actually received and paid by farmers. For
instance, the benefit-cost ratio for farmers might
be much improved by reducing the fertilizer distribution cost through better-organized transport and
storage facilities and more ample supplies of fertilizer at the village level, rather than by subsidies. Similarly, rice prices received by farmers
might be increased by improvements in the marketing
process and by strengthening the farmers' bargaining
position in the local markets through cooperatives.

This is, of course, only a very simple illus-
tration of how farm planning and budgeting can contribute to increase production and income of farms
on the one side, and to formulate agricultural policy on the other. The same approach can be applied
to many other modern practices and inputs, such as
better crop varieties, farm machinery and equipment, harvesting, threshing and storing methods;
more and better use of irrigation water; better and
new livestock enterprises in proper combination with
crop rotations, forage use and feed purchases, so as
to make the best use of the farm's land, capital,
and labor resources throughout the seasons of the
year.

IMPROVING EXTERNAL
ENVIRONMENTAL CONDITIONS

Concerning the improvement of the external economic and institutional conditions affecting the

incentives and ability of farmers to adopt better production plans, we need to identify those external factors that prevent farmers from improving their production efficiency much more specifically and in detail than we have done in the past.

In most farming areas, the research worker is bound to detect several obstacles to progress in farm production. Where rents are too high, we can determine a level of rental charges that would increase the farmer's incentive to raise production; where cost-price relationships are unfavorable, we can indicate how much the input cost would have to be reduced, or the output price raised, to induce farmers to produce more, as we have seen in our example. Where interest rates for credit are too high, we can indicate the interest level at which farmers are willing to borrow for the purchase of fertilizer, pesticides, machinery, and other important factors, and the repayment terms which fit into the timing of their income stream. Where the local marketing facilities are such that the farmer is at the mercy of a few middlemen, or storage facilities and grading standards are absent so that he receives unduly low prices for his products, we can indicate what the storage and grading requirements for the output should be and what kinds and amounts of inputs will be needed under the various production plans in the area as a whole. For new crop and livestock production practices, we can indicate to the extension service the kind of assistance and field demonstrations the farmers will need in order to adopt these practices.

These external economic conditions are amenable to change by cooperative action and government policies. We must remember, of course, that the farmer and the farm planner cannot determine on their own just how much of these production incentives will, in fact, be feasible for implementation through public policy measures, because the various land reform, credit, and price-control programs also have their costs in funds and manpower, and do affect other groups such as landlords, merchants, and urban consumers who will voice their reactions before such

policies can be adopted and effectively carried out
by the government. Nevertheless, the fact remains
that it is very important for planners to know how
farmers feel concerning production incentives, and
how they have responded to them in areas where they
have been offered.

To orient our work to this end requires teamwork with specialists in other fields, such as land
tenure, credit, cooperative organization, agricultural and price policy. But the farm management point
of view furnishes basic specifications of what improvements in these environmental conditions are
needed to motivate farmers toward agricultural progress.

The specialized competence of the farm management worker is to understand the farmer's entrepreneurial problems, to know what motivates him in organizing his production processes, in deciding
between alternative crops or farming practices; and
to observe how he responds to specific incentives
and opportunities, how he accommodates himself to
certain obstacles, risks, and fears. It is this
competence of the farm management worker, who iden-
tifies himself with the farmer, who works with him
in personal contact and gains his confidence, that
plays a crucial role in action-oriented research and
extension work. The farm management worker can in-
terpret farmers' needs, aspirations, and fears to
others--to private merchants, managers of cooperatives, political leaders, and government officials--
and thus, contribute to finding ways for improving
these environmental conditions.

To summarize: There are a number of economic
external conditions that are beyond the control of
the individual farmer, but are amenable to change by
group action, by cooperative or government programs.
The economic location and marketing facilities of an
area can often be greatly improved by roads. Poor
land-tenure systems can be improved by various
agrarian reform measures. Cost-price relations can
be improved by cost reductions and price supports.

For farm development planning, these alterable environmental conditions must be dealt with explicitly and effectively. They can be changed so as to have profoundly favorable effects upon the farmer's production process. And these largely determine the aggregate production performance of agriculture in the context of national economic development.

The agricultural development of Japan offers striking examples of how improvements in environmental conditions stimulated farmers' incentives and motivated them to step up their production rapidly. In the last 100 years, there were two periods of outstanding progress: The first, 1868 to 1912, was marked by a strong development of marketing cooperatives, education and extension services, and improvement of the land-tax system; the second, 1946 to 1960, by a far-reaching land reform, greatly expanded production credit, and a price support and stabilization program for rice and some other key products. There is much to be learned from Japanese experiences in agricultural and general economic development processes, which is of direct concern to many countries.[8] We must realize that farmers' associations and cooperatives can be instrumental in overcoming production obstacles by promoting and helping to implement land reforms, better marketing and credit facilities, farm price supports, etc. Farm management workers are best qualified for getting the facts and interpreting them for practical use in the formulation of farm production plans and agricultural policies.

INCENTIVES FOR FARMERS
IN RURAL DEVELOPMENT PROJECTS

In most underdeveloped regions, among powerful incentives needed to trigger the farmer's motivation to overcome serious obstacles blocking his road toward progress are the following:

(1) Ready availability of modern inputs, such as fertilizers, improved seeds, pesticides, and

machinery;

(2)   Access to credit at terms attractive to farmers, enabling them to buy these production requisites and use them efficiently;[9]

(3)   Favorable cost-price relations with a minimum of uncertainty so as to reduce the price risk that often hampers production increases;

(4)   Tenure conditions that provide two basic incentives for farm development: increasing rewards commensurate with increased production effort of the farmer, and security of his farm occupancy, encouraging him to improve the land and invest in more than short-time "hand-to-mouth" operations. This means that rent, debt, and tax payments must not be allowed to siphon off a major part of the increased farm income;

(5)   Protection against risk, as the farmer sees it, that is involved in adopting new farming methods.[10]

For determining the quantitative and qualitative requirements of these five incentive measures necessary to induce farmers to modernize their farming, the farm management expert has much more to offer than is at present recognized by planners, administrators, and civic leaders. He is familiar with the farm production process, with the farmer's attitudes and aspirations, and the obstacles he has to overcome. He bridges the gap between over-all planning and national policy measures on the one side, and their implementation at the actual farm production level on the other.

FARM MANAGEMENT STUDIES AND EXTENSION FOR MODERNIZED FARMING

The most appropriate place to start this kind of farm management work is in one or several of the country's major agricultural areas, especially those with a considerable production potential. Areas

which have been selected for demonstration of fertilizer or machinery use, farm settlement, irrigation, and other development projects are especially
suited for such studies as they help to guide current farm development in the right direction and to
avoid serious mistakes in the implementation of
these projects.[11]

Such studies need not be costly, nor do they
require a large staff of highly specialized and
theoretically trained personnel. Under the general
guidance of one well-trained farm economist, a series of such studies could be undertaken in various
selected areas, and especially in actual rural-
development projects currently underway. A few
young, bright, and well-motivated graduates of secondary schools or vocational training institutes
could be assigned to him as assistants. It is more
important to start studies along these lines, and
have all persons involved grow in competence in the
process, than to reach for perfection, which will be
beyond reach for many years to come.

Also from the national planning point of view,
we need much stronger enphasis on farm planning and
budgeting for the purpose of changing production
patterns, input and output levels, so as to achieve
a rapidly increasing farm production of a desirable
"product mix," that is a combination of farm products which meets domestic consumption and export
needs. This is essential for increasing the living
level of farmers and the purchasing power of the rural population as well as for promoting general economic development of the country.

The planning of agricultural development, and
particularly the implementation of plans and programs, necessitates the closest cooperation between
economic planners, farm management economist, and
the farmers in the various agricultural areas of the
country.[12]

A TWO-PRONGED APPROACH: PLANNING
FROM THE TOP DOWN AND FROM THE BOTTOM UP

In principle, the nature of the task is as follows:

(1) The economic planner determines one or
preferably several tentative sets of production targets desirable from the national viewpoint, according to population increase, domestic nutritional and
industrial needs, foreign trade prospects and foreign exchange requirements, etc;

(2) The farm development planner indicates, on
the basis of farm plans and budgets for a set of
typical farm types for each major farming area, the
production performance farmers can be expected to
achieve, and the economic and institutional conditions that must be created for enabling and motivating the farmer to implement these production plans;

(3) These farm production plans are summed up
for the various major agricultural areas to yield a
rough estimate of national agricultural production;

(4) At the same time, the national production
targets are broken down by major agricultural areas,
in consultation with the farm development planners
of the various areas;

(5) If the practically feasible production performance of farmers deviates from the nationally desirable production targets, a "feed-back" procedure
is applied to bring about a reconciliation of national targets and practical feasibility of farmers'
performance by readjusting both national production
targets and area farm production plans. This may
also involve certain adjustments in the environmental conditions of the various farming areas and in
some aspects of national economic and agricultural
policies.

This feed-back process is essential for planning and implementing a viable program of

agricultural development and requires active cooperation between farm and economic planners at all levels, from the local farming areas up to the national
planning agency and back down to the local level.
This feed-back process also provides for the dynamic
flexibility of both plans and implementation measures. It facilitates a continuing readjustment and
mutual reconciliation of plans and measures in the
light of experience and changing national and local
situations. Farm management and economic planning
experts have much to learn from each other, have
much to give each other, in a team spirit of dedica-
tion to the urgent task of accelerating agricultural
progress.

This is new, untried, and in many of its administrative and personnel aspects may even be unwel-
come under some existing government and university
types of bureaucratic organization and professional
mentality. It is all the more urgent to realize
clearly the necessity of such cooperation in the
planning and feed-back process, and to invest ingenuity and effort to bring it about.

In this two-pronged approach of aggregating regional agricultural production potentials to national production totals and breaking down national targets by major farming areas, it is often desirable
to interpose a "regional development plan" to serve
as a link between farms and villages and the national level. These regional plans provide also for increases in industrial production and service activities, which complement the agricultural development
through rural processing plants, market and banking
facilities, education and government services. Such
"comprehensive regional development planning" is
gaining ground in some countries--as in Israel, and
on a more limited scale in some European countries.
Also in developing countries, the regional planning
approach promises to play an increasing role, especially in connection with large-scale irrigation
projects and major land development and farm settlement schemes.

Let us be very clear about the nature of this
basic issue: The implementation of a national agricultural development plan requires that the production targets must be broken down to local levels;
increasing agricultural production requires that
modern farming methods be introduced through local
farm production plans. These two approaches must be
harmonized. The agricultural output level and product combination that is nationally desirable must
be matched to what is possible and profitable to
achieve by the farmers.

Farm management economists are in a strong position to help determine the economic and social
factors and the incentives required to achieve the
production targets and to overcome the obstacles
that prevent the adoption of modern farming methods.
In the developing countries today, it is precisely
this function of farm management economists that is
most urgently needed, and is, as yet, least recognized by planners and administrators.

The absence of this two-pronged approach, of
planning from the bottom up as well as from the top
down, is partly responsible for the fact that agricultural development planning on the whole has been
quite ineffective and the farm production response
disappointing. To blow life into a national development plan, one must translate it into the language
of people involved in the production process and mobilize the willingness and ability of local farmers
to raise their production performance.

NOTES TO CHAPTER 12

1. Part of this chapter was published under
the title "Farm Management Research for Planning Agricultural Development," by Rainer Schickele in Indian Journal of Agricultural Economics, Vol. 21, No.
2 (April-June 1966), pp. 1-15.

2. Work in the field of "farm management economics" as used here means research as well as extension work, since there is a desperate need in

developing countries for action-oriented research
designed to guide and hasten the adoption of improved farming systems in conjunction with extension
activities. For an excellent treatment of the
broader aspects of farm management research work,
see W. Y. Yang, <u>Methods of Farm Management Investigations for Improving Farm Productivity</u>, FAO Agricultural Development Paper No. 80 (Rome: FAO, 1965),
pp. 120-253 (revised edition).

3. After six years of such pioneer work undertaken by FAO with the cooperation and support of the
Agricultural Development Council, Inc., the govern-
ments of this Region established a "Working Party of
Farm Management for the Far East" under FAO auspices
and technical guidance. The members of this Working
Party initiated farm management studies in their re-
spective countries and issued the <u>First Farm Manage-
ment Manual for the Use of Agricultural Extension
Workers in Asia and the Far East</u> (Bangkok, Thailand:
Regional Office for Asia and the Far East, Food and
Agriculture Organization of the United Nations,
October 1964). <u>Second Farm Management Manual for
Agricultural Research Workers</u> is in preparation and
scheduled for publication in 1967. The Working Par-
ty also publishes a periodical, <u>Farm Management
Notes for Asia and the Far East</u> under the competent
leadership of its Technical Secretary, Dr. Shao-er
Ong of the FAO Far Eastern Regional Office in Bang-
kok. Its July 1965 issue carried a keynote article
on "Farm Planning and Agricultural Development" by
Dr. W. Y. Yang of FAO, Rome.

4. Government of India, <u>Report on "Intensive
Agricultural District Programme</u>," prepared by the Expert Committee on Assessment and Evaluation, Ministry of Food and Agriculture, Government of India,
1961-63.

5. For an excellent exposition of the approach
used in this Programme, see N. S. Randhawa, "Farm
Planning Project Under Intensive Agricultural District Programme in India," <u>Indian Journal of Agricultural Economics</u>, Vol. XX, No. 3 (July-September
1965), pp. 1-12.

6. Carl C. Malone, "Some Responses of Rice Farmers to the Package Program in Tanjore District, India," _Journal of Farm Economics_, Vol. 47, No. 2 (May 1965), p. 268.

7. Randhawa, "Farm Planning Project Under Intensive Agricultural District Programme in India," _op. cit._, p. 7, reports that in six Indian districts during 1962-63, the crop value-fertilizer cost ratio varied between 2 and 5.6 for the crops fertilized. There may well be areas and years, however, with less favorable value-cost ratios.

8. For a very useful summary of Japan's experiences, see Takekazu Ogura, ed., _Agricultural Development in Modern Japan_ (Tokyo: Japan FAO Association, 1963).

9. This often must include subsistence credit as well, since many farmers depend upon credit to buy food toward the end of the crop year to tide them over to the next harvest. Once they have raised their production through modern techniques, their needs for subsistence credit declines. See Chapter 13).

10. See Stephen A. Marglin, "Insurance for Innovators," _Policies for Promoting Agricultural Development_ (Cambridge, Mass.: Center for International Studies, Massachusetts Institute of Technology, 1965), pp. 257-60.

11. The Food and Agriculture Organization of the United Nations is operating a large number of United Nations Special Fund Projects, in cooperation with many developing countries, in the field of land and water development, farm settlement and pilot development schemes in selected areas. A senior farm economist is usually included in the team of experts to conduct such farm planning studies and determine the major obstacles farmers are facing in adopting modern farming methods.

12. For a tightly reasoned argument for this approach, see Clifton R. Wharton, Jr., "Strategies

for Rural Development," The Agricultural Development
Council, Inc., New York, October 1, 1966, pp. 10-15
(mimeo.).

13. One of the most succinct discussions of the
comprehensive regional planning approach, with con-
crete examples of its implementation, is found in
Raanan Weitz, Agriculture and Rural Development in
Israel: Projection and Planning, The National and
University Institute of Agriculture, Bulletin No. 68
(Rehovot, Israel: February 1963). See also Raanan
Weitz and Yehuda Landan, "Integrierende Landwirt-
schafts Planung auf Nationaler, Regionaler und Ein-
zelbetrieblicher Ehene," Offene Welt, No. 88 (Juli
1965), pp. 185-95 (Köln); and Walter Isard and John
H. Cumberland, eds., Regional Economic Planning:
Techniques of Analysis for Less Developed Areas (Paris: Organization for European Economic Cooperation,
1961). For a clear exposition of economic planning
techniques for establishing national production targets, see Tinbergen, op. cit., pp. 9-28.

13

FARMERS IN GROUP ACTION: COOP-
ERATION, COMMUNITY DEVELOPMENT,
AND PEASANT ORGANIZATIONS

Modern society is much more highly organized in
its production and distribution processes than traditional society. Industry, business, professions,
workers have their organizations representing their
interests in the market, in government policy, in
their respective areas of activities. They bargain
collectively, as groups, in all sorts of formal and
informal negotiations. They articulate their interests, assess their bargaining strength, and through
a process of give and take, arrive at mutual accom-
modations which are more or less acceptable to the
groups concerned on any concrete issue. The individual members of each group participate in formulating its position, and after a certain agreement
has been reached, they are committed to abide by it
until a new round of negotiations start.

In a modern democratic society, the best balance in the bargaining power of these various groups
is that which yields an outcome most conducive to
the economy as a whole, that is to the twin goals of
increasing the national income and reducing poverty.
One of the most vital functions of a democratic government is to provide policy measures which will
bring about such a desirable balance in the bargaining power of the various groups. In practical
terms, this means that public policy aims at
strengthening the bargaining position of the weak
groups and restraining the power of the strong
groups. Herein lies the essence of successful
statesmanship in a modern democracy.

In most of the developing countries, by far the
largest group in a very weak bargaining position
consists of small farmers and agricultural laborers.

322

They are most difficult to organize because they are
widely dispersed, poor, unaccustomed to participation in economic and political group action, and often living under a quasi-servile dependence upon the
good will of a traditional elite. Hence, one of the
key issues of agricultural progress is to strengthen
the farmer's position in his local community, particularly with respect to expanding his economic opportunities and his participation in group activi-
ties--preferably, though not necessarily, with the
acquiescence of the local rural elite.

Let us examine some of the promising approaches
to this end.

MARKETING COOPERATIVES

Farmers work in an institutional environment
which places two rather formidable obstacles in the
way toward progress: (1) a very weak bargaining
position in the market, and (2) a lack of opportunities for securing economies of scale, that is, effi-
ciencies inherent in dealing with large quantities
on their small individual farms. To overcome these
obstacles calls for some kind of organized group action, of cooperation.

A basic purpose of marketing cooperatives is to
strengthen the bargaining power of the farmer in the
market. Without a cooperative, he has often no other choice than selling to the merchant in the village, who may also be his landlord and his moneylender. He must usually sell all his market surplus
at harvest time when prices are lowest, and a good
part of it is used to repay accumulated debts. Under these conditions--particularly if he is illiterate and cannot check the merchant's accounting--he
cannot help but accept any price offered to him.
Yet, if he is to adopt modern techniques and produce
more, he needs prices sufficiently attractive to
give him incentives to do so and money for buying
the modern inputs.

A cooperative gives him an alternative market
outlet and, sometimes, also storage space for part
of his crops for future sale at higher prices.
Since the manager of the cooperative is responsible
to the farmer members, the farmer feels that he can
trust the cooperative, that his sales transactions
are carried out in his interest. This, at least, is
the way a cooperative ought to function. And if it
does, it effectively strengthens the farmer's bargaining power in the market and stimulates progress.

Cooperatives not only strengthen the farmer's
bargaining power, they also bring him benefits of
economies of scale. By handling the combined output of many small farmers, crops can be graded for
quality and higher prices can be paid for good products. The pooling of produce as well as of purchase orders for inputs from many farmers permits
the use of large-scale storage and, often, also processing and packing facilities, which bring higher
prices to farmers for things they sell, and permits
bulk purchases of certain modern inputs (fertilizers, etc.) at lower prices--which improves cost-
price relationships and, again, provides a potent
stimulus for modernization of farming (see Chapter
12).

This aspect of making modern inputs available
to farmers in their villages deserves much greater
attention than it receives, particularly in areas
where the use of these supplies is new.[1] Cooperatives can be instrumental in introducing them into
the area by pooling the orders of the few first innovators, by canvassing the prospective orders for
the coming season and assuring that the supplies of
fertilizer will arrive in time and in the appropriate amounts needed. Beyond that, cooperatives can
put pressure on the government for the assignment of
adequate amounts of foreign exchange for importing
such key supplies as fertilizers.

Cooperatives can also bring economies of scale
to small farmers through the joint use of certain
agricultural machinery and specialized equipment
(e.g., tractors, bulldozers, pesticide sprayers,

threshers, etc.), and technical advice combined with production credit--which is a most powerful combination of inputs for introducing innovations into farming techniques.

Indeed, well-managed cooperatives can bring to small farmers practically all the benefits of economies of scale that large-scale plantations and collective farms enjoy, and still retain the decentralization of initiative and managerial responsibility among farmers that is so important for agricultural progress in view of the nature of the production process and its spatial dispersion. This has been demonstrated impressively by the Scandinavian countries, Japan, Taiwan, and Israel.[2]

There is ample evidence from all parts of the world that, potentially, cooperatives can remove most, if not all, of the handicaps of small farmers regarding economies of scale as well as bargaining strength in the market.

But in actual life, cooperatives have not always succeeded in accomplishing this. There have been many "failures" of cooperatives which were set up with great hopes. Why did they fail? Stories abound of incompetent managers, corruption, and clerks disappearing with the till, of farmers continuing to patronize their old merchants, of governments coddling farmers with subsidies and accepting poor quality products or getting management snarled up with red tape. Many of these stories are true. What conclusion should we draw from them?

Some people are shocked by these failures and conclude that farmers in the developing countries are just not ready for free farmer-controlled cooperatives (and, therefore, should do without them until they are), and that government-sponsored cooperatives are so inefficiently managed that they cannot compete with private merchants. This is a counsel of despair and will not be widely accepted by farmers and governments, for good reasons.

First, farmers have much to learn in group action dealing with modern marketing and production
problems, and they can learn only by doing, by making mistakes and learning from them. Second, what
alternatives are there to overcome the obstacles cooperatives are intended to meet? Increase competition among merchants in all the villages and thereby
raise prices paid to farmers, and lower prices of
things they sell to farmers? No one who is familiar
with the strong positions of the few merchants in
the economy of the typical rural village would know
how to accomplish this. Persuade merchants to pay
farmers the highest price they can afford rather
than the lowest price they have to pay? No farmer
would believe in the efficacy of such persuasion.
The only realistic alternative might be direct government purchase of farm products, which, indeed,
some governments are doing for certain key crops,
such as cotton in the Sudan, rice in Burma and Ceylon, to mention just a few.

In fact, this alternative is quite tempting for
many a government since it provides a ready source
of revenue and government jobs. But it may not be
an alternative better for rural development and more
in the interest of farmers than cooperatives struggling along with some inefficiency and other imper-
fections. These imperfect cooperatives do offer
farmers opportunities for improving their management
and for developing in themselves the qualities of
self-discipline and social responsibility that are
required for any type of group action in a modern
society. Membership participation in a marketing
cooperative involves a farmer in much more concrete
and practical terms than participation in educational or social or political organizations. It will
take time to learn, but learn he will, if often the
hard way.

The tough problem is how to get cooperatives
started and make them function efficiently. In many
parts of the world, one of the most powerful obstacles to successful cooperatives is the silent but
effective opposition of the local rural elite, of
merchants and landlords. Where farmers are very

poor and in a weak bargaining position, they are in-
timidated by the fear of losing the good will of
their landlords and creditors, and with it the only
security they have for their livelihood. It is in
these areas where cooperatives have been especially
difficult to get started and have suffered many
failures. Imagine how afraid a small farmer must be
to join a cooperative if he feels that this will
displease his landlord, who will evict him, or his
creditor, who will refuse him the next loan to carry
his family through to the harvest season. Imagine
how tempting an encouragement from high quarters to
abscond with the money of a co-op can be for a clerk
or the manager. In the assessment of reasons for
failures of cooperatives, these institutional factors are rarely analyzed in detail and, at best,
mentioned in vague general terms. Let us remember
that this opposition can be very effective, even if
it remains silent and does not often lead to overt
reprisals or bribes.[3]

COOPERATIVES, MERCHANTS, AND THE GOVERNMENT

It is precisely in those agricultural areas
where small farmers prevail, where population pressure is heavy, and where local trade is in control
of a small elite of landlords, plantation owners,
and merchants, that the setting up of marketing cooperatives is particularly necessary despite all the
difficulties. Such conditions are typical for large
areas in Latin America and for some parts of Asia
and Africa--except where land reforms have improved
the position of farmers in the market.

Establishing cooperatives in face of the opposition of a strong local elite requires government
support, with trained manpower and finances for organizing and managing cooperatives and educating
farmers in membership participation and responsibilities for a period of years, with provisions for
gradual transfer of management control to the farmer
members, as, for instance, Egypt did fairly successfully under its land reform program.[4] If this is

not possible under the locally prevailing circumstances, direct government purchase of farm products
may be the only practical alternative that would
give farmers better prices. It might well be that
neither cooperatives nor a government purchase organization could be made to function properly until
the area had undergone a thorough land reform in
which the power of landlords and creditors over
farmers had been broken.

Where these obstacles are not as severe, as for
instance in Africa south of the Sahara, and parts of
Southeast Asia, other alternatives for strengthening
the farmers' bargaining power might be found, such
as improving transport and marketing facilities,
which reduce the middleman's margin, price supports
enforceable on private trade, publicly controlled
storage and grading facilities, current price information readily accessible to farmers, and various
tax and credit measures to encourage merchants to
improve the efficiency of their facilities and operations. Usually, these measures are not in conflict
with cooperatives but are benefiting cooperatives
and merchants alike. The interests of farmers and
of agricultural progress might best be served by
fostering farmers' cooperatives side by side with improvements in the functioning of private trade.
There are some farm products, and most consumer
goods, that are more efficiently handled by merchants than by cooperatives. Experience in many
countries shows that cooperatives and private trade
in competition with each other not only strengthen
the farmers' bargaining power, but improve the efficiency of both types of marketing enterprises.

No general principle concerning the role of
private trade in rural areas can be established because much depends on the bargaining position of
farmers, on the control exercised by merchants and
their attitudes toward modernization of the marketing system. In many developing countries, marketing
cooperatives are handling an increasing share of the
farmers' staple food and major export crops, often
including processing and packaging, while farmers
continue to sell their livestock and fruit and

vegetable products to private traders. Similarly, modern inputs, such as fertilizers, pesticides, machinery, etc., may well continue to be distributed mainly through private trade as long as merchants succeed in meeting the quickly rising demand efficiently and at prices that the great majority of small farmers can afford to pay. To this end, governments can help local merchants by extension education in marketing, information services on prices, new sources of supplies, new transport and storage facilities, new types of products, especially modern inputs in farming and the specific time at which they are needed, but also new consumer goods that might appeal to farmers.

Perhaps the most important single factor that will determine the role of merchants in fostering agricultural progress is their ability to win the confidence of the small farmers and to make them feel that merchants respect them as citizens and want to serve them as customers, rather than dominate their fate and exploit their weak position. This change in attitudes of local merchants may be fast in some areas and slow in others; to win the farmers' confidence it must manifest itself in the merchants' behavior toward them, which might well include supporting the farmers' interest in schools, land reforms--and even cooperatives.

This is not as farfetched as it may sound because it clearly is in the enlightened self-interest of merchants to have farmers increase their productivity and income, and become better customers. What private traders may lose in business to the cooperatives, they will more than gain back by the increase in purchases of farm inputs and a whole range of consumer goods. Merchants are elated if a factory moves into a rural town, although the factory manager usually does not buy his supplies from them, nor does he sell his products to them. But the increase in local employment and purchasing power raises the merchants' income just the same. This fact also holds for cooperatives which increase farmers' purchasing power.

Economic progress makes it possible for everyone to be better off. The specific role of cooperatives in bolstering farm production and income brings more rather than less business to merchants, as can be observed in many areas where agricultural progress supported by efficient cooperatives has greatly stimulated private trade. It is a good strategy for agricultural development to win over enlightened progress-oriented members of the rural elite to support the legitimate claims of farmers and the changes required to meet them.

One aspect is very important for agricultural progress that cannot be served by private trade, but for which cooperatives are specifically best suited. Participation in the affairs of a cooperative offers farmers the most practical and constructive opportunity for developing the self-discipline, social responsibility, and cooperative attitude that are requisite to participation in any group organization aimed at improving their economic and social positions.

Such participation is an entirely new experience for farmers. Cooperatives deal with marketing farm products and, hence, involve the farmer's personal interest very deeply and directly. Yet, for generations he has felt individually as helpless vis-à-vis the market forces as vis-à-vis the weather. Through his cooperatives he can exercise some control over market forces, but he must learn to follow a new kind of behavior, one which relates him to his neighbors as a group with a mutual specific interest, which requires of him a certain sense of group responsibility, a trust in his neighbor, an extrafamilial loyalty, a personal obligation to contribute to the group endeavor some new type of effort. This may sometimes involve temporary financial sacrifices in the form of subscriptions to capital stock and foregoing the temptation of selling his products at better prices to traders who may outbid a cooperative just long enough to force it out of business. It takes time for farmers to learn the particular behavior in group responsibility necessary to make a cooperative function efficiently.

We cannot go into detail here on the problems of cooperative management. There can be no question, however, that in developing countries, the establishment of cooperatives usually demands government initiative and support with managerial personnel and finances, at least for an initial period. Training of local personnel preferably drawn from farm families, and local training courses and group discussions on cooperative membership responsibility are also a necessary public function.

The danger that such government-sponsored cooperatives become inefficient, corrupt, bureaucratic, and insensitive to farmers' needs is, of course, a real one, and must be held in check primarily by the farmers themselves. Often there is some local leader with courage and skill for handling issues of this kind who can help farmers in this task. For instance, in a cooperative project of building a school in an Indian village, the committee chairman was found to have embezzled some funds collected from the villagers. A village priest persuaded the chairman to go to the temple, give the misappropriated money as an offering, and beg forgiveness from the gods, with the committee members present. Then, all committee members gave their oath of trusteeship for the project funds, and each agreed to take with him two other committee members to witness each purchase.[5] This is merely an example of how ingenious people can be in handling such moral issues, by taking recourse to local customs that are face-saving for the culprit, and committing to future honesty, him, as well as the others, and thus keeping corruption in check.

There are no foolproof administrative formulas against these dangers of human frailty, but there is plenty of good common sense and devotion to the task among rural people, which can be mobilized through one or the other of the local leaders.

COOPERATIVE CREDIT

Most farmers need credit to survive as well as to buy farm inputs. Even in many areas still under

traditional farming systems, the majority of the
farmers are found to be in debt--and a major part of
the loans is used for living expenses. Usually, a
merchant-moneylender advances a loan to a farmer on
the security of his crop, if not his land, which, in
effect, binds the farmer to his merchant. If the
farmer sells his crop elsewhere, the merchant will
not extend any more credit since the farmer has
shifted his collateral security from his old mer-
chant-creditor to someone else. This makes interest
and repayment collection much more cumbersome for
the merchant. The result is that merchants tend to
respect each others' clientele, and farmers have no
choice but to continue selling their crops to the
same merchant or their landlord.

The same logic, of course, holds for cooperatives. As the farmer sells his crops through the
cooperative, it becomes the natural creditor since
the farmer is under obligation to deliver his crop--
which is the collateral security for the loan--to
the cooperative. However, single-purpose marketing
cooperatives do not extend credit, and single-purpose credit cooperatives do not market crops.

These credit relationships create serious problems in many farming areas. The small farmer is
often in continuous debt to his merchant or moneylender. When his food supply runs out before the
next harvest, he must borrow to survive. When he
sells his crop, part of it goes for repaying his
loan--often at very high interest rates--and the
rest may, again, not be enough to tide him over the
whole crop year. The merchant may prefer not to
collect the loan in full and keep the farmer in debt
because this binds him to the merchant and reduces
competition with other merchants. Hence, if a farmer joins a cooperative, his merchant can immediately
call for the full repayment of the total loan even
before the harvest, which most farmers simply cannot
meet. The farmer then has no alternative but to
continue selling to his merchant.

This makes it very difficult for single-purpose
credit cooperatives to secure their loans, and

therefore, they depend almost entirely on the borrower's character, by requiring mortgages on land and counter signatures of at least two other members, and by being very conservative in the amounts and the purposes for which they are ready to make loans. Such single-purpose credit cooperatives are legally subject to unlimited liability and depend often on their own capital stock contributions as their major source of loan funds. No wonder they, alone, cannot meet the rapidly expanding credit needs of the masses of farmers.[6]

There is a further complication. We have seen why a good part of agricultural credit is used for consumption rather than production purposes. Cooperative credit, however, is usually restricted to production purposes. Merchants, moneylenders, and landlords, however, lend readily for consumption uses because they can charge high interest rates more than ample to cover the risk and tie the farmer's crop even more firmly to themselves. These conditions have greatly retarded the effectiveness of cooperative credit programs and, by the same token, agricultural progress. Cooperative credit must be made to meet the small farmer's need for subsistence credit; otherwise he cannot get a production loan to increase his output so that he will no longer need subsistence loans.

We can get an idea of the magnitude of the problem from surveys made in several areas. In Orissa (India), 50-60 per cent of the total outstanding loans in 1961/62 were used for consumption purposes. In a rice-growing area in the Philippines, 71 per cent of agricultural credit was used for living expenses in 1958.[7] The governments in both these countries have strongly fostered cooperative credit for many years; yet only a small proportion of total loans come from credit cooperatives or other institutional lenders. In an Indian district not far from Delhi, cooperatives furnished only 23 per cent of the total credit of their members, while 62 per cent still came from moneylenders and merchants, and 15 per cent from relatives (in 1958). These members paid 24 per cent or more interest on 46 per cent of

their loans, while non-members paid such high interest on 73 per cent of their loans. Cooperative
credit carried 9.8 per cent interest. In the Philippines (in 1958), only 11 per cent of the loans
came from cooperatives, and 81 per cent from moneylenders and landlords. For much of Southeast Asia,
these "non-institutional" lenders are still supplying 80-90 per cent of the total loans made to farmers.[8]

Commercial banks are not concerned with serving
the credit needs of small farmers; they deal only
with large farmers and plantation owners. For instance, a survey conducted by the University in Iba-
dan in 1961-62 showed that none of the twenty-two
branches of commercial banks in the Western Region
gave loans to small farmers, although they were located in communities where well over 50 per cent of
the people lived on small farms. The bank managers
reported that they gave loans only to borrowers who
had accounts with them or could offer ample collateral security. This, of course, is general practice
of commercial banks, which automatically rules out
the typical small farmer as a borrower.[9]

These conditions show clearly the difficulties
inherent in the traditional dependency of farmers
upon moneylenders and landlords, which farmers and
their cooperative credit programs are facing. Although these conditions have been improving during
the 1960's in India and the Philippines, they are
still far from being satisfactory for rapid agricultural progress. Even in the mid-1960's, interest
rates for the bulk of agricultural loans furnished
by private lenders ranged from 25 to 30 per cent per
year in India, Burma, and Thailand, and from 60 to
200 per cent in Indonesia.[10]

These high interest rates are claimed to be
necessary for covering the high risk involved. The
fact is that they typically amount to exorbitant
"risk premiums" relative to the losses. A moneylender grants many short-term loans; each one is
small, he has known each of the farmer borrowers for
a long time, and he controls, directly or indirectly,

the marketing of their crops. The chances of loss
in the trading or in debt collection are small indeed. The explanation of these interest rates lies
in the weak bargaining position and poverty of the
small farmer and the urgency of his need for money
at critical times during the year.[11]

Another factor is holding back the expansion of
cooperative credit: the unnecessary amount of red
tape and time involved in getting a loan. This must
be changed. Developing countries have reached a
stage where production credit as an instrument for
national development is as important to the economy
as it is to the individual farmer. If the country
wants farmers to get the supplies needed to increase
production, it must pattern the credit arrangements
primarily to fit farmers' needs for getting the job
done. Instead, conventional credit arrangements are
primarily designed to safeguard the creditor's interest, to ease debt collection, and keep defaults
to a minimum.

Long application forms, evidence of credit-
worthiness, affidavits and counter-signatures, and
the checking of these forms up a bureaucratic ladder
to a central authority for decision are all supposed
to reduce risk. But do they? If the farmer cannot
meet his payments, he will default regardless of the
red tape; if the farmer does not want to meet them,
the credit agency has all the legal instruments for
collection at its disposal regardless of the red
tape. The private moneylender lets him have a loan
with just a record in his books. Of course, he
knows the farmer; but so does the local cooperative,
and has a lien on the borrower's crop just as the
moneylender. The only thing that such cumbersome
procedure does is reduce the volume of credit to
those most in need of it.

Local cooperative societies should remain small
enough for the members to know each other. Hence,
the granting of a production loan can well be left
to the discretion of the local cooperative, with a
minimum of paper work just sufficient for certifia-
ble accountability of the legitimate use of funds.

Beside the lien on his crop, the cooperative also
can use the sanction of refusing further credit, or
even cancel his membership in the cooperative. If
the default occurs due to forces beyond the borrower's control, such as drought, floods, or pests, he
should be entitled to reasonable deferment provisions. The members of the cooperatives should be
given the protection of limited liability, as corporations are, and the government could insure them
at low cost for any losses suffered due to causes
beyond their control.

MULTIPURPOSE COOPERATIVES--NEW PARTNERSHIP OF GOVERNMENT AND FARMERS

There are only a few developing countries where
cooperative credit provides a major share of all
short-term loans to farmers. This holds for Japan
and Taiwan where credit is one of the functions of
strong multipurpose cooperatives, along with marketing and extension work and, sometimes also, cooperative use of specialized machinery and the processing of farm products. This requires a well-
trained cadre of managers, technical and administrative personnel, and a strong legislative and organizational support from the government.[12]

The combination of these three basic functions
of marketing, credit, and extension is highly effective in modernizing farming operations, as they
mutually support each other. And since these functions must be closely and currently adapted to widely varying local conditions, the responsible participation of farmers in managing these multipurpose
cooperatives is by far the most efficient organizational principle for carrying out these functions.

Cooperative credit in conjunction with the
marketing of the members' produce provides an ample
pool of collateral security, which can be used to
reduce risk and the interest rate; in conjunction
with extension services, the use of farm loans can
be made efficient through guidance and technical assistance in the application of modern inputs and

production methods, which also reduces risk and permits a lower interest rate.

Several countries are moving in the direction of promoting multipurpose cooperative organizations combining these three functions, such as the Philippines and the U.A.R. When credit is closely linked with marketing in cooperative organizations, production credit tends to be much more widely used, as in Japan and Taiwan with over $200 per hectare of cultivated land and Korea with $97 per hectare, than where credit cooperatives function in the main separately, as in India, Pakistan, Burma, Malaya, and Thailand with only $2 to $3 per hectare.[13]

Table 30 shows the general scope of farmers' cooperatives in a number of developing countries where cooperatives have expanded vigorously in the 1950's and 1960's, usually with strong government support of various kinds. For instance, in Ceylon, the number of cooperatives increased from 68 in 1957 to 4,800 in 1962, serving most of the rice farmers in the first instance. The cooperatives were set up rapidly to serve as purchasing agents for the government, which bought 57 per cent of the total rice crop in 1962 under the Guaranteed Rice Price Scheme.[14] Still, the cooperatives are conceived as multipurpose societies, one for each village or a group of small villages, as farmer-controlled cooperatives for all local activities that are not a matter of national policy, and at the same time as arms of the government on national policy matters they are competent to implement. As long as government policy is favorable to farmers they are not likely to resent this type of government control; if policies become unfavorable, unfairly rigid, or ill-adapted to local conditions, farmers can voice their objections through their cooperative boards and committees.

A new concept, a new philosophy of farmer cooperation is being forged in the developing world, which is quite different from that which guided the cooperative movement in the Western countries. The English Rochdale and German Raiffeisen principles of

TABLE 30

Farmers' Cooperatives in Selected Countries

Type of Cooperative	Number of Local Units	Number of Members (in thousands)
Argentina		
Agricultural Cooperatives, grain, cattle and other products, marketing, milk processing, etc. (1960)	1,394	432
Brazil		
Producers' Cooperatives (1961)	1,456	507
Agricultural Credit Cooperatives, strongest in the States of Rio Grande do Sul, Santa Catarina, São Paulo	253	113
Mexico		
Agricultural Cooperatives of all types, presumably serving farmers outside the ejido system (1961)	838	60
Ceylon		
Multipurpose, one in each village or group of small villages; functions as buying agents for government (e.g., purchased 57 per cent of total rice production under Guaranteed Rice Scheme in 1962)	4,800	n.a.

India

   Mainly Credit Cooperatives, but
with marketing on the increase, especially in supplying fertilizer,
improved seed, implements and serving about one-third of farmers
(1962) — 215,000 — 19,600

Indonesia

   Cooperatives of all kinds, recently
used mainly for supplying farmers
with production requisites (fertilizers, seeds, etc.) at concessional prices (1961) — 38,802 — 6,900

Japan

   Multipurpose Cooperatives, serving
most of the 6 million Japanese farmers; 2,430 cooperatives existing in
1961; these were grouped into 560
associations in 1963 — 2,430 — n.a.

Malaysia

   Cooperatives of all kinds (1962) — 2,912 — 395

Iran

   Multiple purpose, one planned for
each village falling under Land Reform Law of 1962 (15,000 to 18,000
village cooperatives required);
actually established by 1964 — 1,200 — n.a.

Sources: Comité Interamericano de Desarrollo Agrícola, Inventory of Information Basic to
the Planning of Agricultural Development in Latin America, Regional Report (Washington, D.C.: CIDA, 1963), pp. 68-71, for Latin America; Food and Agriculture Organization of the United Nations, The State of Food and Agriculture, 1965 (Rome:
FAO, 1965), pp. 188-89, for other countries.

339

cooperative organization were based upon independence from government financial help, guidance, and
supervision and upon voluntary membership of individuals. These principles do not fit the conditions
in most newly developing rural areas. They require
modifications to take account of the much more active role governments are playing in the agricultural development process, and of the much weaker
bargaining position of the masses of farmers vis-à-
vis the market and the rural elites.

     The new concept of farmer cooperation is based
upon a partnership of government and farmers. The
government augments the loan funds of a cooperative,
contributed by the farmer members to meet the needs
for modernizing farm production; gives initial financial and administrative assistance in the training
of personnel and the management of cooperative marketing and credit activities; and furnishes an extension service to advise and give technical assistance to farmers in modern farming techniques, financed by cooperative production credit. The farmer
assumes the responsibility of management and patron-
age of the cooperative and of gradually taking over
its management by participating in the election of
board and committee members and in the formulation
of cooperative policy and administrative measures,
within the general framework of legislation and government programs relating to cooperatives and their
functions in accelerating agricultural progress.

     In principle, the government's function is lim-
ited to giving financial and organizational support
where needed to supplement the contributions by the
farmers, and to setting certain standards of marketing and pricing practices, credit terms and interest
rates, financial accountability, and other operating
procedures. Within this framework, however, the local cooperative must have ample freedom in the management of its affairs and the responsibility to
adapt its marketing and credit functions to local
conditions.

     This flexibility offers a real opportunity to
implement national development policies and programs

through local cooperatives. The direct involvement
of farmers in the adaptation, testing, and demonstrating of improved marketing and credit practices
is a highly effective device for avoiding costly
mistakes in agricultural program implementation.
Such practices as grading and storing farm products
to realize better prices for farmers and stimulating
them to deliver higher quality products, granting
consumption loans for certain urgent needs, making
fertilizers, better seeds, etc., available to farmers at favorable prices and credit terms--these and
many other practices have to be adapted to local
conditions in order to work efficiently (see Chapter
12). For instance, in the Philippines, the Agricultural Credit and Cooperatives Institute has conducted two pilot projects in different farming areas to
determine the amount and nature of credit needs resulting from farm plans and budgets along the lines
discussed in Chapter 12. This experience led to
changes in loan policies and procedures, designed to
make technical guidance in the use of production
credit available to farmers on an expanding scale.[15]
Highly centralized agricultural programs often break
down or work at a disappointingly low degree of effectiveness, due to the lack of such flexibility and
the failure to draw upon the farmers' keen knowledge
of local conditions.

Many developing countries at present lack the
trained personnel for launching multipurpose cooperatives on a massive national scale. But it is important that the vision of their potential role is
clear in the minds of leaders and farmers. There is
no standard blueprint which will fit all countries,
nor even all rural areas in any one country. Single-
purpose cooperatives are easier to organize and manage. A marketing cooperative handling only one or
two main crops may be best suited in this or that
area at a certain stage, while a credit cooperative
may be most needed in another area. Cooperatives
always involve farmers in group action, in produc-
tion-oriented participation, in community affairs,
in assuming social and managerial responsibilities
for a group with strong common interests--all of
which are experiences of great value to farmers as

well as to the rural community and the nation. As
soon as possible, after a single-purpose cooperative
has gotten over its growing pains and into its
stride, it will be useful to add a few new functions
selected for their complementary nature. Such
growth into multipurpose cooperatives deserves
strong government support and a forward-looking
training program for the personnel required to make
them work efficiently.

The cooperative organization of these functions
may well be worth a rather high price, in terms of
government support and some initial inefficiencies,
just because of this built-in flexibility in adapting national programs to local conditions and involving actively the farmers' knowledge and interest
in the process, and because of the built-in decentralization of administrative responsibility that
permits reduction of red tape and yields a greater
sensitivity to the local needs of farmers. These
two factors are most valuable assets, which are usually lacking in the performance of central government agencies, and whose lack results in much waste
and inefficiency.

COMMUNITY DEVELOPMENT: MOBILIZING
PEOPLE FOR SELF-HELP PROJECTS

The idea of community development by mobilizing
local people and resources for self-help projects of
a wide variety is simple and straightforward. There
is much innate intelligence, accumulated knowledge,
and latent leadership in the population of a rural
community, which can be activated by some assistance
from the government.[16] The basic principle rests
upon the expectation that if an initiative and a
modest support are offered in the form of leadership, administrative, technical, and financial assistance, the local people will respond by active
participation in the planning and execution of development projects.

Governments of many countries, especially in
Southeast Asia, have promoted community development

programs, with widely varying success. Community
development as a "movement" and an integral part of
national development policy is playing an important
role in India, Ceylon, Taiwan, Pakistan, and the
Philippines. A general idea of the scope of this
type of local people's participation in development
projects is given in Table 31, showing the major
types of projects, the percentage of the villages
covered, and the number of rural people served, as
of 1960 or thereabout. Since that time, considerable progress has been made, but at least in India,
Pakistan, and the Philippines, the direct impact of
these programs on the rate of economic progress at
the village level has not been as spectacular as was
hoped by the planners and the government agencies
involved.

In fact, the effectiveness of community development programs on agricultural and general economic
progress has not been very high in many cases. Why
is it that often people fail to respond to initiative and support offered from outside? Why is it
that people's participation is often sluggish and
insufficient to maintain a self-supporting drive for
improving local conditions?[17]

There are no categorical answers to these questions. Group behavior and motivation are very complex processes whose components vary widely. As in
the case of cooperatives, nothing is gained by merely pronouncing community development a "failure" or
a "success." In most cases, elements of both can be
found. Much depends on whether one compares actual
performance with the overt goals, which usually
leads to a negative judgement, or with the situation
prevailing before the program got going, which often
leads to a positive judgement. Let us briefly examine some key issues in the operation and evolution
of community development programs.

(1) Change in people's social values and culture, required for progress, is considered by some
leaders the dominant purpose of community development. People from all walks of life and social
strata of the community are to be brought together

in meetings to discuss what their problems are, and
what they might do jointly to solve them. If some
people feel that the social structure, the caste
system, conditions of land tenure, tribal customs,
and religious taboos stand in the way, these issues
can be brought up and explored. Out of these group
deliberations are to emerge a series of "felt needs,"
which then can be formulated into practical community projects for implementation. Leaders of this
school of thought argue that this is the best way of
securing active and genuine participation of local
people in development projects that they themselves
have decided to want, and of teaching people to work
together toward a dynamic progressive community,
toward higher levels of living, of responsible citizenship, and mutual respect for one's neighbors' human dignity. The government's role is to be merely
one of helping the villagers to implement their program, to help themselves in achieving their aims.

This is basically the concept of community development that emerged in India under the leadership
of Gandhi and his followers, was adopted by the newly independent government, and implemented by an impressive program of organization and training of
village-level workers, block and district officers
in the 1950's.[18] The United Nations has been assisting other countries in organizing similar programs,
with the help of community development experts--many
of whom were drawn from India in the early years.

This idealistic concept is excellent as a motivating principle for guiding the spirit in which
leaders exercise their efforts in stimulating villagers to action. It has proven insufficient, however, as an operating principle for guiding the selection and execution of practical projects by
villagers.

Where the social structure is strongly strati-
fied in groups of widely different levels of social
status, wealth, education, and political power, it
is unrealistic to expect that a comprehensive community development program will emerge out of discussions at village gatherings that will meet even

TABLE 31

Scope of Community Development Programs in
Southeast Asian Countries
(around 1960)

		India	Pakistan (Village Aid)	Ceylon	Taiwan (Farmers' Assoc.)	Phil-ippines
Per Cent of total villages covered (around 1960)	%	68	28	100	91	20
Population of the villages	million	192	17	7	4	4
Number of years from beginning of community development program	no.	8	6	7	6	3
Capital Assets Created:						
Land irrigated	thousand ha.	---	63	---	484	71
Orchards laid out	thousand ha.	288	19	---	29	388
New Implements supplied	thousands	1,595	38	---	219	61
Rural latrines built	thousands	604	16	73	---	---
Drinking wells built	thousands	184	7	14	3	14
School and community buildings		15,579	1,768	5,536	2,134	6,791
Roads constructed	thousand km.	198	5	10	11	6
Literacy Centers	thousands	156	5	---	---	---

Source: United Nations/ECAFE/FAO, "Community Development and Economic Development," Part I, Bangkok, 1960.

345

the most urgent needs of the poor and disadvantaged classes--except in rare cases where some influential leaders articulate the needs of the poor and press for their recognition. Where such progressive leadership appears, it usually comes from the outside, that is from the officers of a progressive government and various religious and political leaders (as in India and Ceylon).

This, of course, is recognized, but it involves the danger that such enthusiastic leaders promote their own "felt needs" and persuade the villagers to adopt a corresponding program. When it then comes to a sustained day-to-day effort of its execution and maintenance, the villagers' participation is much less than enthusiastic and may falter quickly. This has been observed often regarding such projects as latrines and sanitary wells--"needs" which certainly have not been "urgently felt" by villagers in their traditional ways, but which have figured prominently in many community development programs from the beginning.[18] Sometimes these projects don't even last long enough for people to learn from experience their salutary value. On the other hand, school and road-building projects are meeting felt needs, and are genuinely supported and usually maintained, unless the government fails in supplying teachers for the schools.

It is even unrealistic to expect farmers to "feel the need" for modern production techniques, because they don't know about them, or don't believe what they may be told about their miraculous results. The general cultural change approach to community development, therefore, has very little effect on agricultural productivity--except where farm production projects are vigorously promoted by the government and pushed by local leaders.

(2) This leads to another key issue. How much government initiative and guidance is compatible with the community development philosophy? For instance, some Indian leaders blame the government for killing the community development movement by making it "the handmaid of the administrator and

agriculturist." The village-level worker, prompted by the technical officers, "knew what was good for the villager, and so planned it and executed it."[20] The result may be neither a genuine change in social values, nor an efficient adoption of modern agricultural techniques, but merely confusion and disappointment. This, in essence, represents the view of many critics of community development--among whom are economists, planners, and civil servants.

There is, on the other hand, a growing recognition of the need for close cooperation between government agencies and villagers for the sake of accelerating progress. As in the case of cooperatives, a new type of partnership between local groups and government is emerging throughout the developing world. In such a partnership, local groups turn to the government for assistance in improvement and development schemes supported by local effort; at the same time, the government turns to the local groups for adapting national policies to local conditions and for active participation in implementing these policies. Local people need help from the government in securing trained personnel, organizational and financial support for such projects as schools, roads, water supply, marketing facilities, farmers' cooperatives, etc. The government needs the judgement and participation of local people for making national programs (e.g., extension service), introduction of modern farming techniques, supply of inputs and production credit, land reforms, price supports, etc., fit local conditions and work efficiently.

The risks involved in this approach to community development are bound to be smaller than those inherent in a central government authoritative approach of executing stereotyped programs. We must, of course, recognize the risks and face up to the two principal dangers in this partnership: first, the danger that the government loses its responsiveness to local judgement, and with it the confidence of the people and their participation; second, the danger that the small farmers and farm workers who most need to increase their production and income

fail to be effectively represented in the local
groups dealing with the government. This may result
in a continued dominance of the traditional elite, a
dominance that, indeed, may be further strengthened
by its exclusive partnership with the government. A
world-wide study of community development revealed
that "in a society polarized between a few owners of
large blocks of land and a large number of tenants
and landless workers, community development is
greatly restricted in what it can accomplish."[21]
Examples of these dangers can be found in many places.[22]

On balance, the community development approach
to mobilizing local participation and creative effort on one side, and to adapting government programs to local conditions and needs on the other,
deserves the wholehearted support of the farmers as
well as of the government, planners, and political
leaders. Here, as in the case of cooperatives, it
is best to remain flexible and undogmatic as to the
specific types of local organizations and government
functions that might be devised to carry on community development work. Different countries will find
different ways best suited for the task.

In finding out which way promises to be best
suited in a certain area, we must not lose sight of
an important principle: the local unit, which represents the farmers and villagers, must be given a
good deal of discretion, of responsibility for decisions concerning development projects and adoption
of national programs and policies, and possibly powers of taxation for certain local development purposes such as schools, roads, marketing facilities,
etc. This area of discretion also includes at least
an informal or advisory, yet effective, coordination
of all the various government departments and agencies involved in development works and programs at
the local level. The importance of this principle
has become strikingly evident in the experiences of
many different countries, such as the Comilla Rural
Development Project in East Pakistan, the panchayats
in India, the farmers' associations in Taiwan, the
cooperatives and cultivation committees in Ceylon,

the _municipios_ and _barrios_ in the Bicol regions in the Philippines.[23] Unless the local officers of the various government agencies are specifically instructed to work with the community development group, to attend its meetings, to render their services to its committees and members, community development is likely to falter, or to progress at a much slower rate than could be achieved by such cooperation with villagers.

Finally, I want to stress once more the critical relevance of the things we have discussed so far in this chapter to the rate of agricultural progress. With any given amount of personnel and funds a government has available, this amount will go very much further, will yield much greater production and real income, under programs firmly rooted in the rural community, supported by participation, labor, and ingenuity of local farmers, than under programs administered solely by a central government's bureaucratic line--authority, insensitive to the judgement and needs of the local people, unprepared to draw upon their knowledge for adapting national policies to fit the various regions of the country.

PEASANT ORGANIZATIONS: ASCENT TO POLITICAL POWER

Through cooperatives and community development councils, farmers are establishing group relationships with various government units. In dealing with the government, cooperatives speak collectively for their farmer members, and community development councils represent, more or less effectively, the farmers and villagers. This, in itself, means a big step forward in the articulation of the needs and aspirations of farmers as a group. It strengthens their position in the local community, gives them some influence over the course of events. Farmers' participation as a group in a series of specific activities offers them opportunities to improve certain environmental conditions, such as getting better prices and cheaper credit through their cooperatives, better services through extension programs for adults and schools for children, for example.

These group activities on the part of small farmers and farm workers may improve the quality of existing government services, but can have only little direct effect on national policy, on appropriations for agricultural development, on the creation of new programs and new legislation required for accelerating progress. To make their needs and aspirations felt in the nation's body politic, in the legislature, and even in the top echelon of government, farmers must obtain influence in the electorate, in political parties, in organized interest groups that support the farmers' aims.

Peasant organizations that were formed to press for the recognition of their claims by local landlords and employers, by the general electorate, the legislature, and the government, have emerged with remarkable vigor and speed in several areas in Latin America since the mid-1950's and early 1960's. Table 32 shows the approximate number of local units and their membership as of the early 1960's. To put these figures--most of which are bound to be very unreliable--in relationship to the size of the country's agriculture, the total number of farms and a rough estimate of the total membership of the organizations listed are shown. In Cuba and Venezuela, such membership comprised around one half of the farm families, in Argentina and Brazil around one fifth, in Mexico around one tenth of the independent (non-ejido) farmers, and in Chile and Colombia around 5 per cent.

In some areas, for example in Chile, Brazil, and Colombia, rural Catholic priests have played a leadership role in helping farmers organize themselves. Often, farmers received help from urban labor leaders or intellectuals. Sometimes, leaders emerged from their local ranks, as for instance in the peasant revolts in Mexico in the 1910 revolution, and in Bolivia in the 1950's. Small farmers and farm workers are in such a vulnerable position and face such a powerful opposition by large estate owners that their chances of forming organizations

for collective bargaining and participation in the
political process without universal sufferages, outside aid, and the protection of national law are
rare indeed.[24] Even where farmers have succeeded in
establishing organizations, their economic effectiveness in improving local land tenure, wages, housing,
and working conditions has so far, been very limited,
due to their weak bargaining position in the social
structure. This holds for most of the organizations
listed in the table. But it must be remembered that
most of them are very young, less than ten years
old, and that some of them have been more effective
in influencing progressive national legislation than
local conditions. It will take some time for national reform laws to become operative in the villages.

Some of these farmer organizations are affiliated with national political parties, and some are
not. Some of them are sponsored or supported by the
government, some are not. Whether such affiliations
are strengthening or weakening the effectiveness of
farmers' organizations cannot be judged by the fact
of affiliation; it all depends on the nature of the
political party or the government.

If the political party is predominantly controlled by progressive elements in the urban middle
classes or in labor unions, the peasant organizations
can expect strong support for land reform, minimum
wage and housing laws, and low-interest credit, as
the Campesino Federation in Venezuela has received
and the Christian Peasant Union in Chile, for instance. But not much beyond lip service is likely
if the party is under the influence of the traditional elite, which seems at least inofficially to
be the case of rural associations in Brazil and some
of the organizations in Argentina and Colombia.
Similarly, if a strongly progressive government supports local farmers' organizations in areas dominated by a conservative rural elite, this might be the
only effective way open to farmers for exerting
pressure for the implementation of institutional reforms, as was the case in Mexico and recently in
Chile. In 1966, the Chilean Peasant Union, with the

TABLE 32

Farmers' Organizations in Latin America[1]

Type of Organization	Number of Local Units	Number of Members (in thousands)
Argentina: 470,000 farm units; approximate total members[3]		(114)
Sociedad Rural Argentina, mainly owners and operators of large estates.	n.a.	10
Federación Agraria, small owners and tenants	n.a.	40
Confederación Rural, middle-sized farmers.	145	(14)
Farm Laborers' Syndicates	1,000	(50)
Brazil: 2,065,000 farm units; approximate total members[3]		(359)
Rural Associations of various kinds, in 1961: many of them weak and inactive; regarded as "semiofficial" if established under the 1945 law.	1,804	218
Peasant Leagues, began rapid growth in the late 1950's. Members are small owners, sharecroppers, renters, squatters, cattle workers, and wage laborers. The most important peasant leagues were reported in 1962 to have at least 80,000 members, mainly in the States of Pernambuco, Paraíba, Ceará, and Maranhão.	n.a.	80
Rural Syndicates, began rapid growth since 1961. Many in the northeast, some founded by priests, and also by local farmers themselves. They are encouraged by the Federal Agrarian Reform Agency (SUPRA). In the State of Itabuna, about 10,000 of the 150,000 agricultural wage workers are members of syndicates.	n.a.	(Itabuna) 10
Professional Association of Rural Workers, founded by Catholic priests in 1961, mainly in the State of São Paulo.	100	(5)

Federation of Agricultural Workers of São Paulo.   100   (5)

Movement of Landless Farmers (MASTER) and Gaucho Agrarian Front, active in Rio Grande do Sul since 1962--the latter had had seventy-two local syndicates established in 1962.   72   (4)

National Confederation of Agricultural Workers (CONTAG), established December 1963, with 29 federations from 19 states and 743 rural syndicates represented at initial convention.   743   (37)

Chile: 151,000 farm units; approximate total members[3]   (10)

Syndical Association of Chile (ASICH), a Christian social action group founded by priests in 1947, training syndicate leaders; organized in 1960 the Federation of Workers on the Land (UCC), mainly with members in the provinces of Talca and Gruico.   n.a.   n.a.

National Association of Campesino Organizations (ANOC).   n.a.   n.a.

Indian National Federation, founded in 1953.   10

National Federation of Agricultural Workers. These last two are affiliated with the Central Union of Chilean Workers (CUTCH), with a membership of 400,000 workers, or 68 per cent of all trade union members in Chile. Syndicates also have training courses for farm leaders (e.g., 512 farmers got such training January-April 1964).   n.a.   n.a.

Colombia: 1,244,000 farm units; approximate total members[3]   (50)

Sociedad de Agricultura and Confederación Colombiana de Ganaderos are the two largest organizations representing mainly the large landowners' interests. The Sociedad de Agricultura functions as a "consultative body to the government."   n.a.

Federación Nacional de Cafeteros is semiofficial and controls coffee storage, trade, and exports; it has an extension service of its own.   n.a.   n.a.

National Agrarian Federation (FANAL), in 1964 was composed of local unions and associations of low-income farmers and agricultural workers, with 300 syndicates of agricultural workers and 250 "rural community boards," with over 50,000 members.   550   50

353

TABLE 32
(continued)

Type of Organization	Number of Local Units	Number of Members (in thousands)
Cuba: 240,000 farm units; approximate total members[3]		(156)
National Association of Small Farmers (ANAP), established in 1961, comprises 2,611 local organizations.	2,611	156[2]
Mexico: 1,366,000 independent farm units; approximate total members[3]	n.a.	(134)
Confederación Nacional Campesina serves mainly the _ejidatarios_.	n.a.	n.a.
Confederación Nacional de Productores Agrícolas serves independent farmers, as does the	368	(37)
Confederación Nacional Ganadera, and the	973	(97)
Asociación Nacional de Cosecheros.	n.a.	n.a.
Peru: 879,000 farm units; no estimates of membership available		
Sociedad Nacional Agraria is a strong organization with a small membership representing the larger farmers and landowners; it also has a "department for small farmers" offering some technical aid to 200 local committees.	n.a.	n.a.
Committees of Small Peasants affiliated with the National Federation of Peasants, for publicity and information on small peasants' problems.	n.a.	n.a.
Agricultural Syndicates of wage workers on the large sugar, cocoa, and coffee plantations, affiliated with Workers' Confederation of Peru.	n.a.	n.a.

354

Independent Syndicates are increasing and in some places force land-owners to deal officially with their leaders and enter into contracts with them.

Venezuela: 320,000 farm units; approximate total members[3]

Campesino Federation (FCV) is largest of the national peasant organizations in Latin America, it unites 4,000 agricultural syndicates and campesino leagues in a movement covering about 52 per cent of the total rural population over ten years old. In 1963, almost 3,000 legally recognized syndicates had over 145,000 members. The Campesino Federation is affiliated with the

Confederation of Workers (CIV). The syndicates and leagues play important roles in implementation of land reform, in cooperation with National Agrarian Institute (IAN). In some land-settlement projects, the local peasant leagues or syndicates function as de facto local government and carry on community development projects. Also training of farm leaders sponsored by syndicates.

n.a.	n.a.
	(166)
2,936	145
n.a.	n.a.

1. Sources: Comité Interamericano de Desarrollo Agrícola, Inventory of Information Basic to the Planning of Agricultural Development in Latin America, Regional Report (Washington, D.C.: CIDA, 1963), pp. 68-71; and Food and Agriculture Organization of the United Nations, "The Role of Peasant Organizations in Land Reform and Related Community Development Programmes with Special Reference to Latin American Countries," World Land Reform Conference Background Paper No. 4, Rome, 1966, Chapter II, pp. 3-8 (mimeo.).

2. These two figures for Cuba are estimated from data in Food and Agriculture Organization of the United Nations, Country Report: Cuba, World Land Reform Conference, Rome, 1966.

3. Estimated by assuming an average of 100 members per local unit of organizations mainly serving small farmers, and of fifty members per local unit of organizations mainly serving agricultural workers, which roughly corresponds to those organizations for which the numbers of units and of members are available. For Venezuela, the average of "52 per cent of the rural population over ten years old" has been applied to the total number of farms, assuming roughly the same average family size and the same relative incidence of membership of farmers and hired workers. This total membership estimate refers only to the organizations listed showing either local units and/or membership. The numbers of farm units are taken from Comité Interamericano de Desarrollo Agrícola, op. cit.

support of the government, succeeded in reaching an agreement with about forty large estates in the Colchagua Province, after 2,000 farm workers had gone on strike, which guaranteed farm workers a 50 per cent increase in wages. A contract to that effect was negotiated in collective bargaining, and it was expected that the terms of this contract would set wage standards for the whole central valley of Chile, its main agricultural area.[25] It is unrealistic to believe that any affiliation of peasant movements with political parties or the government is necessarily detrimental to the interests of small farmers and farm workers. Particularly where farmers are in a very weak position in the rural community, they will require some outside support from influential groups who share their interests or are sympathetic to them.

The usefulness of affiliation with peasant unions is becoming more and more appreciated by urban-based political parties because of the strong electoral support they can get from the large masses of small farmers and farm workers--which accounts for the affiliation of the Confederation of Workers (CIV) with the Campesino Federation in Venezuela, and that of the Central Union of Chilean Workers (CUTCH) with the Indian National Federation and the National Federation of Agricultural Workers in Chile.

There is a clear advantage, however, in establishing farmers' organizations formally as independent groups--even if they have received help from a political party or the government in getting established. This strengthens the farmers' bargaining power on any specific policy issue and leads to a much clearer articulation of the farmers' problems and aspirations, as compared to farmers joining political parties as individuals, or just voting for the party of their choice--or, perhaps, of someone else's choice. Such parties may, indeed, fight for some legislation in the interest of farmers to keep their votes in the next election. But without an organization of their own, farmers cannot participate in the formulation of specific policy proposals, and in sufficient detail to render them operative once they become law.

Whatever organizational arrangements might
emerge in various areas and countries, agricultural
progress demands that farmers as a group get a hear-
ing in the councils of the nation, where they can
exert their influence in formulating policies in the
interest of their welfare.[26]

NOTES TO CHAPTER 13

1. For a vivid discussion of this issue, see
Arthur T. Mosher, Getting Agriculture Moving: Essen-
tials for Development and Modernization (New York:
Praeger, 1966), pp. 89-98; see also Chapter 10.

2. The comparison between the production efficiency on the large-scale collective farms (Kibbut-
zim) and the family-scale farms (Moshavim) in Israel
is particularly relevant here, because both types of
production organization have been developing side by
side under the same general environment; yet studies
have shown that the individual family-scale farm
complemented by cooperative action is at least as
efficient and in some respects more efficient than
the large-scale collective. See Yehuda Lowe, "Kib-
butz and Moshav, An Economic Appraisal," Ministry of
Agriculture, Israel, August 1958 (mimeo.).

3. See Solon L. Barraclough, "Agricultural
Policy and Land Reform," paper presented at Conference on Key Problems of Economic Policy in Latin
America, University of Chicago, November 6-9, 1966,
p. 57 (mimeo.).

4. See Sayed Marei, Agrarian Reform in Egypt
(Cairo, 1957), pp. 105-13.

5. See K. D. Gangrade, "An Incomplete School:
A Case Record in Rural Community Organization," International Review of Community Development, Nos.
13-14 (1965), p. 113.

6. For a revealing study of these difficulties, see H. B. Shivamaggi, "Provision of Credit for Small Cultivators," _Indian Journal of Agricultural Economics_, Vol. 18, No. 3 (July-September 1963), pp. 23-37.

7. See Misra, _op. cit._; and N. B. Tablante, "The Agricultural Credit Problem in the Philippines," _The Philippine Agriculturist_, Vol. XLIX, Nos. 6-7 (November-December 1965), p. 561.

8. Q. U. Khan, "Rural Credit and Cooperation in the Jamia Development Circle, 1957-58," Jamia Institute of Agricultural Economics and Rural Sociology, 1960, pp. 24-26 (mimeo.). See also Tablante, _op. cit._, p. 560; and the Food and Agriculture Organization of the United Nations, _The State of Food and Agriculture, 1966_, (Rome: FAO, 1965), pp. 178-79. The All-India Rural Credit Survey of 1954 concluded: "Cooperation has failed, but cooperation must succeed." In 1958, India's National Development Council urged that "responsibility and initiative for social and economic development at the village level should be placed fully on the village cooperatives and the village _panchayat_." See United Nations/ECAFE /FAO, "Community Development and Economic Development," Part I, Bangkok, 1960, p. 80. See also Sailesh Kumar Bose, "Cooperative Credit and Agricultural Productivity in India: Experience of a Decade," _Indian Journal of Agricultural Economics_, Vol. 18, No. 1 (January-March 1963), pp. 224-31.

9. See H. A. Oluwasanmi and J. A. Alao, "Role of Credit in the Transformation of Traditional Agriculture: The Nigerian Experience," _Nigerian Journal of Economics and Social Studies_, Vol. 7, No. 1 (March 1965), pp. 31-50.

10. Food and Agriculture Organization of the United Nations, _The State of Food and Agriculture, 1966_, _op. cit._, p. 182.

11. See F. G. Bailey, "Capital Saving and Credit in Highland Orissa (India)," _Capital, Saving and Credit in Peasant Societies_, Firth and Yamey, eds. (Chicago, Ill.: Aldine Publishing Co., 1964), pp.

104-32.

12. United Nations/ECAFE/FAO, "A Study of Farmers' Associations in Taiwan," Community Development
and Economic Development, Part II B, Bangkok, 1960,
p. 95; this is a very useful study of direct interest to many developing countries. In Japan, over
66 per cent of short-term credit in agriculture is
handled by cooperatives, which are the most important source of farm production credit. See Food and
Agriculture Organization of the United Nations, The
State of Food and Agriculture, 1963 (Rome: FAO,
1963) p. 58.

13. For a concise appraisal of the present sit-
uation in India, see M. L. Dantwala, "Institutional
Credit in Subsistence Agriculture," International
Journal of Agrarian Affairs, Vol. V, No. 1 (December
1966), pp. 52-61. See also Arthur Paul, "Credit's
Role in Improving Agriculture," The Asia Foundation
Program Bulletin (San Francisco, September 1965), p.
5.

14. See J. V. Fonseka, "The Guaranteed Price
Scheme in Ceylon," Indian Journal of Agricultural
Economics, Vol. 17, No. 2 (April-June 1963), pp. 1-8.

15. See Tablante, op. cit., pp. 567-72.

16. United Nations/ECAFE/FAO, Community Development and Economic Development, Part I, Bangkok,
1960, p. 1, contains this definition: "1. The term
'community development' has come into international
usage to connote the process by which efforts of the
people themselves are united with those of governmental authorities to improve the economic, social
and cultural conditions of communities, to integrate
these communities into the life of the nation and to
enable them to contribute fully to national progress.
2. This complex of processes is then made up of two
essential elements: the participation of the people
themselves to improve their level of living with as
much reliance as possible on their own initiative;
and the provision of technical and other services in
ways which encourage initiative, self-help and mutual

help and make these more effective. It is expressed
in programs designed to achieve a wide variety of
specific improvements." There are, of course, community development projects in some countries sponsored by non-governmental organizations; while these
may furnish only leadership and trained personnel,
they usually help local people to make use of whatever government services and financial assistance
might be made available.

17. For an excellent analysis of the basic is-
sues in community development, see John Barnabas,
"Whither Community Development," Avard Newsletter,
Vol. VII, No. 4 (July-August 1965), pp. 5-6 and 22.
The pioneering work of Akhteer Hameed Khan and the
Academy for Village Development in Comilla, East
Pakistan, is summarized by Henry W. Fairchild and
Shamsul Haq, "Cooperative vs. Commune," Internation-
al Development Review, Vol. 4, No. 1 (March 1962);
and Akhteer Hameed Khan and A. K. M. Mohsen, "Mobi-
lizing Village Leadership," International Develop-
ment Review, Vol. 4, No. 3 (September 1962).

18. For a critical review of this massive approach by the Indian Government to community development, see A. H. Hanson, The Process of Planning:
A Study of India's Five-Year Plans, 1960-64 (London:
Oxford University Press, 1966), pp. 394-443.

19. For a realistic insight into villagers' problems, see Kusum Nair, Blossoms in the Dust: The
Human Factor in Indian Development (New York: Frederick A. Praeger, 1961).

20. See Barnabas, op. cit., pp. 5-22. He de-
plores the "target mentality" of modern governments
and concludes that "community development, which
started as a movement, a process, deteriorated into
a target-oriented programme."

21. Food and Agriculture Organization of the
United Nations, The Relationship Between Land Reform
and Community Development. Background paper prepared by the Bureau of Social Affairs, World Land
Reform Conference, Rome, 1966, p. 5.

22. For some examples, see Barnabas, op. cit.;
Nair, op. cit., especially pp. 83-84, where a farmer
sums up the results of six years of community development work: "Whether it is the government or the
vikas (community development office), it gives only
to those who already have." See also Barraclough,
op. cit., pp. 40-41: "In one Chilean small holding
community...the government sent in agricultural
agents to give supervised credit and organize a
small holders cooperative. Local merchants and political bosses...quickly took advantage of the credit
and got control of the so-called cooperative. Most
of the small holders received no substantial benefits at all and remain suspicious of the program."

23. See C. de Fonseka, "Shramadana: Mobilization of Unutilized Human Resources," International
Development Review, Vol. 7, No. 1 (March 1965), pp.
14-20; and Bicol Development Planning Board, "Planning and Implementation for Agricultural Development
at the Municipality," Program Series No. 1, the
Philippines, December 1966, and subsequent releases.

24. For an excellent discussion of this issue,
see Ernest Feder, "Societal Opposition to Peasant
Movements and Its Effects on Farm People in Latin
America." Paper presented for a Seminar on Latin
American Peasant Movements, Ithaca, New York, Cornell
University, December 1966. (Mimeo.)

25. See The New York Times, October 30, 1966;
and for Mexico, Food and Agriculture Organization of
the United Nations, "Country Paper," World Land Reform Conference, Rome, June 1966.

26. For a realistically imaginative exposition
of the political processes involved in these relationships between economic interest groups, political parties, and government, see Albert O. Hirschman,
Journeys Toward Progress (New York: Twentieth Century Fund, 1965).

PART IV

INTERDEPENDENCE OF NATIONS

IN ECONOMIC PROGRESS

So far, we have dealt with the national and local problems of economic development. If we were to
stop here, we would close our eyes to one of the
toughest problems in accelerating progress: how to
bring the rich and the poor nations, the industrial
and the agrarian ones, and those that are neighbors,
to realize the nature of their interdependence, and
to do something constructive about arranging their
interrelationship and dealings with each other in
their common interest. Progress in the agrarian
countries can be blocked, and economic stability in
the industrial countries can be shattered, by a
failure in finding solutions to these problems of
international cooperation.

Let us first examine the practical economic and
organizational issues involved in technical assistance and capital aid to developing countries. Then,
in conclusion, we shall take a long-time forward
look at the prospects of the agrarian revolution in
a world perspective.

14

TECHNICAL ASSISTANCE

AND CAPITAL AID

The newly developing countries are desperately
short of people highly trained in modern technology
and economic organization, and of industrial capital
goods and such strategic inputs as fertilizers, pesticides, and farm machinery. Their shortages in
these factors severely limit their rate of progress.
They must turn to countries more advanced in these
fields for assistance. On the other hand, the industrial countries have surplus capacity for producing capital goods as well as consumer goods, and are
desperately in need of expanding markets in the developing world. This market expansion, however,
cannot materialize without a vigorous economic development in these low-income regions where the majority of the world's present and potential producers and consumers live. Herein lies the basic mutuality of economic interest of rich and poor countries.

UNITED NATIONS AND THE FOOD
AND AGRICULTURE ORGANIZATION

At a Conference of the Society for International Development in 1961, the Managing Director of the
United Nations Special Fund, Paul G. Hoffman, made
three key proposals as guidelines for development
assistance:

(1) That rich and poor alike must face
     squarely the stark reality of their
     common fate and promptly adjust their
     actions accordingly...

365

(2) That assistance from one nation to
another must not be considered an act
of charity. Development assistance
is an investment in a more peaceful
and more prosperous world, an act of
partnership between nations in their
common interest...

(3) That the best way to avoid the intru-
sion of defeating factors in aid programs is to channel an increasing
amount and proportion of aid through
the United Nations...[1]

The first two points refer to this community of
interest between countries, the third proposes that
this interest is better served by arranging development assistance through multilateral U.N. agencies
than bilaterally through individual "donor" and "recipient" countries.

The U.N. technical assistance programs are financed by a pool of voluntary contributions from the
member governments of the United Nations. The donor
countries have no control over where their individual contribution will be used, and for what projects. Hence, there are no economic or political
strings attached to these contributions. Each country, eligible for U.N. technical assistance according to its own declaration, submits its own requests
for the kinds and amounts of technical assistance to
the U.N. Technical Assistance Board. These requests
are sorted out by technical subject-matter fields
and turned over to the respective U.N. specialized
agencies. All requests dealing with agriculture,
forestry, and fisheries, for instance, go to FAO for
execution, those dealing with public health go to
WHO, etc. In fields for which no U.N. specialized
agencies exist, units of the U.N. Secretariat function as executing agents. This, for instance, was
the case of requests dealing with industrialization,
until the U.N. Industrial Development Organization
(UNIDO) was established in 1967.

These U.N. specialized agencies appraise the individual country requests and arrange for their execution in cooperation with the government departments concerned. In agriculture, for instance, FAO
selects and hires the experts from whatever countries that have them available, assigns them to the
requesting countries, and provides professional services and general supervision of the technical work
of the experts. The recipient country furnishes the
local support of his work such as office space, sec-
retarial help, transportation, etc., and normally
assigns a senior "counterpart" officer to work with
the expert. Usually, the experts function in advisory, training, surveying, and research capacities.

Since the U.N. Special Fund was created in 1959,
a growing part of technical assistance has been taking the form of an international team of experts
working on a specific but fairly comprehensive project, planned in detail over three to five years in
advance, under the joint management of a local administrative officer and the foreign team leader,
and under the sponsorship of a ministry or a board
in which several ministries are represented. These
projects in the field of agriculture are usually localized in selected areas and deal mainly with "pre-
investment" surveys of land and water resources for
irrigation and settlement; with introduction of modern agricultural techniques, including often pilot
farms or areas for experimentation, demonstration,
and in-service training of local people; with research and training institutions; with processing of
agricultural products, and various other problems.
They follow the principle of organizing a development project around "a focus in a pattern," as we
have discussed earlier.

The point I want to make here is that these U.N.
technical assistance projects are completely worked
into the fabric of the country's own administrative
agencies, with the government contributing around
one-half, and sometimes more, of the total project
cost in the form of local personnel and equipment.

The country considers them its own projects, rather than something foisted upon it by a foreign government. Whatever the nationalities of the foreign experts may be, the fund from which they are paid does not come from any specific nation, and no U.N. expert is permitted to receive any instructions from his home government. These are characteristics that strongly appeal to the recipient country, and which are not typical for bilateral aid given by individual donor countries.

Technical assistance under United Nations auspices consists mainly of highly trained experts and student fellowships. Only a minor part of the total funds are used for equipment, instruments, and vehicles necessary for the experts to function effectively and not available in the recipient country. In 1965, the U.N. Technical Assistance Programme amounted to around $300 million (see Table 33).

BILATERAL FOREIGN AID

Under bilateral foreign aid, the emphasis is usually on capital equipment, food, medical, and other supplies. Technical assistance experts are furnished along with such goods to help in their installation and use. Some countries, especially France and the United States, contribute large numbers of teachers, student fellowships for studies in the donor countries, volunteers, and technical and administrative advisers. However, of the total bilateral public aid of $5.8 billion in 1965, only 18 per cent (or $1 billion) was used for technical assistance personnel of all kinds, including the cost of students and trainees. In absolute size, however, the bilateral technical assistance program is three times larger than the United Nations program. The number of people involved in this part of bilateral foreign aid is quite impressive, as seen in Table 33. Over 92,000 experts and volunteers served in developing countries in 1965, sent there by individual donor countries, and 61,000 students and trainees received educational grants in one form or another, many of them spending at least some months in

TABLE 33

Technical Assistance Personnel Publicly Financed
Under Bilateral Aid Programs, 1965[1]

	All Donor Countries[2]	U.S.A.	France	U.K.	Germany
	. . . . 1,000 persons				
Experts and Volunteers:					
Total	92.1	21.1	43.5	16.8	2.6
Personnel in Education	40.2	2.6	29.2	3.5	0.8
Operational Personnel	23.1	---	10.0	10.7	0.4
Advisers	12.8	6.7	4.0	0.4	0.5
Volunteers	16.0	11.8	0.3	2.2	0.9
Educational Grants:					
Total	60.8	15.8	12.4	8.9	10.6
Students	30.0	8.5	4.6	3.6	5.1
Trainees	30.8	7.3	7.8	5.3	5.5

1. Organization for Economic Cooperation and Development, Development Assistance Efforts and Policies, 1966 Review (Paris: OECD, September 1966), pp. 162-63.

2. The cost of this technical assistance represents 18.2 per cent of the Total Public Bilateral Net Contribution.

the donor country. France stands out with 47 per
cent of its foreign aid contributed in the form of
technical assistance in 1965. The U.S. furnished
nearly 75 per cent of the total volunteers mostly
through its Peace Corps program.

Still, for bilateral public aid as a whole,
more than 80 per cent goes into capital goods, food
shipments, and other supplies, and the services con-
nected with them.

These resources are made available by a specific "donor" country to a specific "recipient" country
under bilaterally negotiated agreements. The projects in the various fields are not as closely tied
into the local institutional structure as under U.N.
programs, and, indeed, are sometimes operated quite
separately under the direct control of the donor
country--until the project is turned over to the
government after completion. The experts work under
general instruction of their home government, and
the types of projects and kinds of capital goods are
often determined by the donor country's economic and
trade interest. The recipient country must, of
course, approve the projects. The specific contributions which the recipient government agrees to make
to any particular bilateral aid project vary widely
and are negotiated case by case.

From a strictly technical viewpoint, this mode
of operation may have some advantages, as the donor
country is less dependent upon the administrative
and logistic services of the local government, which
are often ill-adapted to modern techniques and organizational requirements; from the viewpoint of improving the efficiency of these government services,
it has disadvantages, as some of the projects may
deteriorate for lack of effective local support after
they have been turned over to local operation. Economic progress demands a larger and better-trained
staff of technicians, professional and administrative officers--especially in agriculture and at
middle-echelon and field levels--than most developing countries have now. In this area, U.N. and
other multilateral agencies working within the local

administrative channels and through teams of inter-
nationally recruited experts are bound to be more
effective than bilateral aid programs. Neglect of
this area of technical assistance causes the much-
debated problem of the "absorptive capacity" for
capital aid.

A good part of bilateral foreign aid is provided by means of loans repayable by the recipient
countries, and the terms concerning amortization,
interest rates, and means of payment in hard or local currencies or commodities are negotiated bilaterally between the donor and the recipient countries. Accumulating debt obligations arising from
bilateral aid are creating serious debt-service problems for a number of developing countries. In recent years, the debt service absorbed 25 per cent or
more of the export earnings of several countries.
The study of a sample of forty countries (representing 80 per cent of the population in the developing
regions) revealed that their external debt service
on public and publicly guaranteed private loans
amounted to $2.8 billion in 1965. Comparing this
with 80 per cent of the total public financial flow
in 1965, i.e., $6.7 billion, this debt-service obli-
gation alone (which does not include that of private
bilateral loans) represents 42 per cent of the total
net inflow into developing countries for that year.[2]
Some of these countries have debt payments exceeding
the new financial aid received in the same year.
This burden is particularly heavy for countries with
loans of less than five years maturity (the traditional commercial credit limit), high interest rates,
and projects that have a long gestation period for
getting into full production.

It is useful to distinguish three sources of
financial aid: (1) public bilateral aid representing about 54 per cent of the total financial flow in
1965; (2) private bilateral aid with 30 per cent;
and (3) multilateral aid with 16 per cent (see Table 34). Bilateral loans, especially from private
sources, usually have a shorter maturity and higher
interest rates than multilateral loans under the
IBRD and other agencies. This heavier burden of

debt service is only partly offset by the fact that
over half of the aid from public bilateral sources
represents grants--often in the form of food shipments, medical and other supplies, technical assistance experts, and similar services.[3] Private bilateral aid consists almost entirely of loans, except
for non-commercial programs sponsored by such private eleemosynary organizations as CARE and various
religious groups.

On the whole, about two thirds of the total bilateral and multilateral flow of financial resources
in 1965 represented loans that the developing countries are paying back, a good part of them at rather
"hard" terms of interest, maturity, and currencies.
Strictly speaking, the term "aid" is applicable only
to grants and to that part of loans that is offered
on terms more favorable to the borrower country than
those customary under commercial credit arrangements.
Hence, the dividing line between "aid" and "trade"
is blurred for a wide area of foreign aid; if one
were to make a clear-cut distinction, over half of
it would probably have to be classified as "trade"
and not as "aid." Most of the bilateral private contributions could be called "trade transactions,"
since they directly promote the donor countries' own
commercial interests in the markets of the developing countries.

MULTILATERAL AID
AND AN INTERNATIONAL CAPITAL MARKET

In recent years, multilateral financial sources
for capital investment have expanded at a much greater rate than bilateral sources. Annual commitments
of the World Bank (IBRD) and its associates, the International Development Association (IDA) and the
International Finance Corporation (IFC), have doubled between 1960 and 1965, and a number of regional
multilateral lending agencies are getting into their
stride. Beside the Inter-American Development Bank
(IDB) and the Economic Development Fund of the OECD,
Regional Development Banks for Africa and Asia are
just beginning their operations. These multilateral

lending agencies contributed 8.5 per cent to the total flow of financial resources to developing countries in 1960, and increased their share to 16 per
cent in 1965, as shown in Table 34. Their boards of
directors or governors include borrowing as well as
lending countries.

Perhaps there is a possibility of organizing an
international capital market around these multilateral lending agencies, establishing close cooperation between them and the individual lender countries through consortia or groups made up of borrower countries as well as of lender countries. Such
a newly organized capital market might succeed not
only in assembling much larger financial resources
from both private and public investors for the specific purpose of economic development, but might also work out terms and operational procedures much
better adapted to the needs and conditions of the
developing countries. For 1961, the World Bank estimated that the developing countries could have made
effective use of $3 to 4 billion more of public bi-
lateral and multilateral aid than the $6.1 billion
they received.[4]

For many years to come, most of the heavy machinery and equipment required for modern industrial
plants, transport and communication facilities, major irrigation and land reclamation works, and in
agriculture also, much of the operating capital,
such as fertilizers, pesticides, and farm machinery,
etc., must come from the industrialized countries
and must become available at terms the developing
countries can meet without stunting their own growth.

We are gathering already a great deal of experience in handling international credit problems, in
experimenting with various new procedures, and adjustments of old ones. For instance, since 1958,
the IBRD has organized "consortia" or "consultative
groups" which include representatives of governments
interested in bilateral development financing or
technical assistance in a specific recipient country.
The IBRD arranges for meetings of such a consortium
with government and national bank officers of a

TABLE 34

Flows of Financial Resources to
Less-Developed Countries[1]

	1960	1965	Increase 1960-65	1965 Per Cent of Total
	billion U.S. $		%	%
Total: All Sources	8.2	12.0	46	100
Total: Bilateral	7.5	10.1	35	84
Net Outflow from DAC Countries:[2]	7.1	9.4	32	78
Public ("official") Funds	(4.3)	(5.8)	35	(48)
Private Funds	(2.8)	(3.6)	28	(30)
Outflow from Non-DAC Countries[3]	0.4	0.7	75	6
Total New Commitments by Multilateral Agencies[4]	0.7	1.9	172	16
IBRD, IDA, and IFC	0.5	1.0		
IDB	---	0.3		
EEC	0.1	0.3		
U.N. Agencies	0.1	0.3		

1. Based on Organization for Economic Cooperation and Development, Development Assistance Efforts and Policies: 1966 Review (Paris: OECD, 1966), pp. 30 and 36.
2. The Development Assistance Committee of the Organization for
   Economic Cooperation and Development includes: Australia,
   Austria, Belgium, Canada, Denmark, France, Germany, Italy, Japan, the Netherlands, Norway, Portugal, Sweden, United Kingdom, and U.S.A.
3. Non-DAC countries for which estimates could be made include
   Switzerland, New Zealand, and Sino-Soviet countries. Most of
   these funds are probably of a "public" or "official" nature.
4. International Bank for Reconstruction and Development (IBRD),
   International Development Association (IDA), International
   Finance Corporation (IFC), Inter-American Development Bank
   (IDB), European Economic Community (EEC), United Nations Agencies.

recipient country to appraise its development plan
and the priorities of various projects for external
financing, and encourages the members of the consortium to pledge specific amounts of capital for specific projects, complementing its own multilateral
loans. These consortia provide a framework of orderly consultation with developing countries on their
needs for development capital and technical assistance. The OECD and the Inter-American Bank are also
using such consortia or consultative groups for improving the coordination of external financing and
technical assistance by various donor countries and
for increasing such resources at more favorable
terms to the developing country.[5]

We must remember, however, that the membership
of these consortia is determined by the sponsoring
multilateral banks or funds, and represents primarily the interests of the lending countries and agencies. Membership varies for different recipient
countries and does not include representatives of
them. These consortia may reduce competition between donor countries and weaken the bargaining position of the developing countries; but they also may
improve over-all effectiveness of development aid by
its allocation to more viable and mutually complementary projects and by a stronger pressure upon the
recipient country to improve its own administration
and increase its local contributions.

It is still true, however, that the consortia
are bodies of the donors and lenders, of the industrialized high-income countries. From the viewpoint
of the developing countries, it is easy for local
critics to argue that they are devices of the rich
nations to gang up on the poor ones and determine
among themselves how much and what kind of financial
resources, and at what terms, they want to make
available to each recipient country, one by one.
The fact that the consortia usually meet outside the
recipient country, on "foreign" territory and behind
closed doors, does not enhance their popularity with
the rank and file of the developing world.

Perhaps the general idea of the consortium's role could be broadened and made more effective by including recipient countries in its membership, and by meeting in the recipient country and holding some sessions open for participation of local government agencies, investment firms, and technical experts in the discussions. The consortium's function is consultative only, not executive, and a more nearly equal representation of the developing countries might greatly raise its prestige and confidence in its judgement. Including borrower countries in the consortium might broaden and deepen its insights and factual knowledge of the issues well beyond what their present composition can provide.

Another promising experiment is carried on by the Joint IBRD-FAO Program, dealing with feasibility appraisals of proposed agricultural development projects and of current projects whose progress is retarded by the lack of critical financial and technical assistance resources. The combination of the experiences and specialized knowledge of multilateral lending and U.N. technical assistance agencies might contribute greatly to raising the "absorptive capacity" for development capital and its productivity, as we shall see later.

The International Development Association (IDA) is also a new approach to better meet the needs of development capital for certain kinds of infrastructural investment that will not yield immediate and readily calculable returns, such as schools and hospitals and other projects of a social service nature. The IDA finances these types of investments on "soft" terms of long-maturity loans and low-interest rates.

A well-organized international capital market designed to meet development needs must accomplish a number of tasks that traditional arrangements have not been able to do. More funds must become available at terms that the developing country can pay without jeopardizing its fiscal and foreign exchange position to the detriment of continued progress. This might require setting up a new system of measures for the industrial countries to make adequate

amounts and kinds of capital available at concessional terms for specific development purposes, and for
low-income agrarian countries to assume specific obligations concerning the planning and effective use
of such capital investment. There certainly is no
lack of potential capital in the rich nations, nor
lack of opportunities to use such capital produc-
tively in the poor nations. The lack is in imaginative and courageous leadership on both sides.

ABSORPTIVE CAPACITY
FOR DEVELOPMENT CAPITAL

The problem of the absorptive capacity for development capital is of growing concern to multilateral lending agencies and to individual lender countries.

There are indeed some externally financed investments that have not yielded the expected returns.
I have seen irrigation projects that a few years after completion deteriorated quickly with accumulation of salts in the soil due to poor drainage and
inefficient water use, or that never were fully utilized because crop production and farming techniques
were not modernized and adapted to take advantage of
the greatly increased potential productivity of the
land and water resources. There are warehouses
standing idle because the expected increase in the
production and trade of the area did not materialize.
There are factories working at much less than full
capacity because of lack of raw materials or of poor
demand for the product due to the widespread poverty
of the people. Many tractors have broken down after
short use due to lack of mechanics and repair shops
and spare parts. Similar examples can be cited ad
infinitum.

Some malallocation and misuse of capital is, of
course, not surprising and is a price paid for poor
planning and administration of development processes,
for insufficient training of people in the use of
the new resources and modern production techniques,
for inadequate opportunities and incentives offered

to farmers and workers, as we have discussed in earlier chapters. These things explain failures, but
do not justify them. However, many people in developing countries have become more conscious of these
changes than they were five or ten years ago, and
are learning to cope with these problems. Let us
look at some of the ways they can be tackled.

First, on the part of multilateral agencies and
the industrial countries, much more emphasis might
well be given to technical assistance and training
in connection with development projects. One of the
most effective means for assuring the success of a
project is its realistic preparation and programming
over time, the training of local people in its execution, and the follow-up, after completion of construction, with technical assistance and training of
local managers, supervisors, farmers, and workers in
using the resources and applying modern production
techniques efficiently. Many developing countries
do not have the people trained and experienced in
these tasks. This holds particularly for agricultural development projects where technical assistance and training requirements are usually more complex and difficult to meet. The lending agencies
might insist on good support along these lines, and
if the country cannot provide it out of its regular
U.N. Technical Assistance allocation, the loan could
cover the cost of this function, either directly or
through a special assignment to the appropriate U.N.
specialized agency. The Joint FAO-IBRD program
might possibly be useful in working out arrangements
along these lines.

Second, on the part of the developing countries,
more effort is needed in breaking down national development plans into sets of specific operational
policies and projects, as we have seen earlier (see
Chapter 3 and Chapter 12). There is a good deal of
work the country itself must do in the project preparation, training of local people, and follow-up in
the operation of the project after construction that
foreign experts cannot do. Hence, the government
must be responsible for matching technical assistance with its own contributions in local personnel

and organizational arrangements and policy measures, which will make producers willing and able to use the new resources efficiently. This may often require certain land reforms or credit and marketing facilities, extension service, etc.

These are the most promising approaches for keeping the absorptive capacity for capital in line with development requirements.

DEVELOPMENT CAPITAL AND WORLD TRADE

Finally, a serious stumbling block for developing countries in meeting their increasing debt-service obligations lies in the vagaries of certain world commodity markets and the inconvertibility of most currencies.

We have already seen how the burden of foreign-debt payments is rising in many of the poor countries and threatening to thwart their continued growth. Again, there are several ways that might offer at least partial solution of the problem.

In many cases, the maturity of development loans could be lengthened. The maturities of official bilateral loan commitments in 1965 by 6 donor countries averaged 15 years or less, by 4 countries 16-20 years, by 3 countries 21-24 years, and only by 2 countries (U.S. and Canada) 28 and 30 years, respectively.[6] Bilateral private loans often have much shorter maturities, such as 10 years or less. The interest rate could be lowered. In 1965, official bilateral loan commitments averaged 3.6 per cent, but 6 of the 15 DAC countries charged over 4 per cent. The U.S., with by far the largest amount of loans, raised its interest rate from 2 per cent in 1963 to 3.3 per cent in 1965; Canada lowered its rate from 6 per cent in 1963 to 3.8 per cent in 1965. There is obviously a great deal of flexibility in the interest rates charged by any donor country.

The most important aspect of the debt-service burden, however, lies in the typical developing

country's balance-of-payments difficulties and the
inconvertibility of its currency. We cannot go here
into the details of this thorny problem. We can only stress that many developing countries are extremely vulnerable to price fluctuations in the
world markets of a few key commodities like tea,
coffee, cocoa, sugar, rubber, and a few more, and
that even minor price declines may seriously jeopardize their balance-of-payments position. Improvement
in the price stabilization of these commodities and
arrangements for a much wider convertibility of
their currencies are extremely urgent for their economic development.

This whole complex of problems was brought up
for discussion before a world-wide forum at the
first meeting of the United Nations Conference on
Trade and Development (UNCTAD) in 1964. At this conference, the developing countries presented striking
evidence of the intolerable handicaps that their
weak bargaining position in these world markets and
in the currency convertibility system placed upon
them.

In the long-time view--and economic development
is by nature a long-time process--an objective appraisal of this problem leads to the conclusion that
the industrial high-income countries have the choice
of three approaches:

(1) Stabilize the world markets of a few key
commodities and reduce obstacles in their trade,
such as tariffs and quotas, etc.;

(2) Arrange for much wider convertibility of
soft currencies; and

(3) Make an increasing part of total debt-
service obligations payable in the borrower's currency or in terms of commodities. These basic approaches are not mutually exclusive; they can be
pursued at the same time. But the more we promote
the first and second, the less need there will be
for the third.

As to the first approach, we have gained some limited experiences. Various price-stabilization plans have been in operation for wheat (since 1949), coffee (since 1963), and sugar (folded in 1961), and similar international commodity agreements for cocoa, tea, rubber, and various others are still under study by the FAO Committee on Commodity Problems—some of which have been "under study" since before World War II. Except for wheat, the bulk of world exports of these commodities come from developing low-income countries, each in a weak bargaining position, and are imported by the industrial high-income countries in a very strong bargaining position. Since the basic purpose of these commodity agreements is to protect the export-producers from the often ruinous impact of price declines on their economies, and the import-consumers feel that they might lose rather than gain by such protection of the exporters, it is small wonder why these commodity agreements don't get off the ground. With wheat, the bargaining position between exporters and importers is reversed. The U.S. produces nearly half of the world export, and together with Canada and Australia about 80 per cent of it. No wonder that these three high-income countries with very strong bargaining positions can negotiate a wheat agreement and make it work for nearly two decades.

After years of study and negotiations for a cocoa agreement, the exporting countries gave up hope in 1963 and established an organization of their own, the Cocoa Producers' Alliance. It remains to be seen whether they can master sufficient strength to stabilize prices and improve the functioning of the market in their favor.

Reducing trade obstacles in these commodities is an issue closely related to that of price stabilization. The General Agreement on Tariffs and Trade (GATT), whose membership represents largely the high-income countries, included in 1963, for the first time, agricultural products in the Kennedy Round of tariff negotiations. This Round was completed in the spring of 1967 without benefiting the low-income

exporters of these key commodities in any significant way.

Perhaps the Trade and Development Board of
UNCTAD and its various committees could make a fresh
start in coming years with international commodity
agreements and reduction of specific trade obstacles
that mean little to importing countries but hurt exporters very badly. If high-income countries can be
persuaded that it is in their long-time interest to
refrain from the full exercise of their bargaining
power and make concessions that would be of minor
cost to them but of very high benefit to developing
countries, international commodity agreements could
play a constructive role in promoting economic progress.

As to the second approach of widening the convertibility of soft currencies, especially of those
developing countries that are peculiarly vulnerable
in their balance-of-payments position (e.g., those
depending mainly upon one or two export crops for
their foreign exchange earnings), very little progress is being made. Since 1963, the International
Monetary Fund (IMF) has been authorized to increase
the drawing privileges from the Fund's recourses for
export countries whose liquidity is threatened by
temporary shortfalls in export earnings. This is
the mildest of various proposals made for "compensa-
tory financing" of shortfalls in export earnings;
others designed "to insure the developing countries
against the effects of a long-term deterioration of
their terms of trade so as to permit the uninter-
rupted implementation of the country's economic development plans"[7] have, so far, not even been tried
out on an experimental basis anywhere. These problems of reforming the international monetary system,
however, are beginning to be explored by the World
Bank and by UNCTAD under the mounting pressure from
the developing countries.

As long as there is no world currency into
which every national currency is freely convertible,
and as long as many developing countries depend on
only a few agricultural export products as their

main source of foreign exchange, it is obvious that
they require a type of long-range financing of their
development-capital imports that has not been established yet. The longer it takes to work out such
arrangements for an international capital market
that will really meet the legitimate needs of developing countries, the worse will become the disruptive and progress-retarding effects of balance-of-
payments difficulties.

Here, as in the case of international commodity
agreements and trade obstacles, the key to finding
practical solutions lies in the willingness of the
industrial countries to yield only a little of the
advantages they derive from their wealth and strong
bargaining power, in order to increase greatly the
access of developing countries to capital. This
would be clearly in the long-time self-interest of
the industrial countries also, since they will find
it impossible to isolate their economies from the
impact of stagnation, hunger, unemployment, and un-
abated poverty, which are bound to harass the developing countries unless they can achieve a vigorous
rate of progress.

Stabilization of certain world commodity markets and widening the convertibility of soft currencies are by nature matters for multilateral action.
The third approach outlined above, namely making
foreign aid and debts payable in local currency or
in commodities, can be readily used on a bilateral
basis. A considerable part of the foreign aid from
the U.S.A. and the U.S.S.R. is provided on such
terms.

For instance, in 1965, the U.S. made 45 per
cent of a $2.1 billion total of loans or supplies to
developing countries repayable in recipients' currencies or through sales for recipients' currencies.[8]
That the U.S. does not use these payments for importing local goods to the U.S. is its own choice, presumably because the U.S. Government does not want to
get into the U.S. import trade. Instead, these local payments to the U.S. are made available to the
recipient government for its domestic use in

developmental activities--but only with U.S. approval. Hence, in foreign aid statistics, they are classified as "grants" rather than "loans" or "sales." Hardly any of the other Western countries uses this debt-service payment method.

The U.S.S.R., however, often arranges debt payments in terms of commodities produced by the recipient countries--such as cotton, rice, dates, etc.--scheduled over ten or twenty or more years ahead, with some flexibility as to quantities and prices left for future negotiation within certain limits. From discussions I had in a number of developing countries, I have gained the impression that these arrangements for debt payments in locally produced commodities are more popular with the recipient countries than the U.S. arrangement for payments in local currencies for domestic use, but under U.S. control.

For a real breakthrough in establishing a well-functioning world capital market and provisions for debt-service payments, the most promising approaches seem to lie with stabilizing and expanding certain key commodity markets, and with widening the convertibility of soft currencies.

NOTES TO CHAPTER 14

1. Paul G. Hoffman, "Development Priorities," International Development Review, Vol. IV, No. 1 (March 1962), pp. 6-9.

2. The New York Times, May 7, 1967, report on India's negotiations with the Consortium to lighten her debt burden. Her 1967 debt-service obligation of $450 million represents one-fourth of her total export earnings, and 40 per cent of the new development loans pledged to India by the member nations of the Consortium.

3. See Organization for Economic Cooperation and Development, op. cit., pp. 150-51.

4. See the Food and Agriculture Organization of the United Nations, _The State of Food and Agriculture, 1966_, op. cit., p. 46.

5. For a review of the functions of consortia and consultative groups, see Organization for Economic Cooperation and Development, op. cit., pp. 126-30.

6. See ibid., p. 160.

7. See the Food and Agriculture Organization of the United Nations, _The State of Food and Agriculture, 1965_, op. cit., p. 52.

8. See Organization for Economic Cooperation and Development, op. cit., p. 157.

15

AGRARIAN REVOLUTION
IN WORLD PERSPECTIVE:
AN EPILOGUE

EMERGENCE OF A WORLD CONSCIENCE

We are witnessing the dawn of an era of world
organization. This fact is not easy to grasp because we also observe a rise of intense nationalism
throughout the countries of the developing world.
This nationalist accent, with its emphasis upon local cultural traits, is more tangible and more easy
to see than the emergence of a world consciousness.
Yet, it is fallacious to view these two currents as
antagonistic to each other. In a deeper sense, they
are complementary. The emotional source of nationalism is the urge of people for self-determination--
an aspiration that can only be realized by a world
organization of nations guaranteeing, through accepted systems of peaceful negotiation, the mutuality of
respect for the rights and responsibilities of any
individual nation by all other nations.

We have moved from the fragmentary League of
Nations of the 1920's to the much more inclusive,
far-flung, and functionally differentiated United
Nations Organization and a score of specialized
world agencies, among which the FAO is holding a
crucial position for contributing to agricultural development all over the world.

All this is very new. In earlier centuries,
international organizations were of an imperialist
or private economic nature, such as the British East
India Trade Company, the various colonial empires,
and the I. G. Farben cartel. Their purpose was self-
seeking in terms of economic and military power politics. Now, in the middle of the twentieth century,
the various world organizations represent many

sovereign nations and employ large staffs of inter-
nationally recruited personnel whose work is not
controlled by any individual nation and whose purpose is to serve all nations, each in accordance
with its own needs, and all in their mutual long-
time interest. Their purpose is the forging of a
world society of nations in which all major issues
of friction and controversy can be resolved by peaceful means of study and negotiation, to the end that
people may grow together instead of apart, may pros-
per together instead of exploiting each other.

We are witnessing the birth of a world conscience that is beginning to permeate the views of
ever-increasing numbers of people, in all countries.
We individuals often feel discouraged by the slow
progress and many setbacks in making the United Nations function effectively. But let us remember
that this slow growth, these partial failures and
doubtful successes of the U.N. and its agencies are
mainly due to our own individual governments refusing to permit the U.N. to function the way it should.
Despite all its operational weaknesses, especially
in its peace-keeping functions, the United Nations
does exert a moral force upholding humanist-democratic principles in the world-wide forum of nations.

No individual nation, however powerful, nor any
political alliance could possibly create such a moral presence of mankind's conscience in the affairs
of nations. It is quite conceivable that had it not
been for the United Nations, some of the local wars
might have gotten out of hand and plunged the world
into unprecedented destruction. This still could
happen--but it certainly could not be blamed on the
United Nations, but only on a few powerful nations
betraying its principles.

THE AGRARIAN SCENE: A CENTURY AGO

Around 1850, agricultural conditions in the
Western world were very different from today. In
Western Europe, many tenants paid oppressively high
rents, were insecure in their occupancy of the land,

and had to render personal services to the landowners. These tenants were at the mercy of their landlords, without bargaining power and without ways of
making their frustrations felt except through violent uprisings, which often left them weaker than
before. In Eastern and Southern Europe, tenants and
farm workers were still close to the place they occupied in the feudal tenure systems of the Middle
Ages. In the South of the United States, the plantation system with its Negro slaves was still in
full swing. The vast unsettled land toward the West
of the United States was sold in large blocks to
land speculators and land companies that exploited
the poor settlers and refugees from the eastern
sweatshop industries by all sorts of ingenious
fraud and misrepresentation. Over most of Latin
America, peasants and workers lived under quasi-
feudal conditions, in various forms of bondage and at
the bare level of subsistence. In Asia and Africa,
the colonial empires either reinforced the power of
the indigenous chiefs and landowners or imposed
their own in the process of developing plantations
and siphoning off the natural resources by the coercive use of the labor of the "inferior" natives.

There was a remarkably common trait in these
different agrarian systems: No matter how rich or
poor the land, what terms of rental rates or wages
were in effect, they all left the families working
on the land at the same bare subsistence, just
enough to do the work and propagate. The economics
of labor under these widely varying conditions was
very akin to the economics of work horses--an economics that has produced the well-known theory of
the Iron Law of Wages and the still better-known Communist Manifesto.

So much for the general conditions of the people living and working on the land. The landowners,
on the other hand, formed a landed gentry, an elite:
provided the rulers, army officers, and civil officials, and governed, directly or indirectly, not only the lives of persons and community affairs of
their own estates, but of the regions and the nation
as well. A self-appointed elite governed over

inferior groups, over peasants and farm workers who
had no peaceful means of making their needs and aspirations felt in a way that would make it necessary
for landlords and governments to heed the farmers'
and workers' wishes.

Sketched in broad strokes, these were the typical features of the agrarian structure throughout
most agricultural regions of the world a century
ago. Let us keep these features in mind, as bench
marks, against which to chart the path of progress
over the last 100-150 years.

THE UNITED NATIONS: A MORAL FORCE

There has been a common core in the evolution
of agriculture. The general direction has been toward the emancipation of the families living and
working on the land, toward expanding their opportunities and responsibilities, their living level
and managerial freedom, their education and individual dignity, civil rights and influence in public
affairs. Associated with these changes was greater
productivity of labor as well as of land, hence
greater total production of food with increasing efficiency of resource use, and higher family incomes.

In the West, this broadening of incentives, of
opportunities and rewards over a rapidly increasing
proportion of the working people unleashed undreamed
of forces of energy, discovered unsuspected riches
in people's talents, efforts, and capability of self-
discipline. Without them, the Western world could
not have experienced such a breath-taking splurge of
technological, economic, and social development as
we have witnessed during the last hundred years.
The greatest discovery of all was the vast riches of
talents, energies, and capacity for responsibility
that had lain hidden and dormant in the great numbers of poor, uneducated, downtrodden people of all
regions and races. The means by which these precious human resources were developed and put to use
were the socio-political institutions of a humanist-
democratic social order, and the widespread

application of scientific technology down to the
millions of small farms and factories.

This development process has started only recently, since around 1950, in the whole newly developing world, in most places haltingly, in fits and
spurts here and there, in some places remarkably
fast, as in Japan, Russia, Yugoslavia, and Mexico,
for example. It is clearly headed in the same general direction as it was during the last 150 years
in the West, although the detailed forms of social
and economic arrangements may turn out quite differently, in current adaptations to the great variety
of cultures and under more or less democratic home
rule. The seriousness of the race between food and
population in the newly developing world makes necessary a rate of progress considerably faster than
that achieved in the West during the 1800's. The
race is close, but need not be hopeless. Its outcome will hinge on whether people will manage to
bring about the transformations in their social and
economic ways of life fast enough to take full advantage of modern production technology without which
the race cannot be won.

In this process, the United Nations, its specialized agencies, and various other multilateral
world organizations like the World Bank and regional
development banks are playing a role much more powerful than their current operational programs render
visible. This role is one of a patient but firm
search for evolving moral standards of national conduct that transcend the immediate self-interest of
the individual nation, restrain the exercise of its
full economic and military power over weaker nations,
and formulate world-wide peaceful means for resolv-
ing conflicts between nations in the interest of a
humanist world community.

PROSPECTS AND THE WILL TO PROGRESS

Evolution is a slow and continuous process. As
one problem is met, another arises and calls for new
solutions. Ideas and aspirations of people change,

patterns of political forces change, occupational
distribution and economic relationships change, technology changes--and all these changes must be reflected in the transformation of institutions, of
the organization of social and economic processes,
of practical working procedures between groups within a country, and between countries in the world.
This process takes time, achieves a breakthrough
here and suffers a setback there, and severely taxes
the patience of progressive planners and leaders, of
farmers, workers, and intellectuals in all walks of
life. At any particular time and place, it is easy
to lose faith in man's capacity for creating a peaceful world, and to turn cynic. Cynicism is indeed
effective in dramatizing what goes wrong, but dead-
ens the will to act, to work for what is right, as
it sees no hope and predicts disaster. Hence, extreme cynicism leads to a sullen disgust of the
world around us, to withdrawal from involvement in
public affairs; or, in people with a driving lust
for life and power, cynicism leads to brazen oppor-
tunism.

    In these pages, I have deliberately taken the
approach of demonstrating what might be done rather
than prophesying what will not be done. It is for
the nascent enlightened leadership to take heart and
devote itself to fighting for the needed reforms. I
have presented facts and arguments, experiences and
ideas concerning major obstacles to progress and
possible means to overcome them, for leaders, planners, and students everywhere to weigh, to decide
upon, and to use in their own countries, with their
own people, in their own activities. It is they who
must undermine the folklore of the traditional ruling elites, by winning more and more defectors from
their rank and enlisting them in the struggle for
progress.

    If some countries move fast enough to escape
violent upheavals and starvation, is this not proof
that it can be done? And does it not challenge the
laggards to pull their ostrich heads out of the sand
and start running?

As a social scientist, I can only use the
skills and the "soft-ware" weapons I have learned to
handle. They aim at minds, not bodies; they aim for
peaceful evolutionary change, not for bloody revolutions. Having observed the rate of social change
over nearly half a century in several countries, I
have learned to think in decades, not in years.

Western people with a strong materialist bias
are much more impatient for achieving economic affluence than most of the people in the developing
countries, even the masses of poor peasants and
workers. They want to get out of poverty, yes, but
they won't mind waiting another decade or two for
automobiles and bathtubs. They are much more anxious to get out of their status of subservience, of
dependence upon the good will of landlords, moneylenders, and employers, and for that they don't need
an economic growth rate of 6 per cent per year indefinitely. Hence, my emphasis on reducing poverty
rather than maximizing national production per se,
on universal education, cooperatives, farmers' unions, and community development rather than economic
growth models and imput-output matrixes.

On this human dignity front, people in many
countries have progressed faster than on the economic
front. Primary education is becoming universal rapidly throughout the world (more slowly in rural than
in urban areas); so is voting in political elections.
Corporal punishment of people by landlords and employers, prohibition of leaving the estate, and other aspects of serfdom--still generally accepted a
decade or two ago in much of Latin America and
throughout much of the colonial territories in Africa and Asia--are on the way out quite precipitously.
In historical perspective, these changes are occur-
ring remarkably fast--though, of course, still much
too slow for vigorous progress. Moreover, these
changes are irreversible: there is no turning back
to the old feudal days. In the long run, the traditional leaders can only reform or perish--or grudg-
ingly accommodate to the new social power structure
arising from the political ascendancy of the poor,
as many of them are bound to do for want of courage

and insight. In the meantime, however, many of them will resist reforms and fight for the status quo.

This new social structure is being formed by two dynamic forces that are eroding the power of the traditional leadership and its unquestioned acceptance by the people:

(1) The growth of an educated middle class, an intelligencia of professionals, of clerical, administrative, and many other skilled workers and civil servants whose orientation is fundamentally humanist-democratic; and

(2) The political ascendancy of the poor to modern citizenship, to active participation in public affairs through voting in elections, organizing into parties and cooperatives and unions articulating their views and promoting their interests.

The process of this socio-political transformation is slow by nature--even under revolutions. The American Revolution took a century to abolish slavery, and two centuries, including a devastating civil war, to establish civil rights in the South. In continental Europe, the French Revolution was succeeded by an enlightened military dictatorship under Napoleon and a gradual transfer of political power from absolute monarchies to popularly elected parliaments, which also took more than a century. The Mexican and Russian revolutions are approaching functional maturity in their new social order only recently, since the 1950's. And during these transitional periods of a century, more or less, there were wars and counterrevolutions (notably fascism in Italy, Spain, and Germany), setbacks and stagnation and spurts of progress, civil strife, industrial and agrarian unrest--but one cannot deny the perseverance of a dominant long-time trend in the basic orientation of this social transformation toward humanist democracy.

In most of the developing countries, this process of social transformation began around 1950, less than twenty years ago, with the demise of the colonial empires and after the creation of the United Nations. It would be most unrealistic to expect that by some miracle the newly developing countries would be spared the pains of this social transformation process.

This backward look over history does not presage a rosy prospect. The picture of the future has still a lot of canvas on which the coming decades will paint human misery, violence, and oppression. There will be plenty of it in the years to come, in a lot of places. There always has been plenty of it, everywhere. But as to the prospects of the two great challenges of our era--the conquest of poverty, and the human dignity of every person as a responsible and participating citizen of society--they seem to me to be en marche, barring an atomic world war and a "Brave New World" under computer rule.

I don't rule out either of these possibilities, but I don't see any way of trying to block their chances other than bolstering people's faith in humanist progress and learning to employ technology and socio-political reforms in the service of that faith. This would even be worth trying if a world-opinion poll put the combined probability of the triumph of atom bomb and computer over mankind at 90 per cent. Would you put it that high, say by the year 2000? I would not. Still, I don't see how these guesses at the probability of future doom--and these can be only vague guesses, there is no certainty in matters of this kind--can be relevant to the question of how best to accelerate progress in the developing world.

Having disposed of these two extreme possibilities of universal suicide and computerized technocracy (at least for the next forty years or so), economic development can, of course, follow paths not in accord with humanist ideology. The most dangerous one is a renaissance of a feudal society in modern idioms. The Union of South Africa is the best example at present: a self-appointed white elite, small in number, ruling over masses of black people by sheer police force, but allowing home rule of

tribal groups whose limits are set unilaterally
without recourse to a superior authority or to negotiation on equal terms. There are a few other countries that one might consider museum pieces of medi-
eval feudal orders. Not one of the major countries
today heralds these feudal regimes as the pacesetters for economic progress and paragons of modern
society.

There is Mainland China: a small orthodox leadership of old revolutionary heroes and functionaries,
for the last year in a ruthless survival struggle
with their younger, much less orthodox peers. His-
torically, the Mao Regime might well be now where
the Russian Regime was before Stalin's death: at
the end of the dictatorship period of the original
party elite. Chances are that in the next decade, a
liberalization and humanist democratization will begin, similar to that which has been taking place in
Russia since the 1950's, and headed in the general
direction toward which the modern Communist and non-
Communist countries are converging. The Mao Regime
has lost the support of Russia and of most Communist
countries, and many of the Communist parties in other countries as well.

All this means that the dictatorships of the
feudal Right and the orthodox Left are losing ground
throughout the world. The newly developing countries are not committed to the orthodoxy of either
European or Russian economic systems, selecting features from both and inventing new ones themselves to
meet their own conditions.

The recognition of this trend does not solve
the many concrete problems people are facing in
their economic development. There will continue to
be many obstacles retarding progress. There will be
military coups to protect the privileged position of
traditional leaders when they feel that social reform groups, such as labor unions or farmers, are
getting too strong, as has been typical of Latin
America. There will be much silent, covert repres-
sion of progress by landlords obstructing implementation of land reforms and primary education, by

employers doing the same with labor legislation, and
merchants with marketing and credit cooperatives.
There will be much inefficiency and corruption in
rapidly expanding civil service ranks. There will
be rivalry between tribes, family clans, political
parties, for privileges and power, and abuse of power by strong charismatic leaders.

But there will also be much soul-searching by
leaders for ways to accelerate progress, to gain and
keep the confidence of farmers and workers and professionals and their support in elections. There
will be much devotion, by groups and individuals, to
bringing about better economic conditions, wider opportunities for themselves and their children, more
participation of people in public affairs, in education, organizations, and government programs.

Humanist ideas and modern technology demand progress in the directions of universal citizenship,
with its rights and responsibilities, and the abol-
ishment of poverty, by distributing productive capacity and purchasing power widely among the people.
Human dignity and economic progress would both with-
er away if they were restricted to a privileged
minority.

SELECTED BIBLIOGRAPHY

SELECTED BIBLIOGRAPHY

Books

Bailey, F. G.   "Capital Saving and Credit in High-
       land Orissa (India)," in Capital, Saving and
       Credit in Peasant Societies, eds. Firth and
       Yamey. Chicago, Ill.: Aldine Publishing
       Co., 1964.

Bergson, Abram, and Kuznets, Simon (eds.).   Economic
       Trends in the Soviet Union. Cambridge, Mass.:
       Harvard University Press, 1963.

Currie, Lauchlin.   "The Capital Formation Approach,"
       in Accelerating Development: The Necessity
       and the Means. New York: McGraw-Hill Book
       Co., 1966.

Gaitskell, Arthur.   Gezira; A Story of Development
       in the Sudan. London: Faber & Faber, 1959.

Galbraith, John Kenneth.   Economic Development in
       Perspective. Cambridge, Mass.: Harvard
       University Press, 1962.

Gandhi, Mohandas Karamchand.   All Men Are Brothers;
       Life and Thoughts of Mahatma Gandhi as Told
       in His Own Words. Paris: UNESCO, 1958.

Hanson, A. H.   The Process of Planning: A Study of
       India's Five-Year Plans, 1960-64. London:
       Oxford University Press, 1966.

Hapgood, David (ed.).   Policies for Promoting Agri-
       cultural Development. Cambridge, Mass.:
       Massachusetts Institute of Technology, 1965.

399

Hirschman, Albert O. The Strategy of Economic Development. New Haven, Conn.: Yale University Press, 1958.

Kuznets, Simon. Modern Economic Growth. New Haven, Conn.: Yale University Press, 1966.

Lewis, W. Arthur. "Aspects of Economic Development," in Africa: Progress Through Cooperation, ed. John Karefa-Smart. New York: Dodd, Mead & Co., 1966.

_____. Theory of Economic Growth. London: George Allen & Unwin, 1955.

Malinovsky, Branislaw. The Dynamics of Culture Change. New Haven, Conn.: Yale University Press, 1945.

Mason, Edward S. Economic Planning in Underdeveloped Areas: Government and Business. New York: Fordham University Press, 1958.

Mellor, John W. The Economics of Agricultural Development. Ithaca, N.Y.: Cornell University Press, 1966.

Mosher, Arthur T. Getting Agriculture Moving: Essentials for Development and Modernization. New York: Frederick A. Praeger, 1966.

Myrdal, Gunnar. Economic Theory and Underdeveloped Regions. London: Methuen and Co., 1957.

Nair, Kusum. Blossoms in the Dust: The Human Factor in Indian Development. New York: Frederick A. Praeger, 1961.

Paddock, William and Paul. Hungry Nations. Boston, Mass.: Little, Brown and Co., 1964.

Robinson, Joan. Economic Philosophy. Chicago, Ill.: Aldine Publishing Co., 1962.

Schickele, Rainer. Agricultural Policy. Lincoln, Neb.: Nebraska University Press, 1964.

Schultz, Theodore W. The Economic Value of Education. New York: Columbia University Press, 1963.

_____. Transforming Traditional Agriculture. New Haven, Conn.: Yale University Press, 1964.

Shukla, Tara. Capital Formation in Indian Agriculture. Bombay: Vora and Co., 1965.

Smith, T. Lynn. Brazil: People and Institutions. Baton Rouge, La.: Louisiana State University Press, 1954.

Staley, Eugene, and Morse, R. Modern Small Industry for Developing Countries. New York: McGraw-Hill Book Co., 1965.

Theobald, Robert (ed.). The Guaranteed Income. New York: Doubleday & Co., 1965.

_____. The Rich and the Poor. New York: New American Library, Inc., 1960.

Tinbergen, Jan. Design of Development. Baltimore, Md.: Johns Hopkins Press, 1958.

Vernon, Raymond. The Dilemma of Mexico's Development: The Roles of the Private and Public Sectors. Cambridge, Mass.: Harvard University Press, 1965.

_____ (ed.). Public Policy and Private Enterprise in Mexico. Cambridge, Mass.: Harvard University Press, 1964.

Ward, Barbara. The Rich Nations and the Poor Nations. New York: W. W. Norton & Co., Inc., 1962.

Ward, Barbara. Spaceship Earth. New York: Colum-
     bia University Press, 1966.

Waterston, Albert. Development Planning: Lessons of
     Experience. Baltimore, Md.: Johns Hopkins
     Press, 1965.

Wiles, Peter. "Convergence: Possibility and Proba-
     bility," in Planning and the Market in the
     USSR: The 1960's. New Brunswick, N.J.:
     Rutgers University Press, 1967.

Yamey, B. S. "The Study of Peasant Economic Sys-
     tems: Some Concluding Comments and Ques-
     tions," in Saving and Credit in Peasant So-
     cieties, eds. Firth and Yamey. Chicago,
     Ill.: Aldine Publishing Co., 1964.

          Reports and Official Publications

Abbott, J. C. "The Role of Marketing in the Growth
     of Agricultural Production and Trade in Less
     Developed Countries," in Monthly Bulletin of
     Agricultural Economics and Statistics. Vol.
     IX, No. 9, September 1960.

Australian National University, Research School of
     Pacific Studies. Bulletin of Indonesian
     Economic Studies. Canberra: No. 3, Feb-
     ruary 1966.

Chang, C. W. Extension Education for Agricultural
     and Rural Development. Bangkok: FAO Re-
     gional Office for Asia and the Far East,
     March 1963.

de Wilde, John C. Experiences with Agricultural De-
     velopment in Tropical Africa. Washington,
     D.C.: International Bank for Reconstruction
     and Development, June 1966.

Drewnowski, Jan, and Scott, Wolf. The Level of Liv-
     ing Index, U.N. Research Institute for Social
     Development, Report No. 4. Geneva: U.N.

Research Institute for Social Development, September 1966.

Flores, Edmundo. Land Reform and the Alliance for Progress, Woodrow Wilson School of Public and International Affairs, Policy Memorandum No. 27. Princeton, N.J.: Princeton University Center of International Studies, May 20, 1963.

Food and Agriculture Organization of the United Nations. Agricultural Development in Nigeria, 1965-1980. Rome: FAO, 1966.

_____. First Farm Management Manual for the Use of Agricultural Extension Workers in Asia and the Far East. Bangkok, Thailand: Regional Office for Asia and the Far East, FAO, October 1964.

_____. The Relationship Between Land Reform and Community Development. Rome: Bureau of Social Affairs, World Land Reform Conference, 1966.

_____. "The Role of Peasant Organizations in Land Reform and Related Community Development Programmes with Special References to Latin American Countries," World Land Reform Conference Background Paper No. 4. Rome: 1966.

_____. The State of Food and Agriculture, 1966. Rome: FAO, 1966.

_____. Yearbook of Food and Agricultural Statistics. Rome: FAO, 1958.

Gray, Jack. "Agrarian Policies in China Today," in Bulletin for Atomic Scientists. Vol. 22, No. 6, June 1966.

Marglin, Stephen A. "Insurance for Innovators," in Policies for Promoting Agricultural Development. Cambridge, Mass.: Center for

International Studies, Massachusetts Institute of Technology, 1965.

Mathieu, M. "Field Progress Report No. 29," Near
East and North Africa Region, FFHC-FAO Fertilizer Program, October 27, 1966.

Ogura, Takekazu (ed.). Agricultural Development in
Modern Japan. Tokyo: Japan FAO Association,
1963.

Organization for Economic Cooperation and Development. Development Assistance Efforts and
Policies: 1966 Review. Paris: OECD, 1966.

Paul, Arthur. Credit's Role in Improving Agriculture. The Asia Foundation Program Bulletin.
San Francisco, September 1965.

Richardson, H. L. "The Freedom from Hunger Campaign
in Five Years of the FAO Fertilizer Programme," in Outlook on Agriculture. Vol. V,
No. 1, 1966.

Sakoff, A. N. "The Private Sector in Soviet Agricul-
ture," in Monthly Bulletin of Agricultural
Economics and Statistics. Vol. 11, No. 9,
September 1962.

_____. "Rural Population and Agricultural Labor
Forces in the USSR," in Monthly Bulletin of
Agricultural Economics and Statistics. Vol.
15, Nos. 7 and 8, July-August 1966.

United Nations. Statistical Yearbook, 1964. New
York: United Nations, 1964.

_____. World Population Prospects as Assessed in
1963. New York: United Nations, 1963.

_____. Yearbook of National Accounts Statistics,
1965. New York: United Nations, 1965.

United Nations/ECAFE/FAO. "A Study of Farmers' Associations in Taiwan," in Community Development

and Economic Development. Bangkok, Part II
B, 1960.

United States Government. Department of Agriculture.
Agricultural Statistics, 1965. Washington,
D.C.: Government Printing Office, 1965.

_____. Department of Commerce. Statistical Ab-
stract of the United States, 1965. Washington, D.C.: Bureau of the Census, 1965.

_____. Economic Report of the President Trans-
mitted to the Congress January 1966. Washington, D.C.: Government Printing Office,
1966.

Weitz, Raanan. Agriculture and Rural Development in
Israel: Projection and Planning. The National and University Institute of Agriculture, Bulletin No. 68. Rehovot, Israel,
February 1963.

Wharton, Clifton R., Jr. "Strategies for Rural Development." New York: The Agricultural Development Council, Inc., October 1, 1966.
(Mimeo.)

Wilcox, Clair. The Planning and Execution of Economic Development in Southeast Asia, Occasional Papers in International Affairs, No.
10. Cambridge, Mass.: Center for International Affairs, Harvard University, January 1965.

Yang, W. Y. Methods of Farm Management Investiga-
tions for Improving Farm Productivity, FAO
Agricultural Development Paper No. 80. Rome:
FAO, 1965. (Revised edition.)

                    Articles and Newspapers

Barraclough, Solon L. "Agricultural Policy and Land
Reform," paper presented at Conference on

Key Problems of Economic Policy in Latin America, University of Chicago, November 6-9, 1966.   (Mimeo.)

Barraclough, Solon L., and Domike, Arthur L.   "Agrarian Structure in Seven Latin American Countries," Land Economics, Vol. XLII, No. 4 (November 1966).

Belarmino, Isagani C.   "The Rice Problem: An Appraisal," Economic Research Journal, Vol. XII, No. 1 (June 1965).

Bicanic, Rudolf.   "Economics of Socialism in a Developed Country," Foreign Affairs, Vol. 44, No. 4 (July 1966).

Bose, Sailesh Kumar.   "Cooperative Credit and Agricultural Productivity in India: Experience of a Decade," Indian Journal of Agricultural Economics, Vol. 18, No. 1 (January-March 1963).

Boulware, James H.   "India's Fourth Five-Year Plan Focusses on Agriculture," Foreign Agriculture, Vol. IV, No. 40 (October 3, 1966).

Cochrane, Willard W.   "The World Food Budget: A Forward Look to 2000 and Beyond," World Food Forum, Washington, D.C., January 1963.

Dantwala, M. L.   "Institutional Credit in Subsistence Agriculture," International Journal of Agrarian Affairs, Vol. V, No. 1 (December 1966).

de Fonseka, C.   "Shramadana: Mobilization of Unutilized Human Resources," International Development Review, Vol. 7, No. 1 (March 1965).

Duboy, D. C., and Sutton, Willis.   "A Rural Man in the Middle: The Indian Village Level Worker in Community Development," Human Organization, Vol. 24, No. 2 (Summer 1965).

Fairchild, Henry W., and Haq, Shamsul. "Cooperative
    vs. Commune," International Development Re-
    view, Vol. 4, No. 1 (March 1962).

Fonseka, J. V. "The Guaranteed Price Scheme in Cey-
    lon," Indian Journal of Agricultural Econom-
    ics, Vol. 17, No. 2 (April-June 1963).

Gangrade, K. D. "An Incomplete School: A Case Rec-
    ord in Rural Community Organization," Inter-
    national Review of Community Development,
    Nos. 13-14 (1965).

Hapgood, David. "Rural Animation in Senegal," Inter-
    national Development Review, Vol. VI, No. 3
    (September 1964).

Herdt, Robert W., and Mellor, John W. "The Contrast-
    ing Response of Rice to Nitrogen: India and
    the United States," Journal of Farm Econom-
    ics, Vol. XLVI, No. 1 (February 1964).

Hoffman, Paul G. "Development Priorities," Interna-
    tional Development Review, Vol. IV, No. 1
    (March 1962).

Hopper, W. David. "Mainsprings of Agricultural
    Growth in India," Indian Journal of Agricul-
    tural Science, Vol. 35, No. 2 (June 1965).

Karcz, Jerzy F. "The New Soviet Agricultural Pro-
    gramme," Soviet Studies, Vol. XVII, No. 2
    (October 1965).

Keating, Robert B. "Research for Transportation De-
    velopment," Development Research Digest,
    Vol. II, No. 1 (July 1963).

Khan, Akhteer Hameed, and Mohsen, A. K. M. "Mobi-
    lizing Village Leadership," International De-
    velopment Review, Vol. 4, No. 3 (September
    1962.

Kuznets, Simon. "Quantitative Aspects of the Econom-
    ic Growth of Nations," Economic Development

and Cultural Change, Part II, Vol. V, No. 4
(July 1957).

Lampman, Robert J. "Approaches to the Reduction of
Poverty," American Economic Review, Vol. 55,
No. 2 (May 1965).

Long, Erven J. "The Economic Basis of Land Reform
in Underdeveloped Countries," Land Economics,
Vol. 37, No. 2 (May 1961).

MacDougall, Colina. "A Peking Commune," Far Eastern
Economic Review, Vol. LI, No. 2 (January 13,
1966).

Malone, Carl C. "Some Responses of Rice Farmers to
the Package Program in Tanjore District, India," Journal of Farm Economics, Vol. 47,
No. 2 (May 1965).

Manglapus, Raul S. "Asian Revolution and American
Ideology," Foreign Affairs, Vol. 45, No. 2
(January 1967).

McLoughlin, Peter F. M. "The Sudan's Gezira Scheme:
An Economic Profile," Social and Economic
Studies, Vol. 12, No. 2 (June 1963).

Mehta, Shri Asaka. "Toward an Agricultural Revolution," Indian Journal of Agricultural Economics, Vol. XX, No. 1 (January-March 1965).

Misra, B., et al. "Possibilities of Capital Forma-
tion in Agriculture in Cuttack (Orissa),"
Indian Journal of Agricultural Economics,
Vol. XX, No. 1 (January-March 1965).

Morgan, Robert W., Jr. "Occupational Prestige Ratings by Nigerian Students," The Nigerian
Journal of Economic and Social Studies, Vol.
7, No. 3 (November 1965).

Mosher, A. T. "A Note on the Evolutionary Role of
Extension Workers," Land Economics, Vol. 42,
No. 3 (August 1966).

Moskos, Charles C., and Bell, Wendell. "Some Impli-
    cations of Equality for Political, Economic
    and Social Development," International Re-
    view of Community Development, Nos. 13-14
    (1965).

Ojha, P. D., and Bhatt, V. V. "Pattern of Income
    Distribution in an Underdeveloped Economy:
    A Case Study of India," American Economic
    Review, Vol. 54, No. 5 (September 1964).

Oluwasanmi, H. A., and Alao, J. A. "Role of Credit
    in the Transformation of Traditional Agricul-
    ture: The Nigerian Experience," Nigerian
    Journal of Economics and Social Studies,
    Vol. 7, No. 1 (March 1965).

Pearse, Andrew. "Agrarian Change Trends in Latin
    America," Latin American Research Review,
    Vol. I, No. 3 (Summer 1966).

Peaslee, Alexander L. "Elementary Education as a
    Prerequisite for Economic Growth," Interna-
    tional Development Review, Vol. VII, No. 3
    (September 1965).

Quintus, Paul E. "France Moves Ahead in Its Program
    of Farm Restructuring," Foreign Agriculture,
    Vol. IV, No. 36 (September 5, 1966).

Randhawa, N. S. "Farm Planning Project Under Inten-
    sive Agricultural District Programme in In-
    dia," Indian Journal of Agricultural Econom-
    ics, Vol. XX, No. 3 (July-September 1965).

_____. "Returns to Scale and Cooperative Farm-
    ing," Indian Journal of Agricultural Econom-
    ics, Vol. 15, No. 3 (July-September, 1960).

Ruttan, Vernon W. "Equity and Productivity Objec-
    tives in Agrarian Reform Legislation: Per-
    spectives on the New Philippine Land Reform
    Code," Indian Journal of Agricultural Econom-
    ics, Vol. XIX, No. 3 (July-December 1964).

Schickeie, Rainer. "Evolution of Land Tenure in
        World Perspective," AICC Economic Review,
        Vol. VI, Nos. 18-19 (January 21, 1955).

_____. "Farm Management Research for Planning
        Agricultural Development," Indian Journal of
        Agricultural Economics, Vol. 21, No. 2
        (April-June 1966).

Shivamaggi, H. B. "Provision of Credit for Small
        Cultivators," Indian Journal of Agricultural
        Economics, Vol. 18, No. 3 (July-September
        1963).

Siemans, Alfred H. "New Agricultural Settlement
        Along Mexico's Candelarie River: Implica-
        tions of Commitment to Planning and the Eji-
        do," Inter-American Economic Affairs, Vol.
        20, No. 1 (Summer 1966).

Skinner, G. William. "Marketing and Social Struc-
        ture in Rural China," The Journal of Asian
        Studies, Vol. XXIV, No. 3 (May 1965).

Tablante, N. B. "The Agricultural Credit Problem in
        the Philippines," The Philippine Agricultur-
        ist, Vol. XLIX, Nos. 6-7 (November-December
        1965).

Takasuga, Yoshihiro. "The Efflux of Labour from
        Japanese Agriculture and the Rise in Prices,"
        Rural Economic Problems, Tokyo, Vol. 3, No.
        2 (December 1966).

Walters, Harry E. "New Soviet Plan Implies Major
        Farm Policy Switch," Foreign Agriculture,
        Vol. IV, No. 12 (March 21, 1966).

Weitz, Raanan. "Rural Development Through Regional
        Planning in Israel," Journal of Farm Econom-
        ics, Vol. 47, No. 3 (August 1965).

ABOUT THE AUTHOR

Rainer Schickele, an Associate of the Agricultural Development Council, Inc., New York, and since 1967 Visiting Professor of Agricultural Economics at the University of Ceylon, has been intimately concerned with problems of planning and with implementing policies for economic and agricultural development in Asia, Africa, and Latin America.

From 1954 to 1965, he was Director of the Land and Water Development Division of the Food and Agriculture Organization of the United Nations, where he was responsible for guiding the planning and operation of many technical assistance projects throughout the developing world. His travels brought him in close contact with leading government officials, economists, agriculturalists, and farmers in many countries and exposed him to the complex practical problems of translating programs into action, of making policies work at the grassroots level. This book is based on his experience and on his comparative study of technical assistance and national development policies in various parts of the world.

Mr. Schickele received his Ph.D degree from the College of Agriculture, University of Berlin. He conducted research and lectured at Iowa State and George Washington universities and at the U.S. Department of Agriculture. In 1947, he became Head of the Agricultural Economics Department of North Dakota State University. As a Postdoctoral Fellow of the Social Science Research Council, he devoted himself to problems in econometrics, political science, and methodology in the social sciences at Harvard University.

His publications cover a wide range of subjects in many professional journals. His book Agricultural Policy: Farm Programs and National Welfare is well-known in the United States and in developing countries.